→1850

Metal-Mining in Peru, Past and Present

W. F. C. Purser

Metal-Mining in Peru,
Past and Present

Praeger Publishers   New York   Washington   London

PRAEGER SPECIAL STUDIES IN INTERNATIONAL ECONOMICS AND DEVELOPMENT

PRAEGER PUBLISHERS
111 Fourth Avenue, New York, N.Y. 10003, U.S.A.
5, Cromwell Place, London S.W.7, England

Published in the United States of America in 1971
by Praeger Publishers, Inc.

Library of Congress Catalog Card Number: 78-167621

Printed in the United States of America

This book attempts to give an account of the nature, history and importance of the mines of Peru. Part I of the book sketches the background of Peru and its mining history. The mines actually in production today are discussed in Part II, which is divided into five chapters for the five mining areas of Peru. Part III is concerned with the economic significance of the mines today.

The point of view assumed throughout this book is Peruvian. The industry is discussed or its history analyzed against the criterion of its importance or utility to the country in which it exists. The Peruvian mining industry is, of course, important to other people such as the foreign mining companies that operate there, or the consumers of the richer countries of the world who need its products. However, these people are well able to look after their own interests and being so noticeably more prosperous than the inhabitants of Peru I feel that I owe them no apology in adopting the views that I have. Should, by any chance, my remarks about the foreign mining companies cause offense, I should like to apologize in advance. I have received nothing but help and interest from those companies, and my objective in criticizing them is not intended as a show of ingratitude. It is the central thesis of this book, when discussing the economics of the mining industry, that the interests of the foreign companies and consumers and the interests of Peru are very largely incompatible. It is necessary to "take sides." This book, while attempting to be as objective and factual as possible, is essentially concerned with the interests of the inhabitants of Peru, and to them it is dedicated.

I should like to add my thanks to the Overseas Development Institute (ODI) of London, which awarded me a two-year fellowship to do the study on which

the book is based, and to the Ford Foundation--the
ultimate source of finance. Both the ODI and the
Foundation have been of continuous assistance and
have given much encouragement. The book, of course,
represents my own views, which are in no way connected with those of the two institutes.

Since leaving Peru in January 1970, there have
been many major changes in national mining policy
that will affect medium- and long-term development
profoundly. Where possible, I have tried to incor-
porate these changes into the text and hope that the
information, largely gleaned from the press, is accurate.

CONTENTS

Appendix   Page

                          APPENDIXES

                           INDEXES

Index

LIST OF MAPS AND TABLES

GEOGRAPHY
AND
HISTORY

1

THE
LAND
OF PERU

Peru is the third largest country in South
America in terms of area. Its 125 million hectares
make it roughly equivalent to Europe west of the
Rhine. Geographers conventionally divide the country
into three topographical units--the coast, the sierra
(mountains) and the jungle--although, of course, these
units contain considerable variations within themselves.

THE COAST

The coastal strip runs from the Ecuadorian frontier to Chile, a distance of some 2,000 kilometers
(kms.) in a general north northwest-south southwest
direction. Despite the fact that this entire length
lies within the tropics, the temperatures are relatively cool. Except for the valleys irrigated by
the rivers that run down to the Pacific, the area is
almost completely desert--a desert that stretches
well into Chile and is at its most impressive in the
Atacama region of that country. Although there is
almost no rain, the coastal strip is often overcast
by a low cloud for half the year (May-November),
which forms a layer some 400 meters thick at an altitude less than 1,000 meters. At times, this cloud
descends almost to sea level, forming the garua,

which swirls around the treetops and tall buildings
of Lima, sometimes blotting them out completely. The
garua is less persistent in the north and south of
the country.

The cause of this strange climate is to be found
in the neighboring ocean. Off the coast lies a tremendous trench of depths up to 6,000 and even 7,000
meters, and more or less along the line of this
trench from south to north flows the Humboldt Current.
The current has a speed of some 8 kms. per hour, is
not wide (less than 200 kms.) but is noticeably cold
with temperatures around 15°C. The existence of this
current, with its incredibly rich marine and associated bird life, has always been known to the inhabitants of the Peruvian coast, but Humboldt was the
first man to recognize its effect on the neighboring
land. In fact, the cold current so cools the air
above it as to produce a strong temperature inversion.
The low cloud that drifts inland is either evaporated
or condenses but never really causes rain, while the
temperature inversion effectively prevents the formation of strong upcurrents, which might cause violent precipitation. That these conditions have not
always been so is amply evidenced by the coastal
hills, heavily eroded and cut by water courses that
are now completely dry. When this change took place
is not yet known--although there is some evidence
that heavy, if infrequent, rains occurred up till
1000 B.C. or so.

The coast may be conveniently divided into
three sections: Ecuador to Trujillo in the north,
Trujillo to Canete (south of Lima), and Canete to
Chile. The northern section is the widest. If we
consider the 1,000-meter contour as its inland limit,
it decreases from 150 to some 40 kms. As we move
south, the distance to the continental divide decreases from some 200 to 100 kms. In the northwest
are some of the largest exposures of Tertiary formations in coastal Peru, which include the oil fields
of Talara, Zorritos, etc. Across this area run a low
chain of hills, the Amotape, whose direction con-
trasts with that of the main Cordillera Andina. To
the southwest of the widest part of the desert the

coastal promontories of Paleozoic rock form the northern end of the former Cordillera de la Costa. This
range, which to the south has sunk beneath the sea
and only shows itself by a few islands, reappears
again at Paracas. This sinking and lifting of coastal areas is characteristic of the entire seaboard,
as shown by innumerable block-faulting and raised
beaches. The northern section of the coast is completely arid in some parts, e.g., the Desert of
Sechura (where there are large phosphate deposits),
but nearer the Andes is more like a savannah, with
low scrub and trees in eastern Piura.

The stretch from Trujillo to Canete is very narrow, with only 30 to 40 kms. to the 1,000-meter contour. The Continental Divide is a mere 100 kms.
away, and the rivers in consequence are all short
and abrupt. An exception is the Santa River, which
for a considerable distance flows parallel to the
coast along the line of a graben, between the Cordilleras Negra and Blanca.

From Canete southward, the Cordillera de la
Costa reappears from the sea (the width of the continental shelf in the central section gives proof of
its submarine continuance) and, with the whole line
of the Andes, turns more easterly until the Chilean
border. From Canete to Lomas, there is a wide table-
land of some 70 kms. in width, in which the rivers
from the sierra lose themselves before they ever find
the Pacific. The coast itself is savage and unin-
habited, but inland are the main vineyards of Peru
at Ica and Ocucaje. Strangely, this area seems, too,
to have been popular in prehistoric times, the Nazca
and Paracas regions affording the best examples of
pottery and textiles from about 2,000 years ago.
One is tempted to conjecture that the climate, which
is now extremely arid, was once more favorable, and
a study of the irrigation systems of prehistoric
Nazca and the elaborate designs in the surrounding
desert (thought to be connected with astronomical
observations for determining the seasons) might
yield some information. A very interesting feature
of this part of the coast is the Nazca Ridge, a submarine mountain chain running at right angles to

the main Cordillera, for perhaps 1,500 kms to the
southwest. This chain is at a depth of about 2,500
meters and rises from the Pacific floor at about
4,500 meters. The presence of "guyots"* and evidence
on the coast suggest that this chain has sunk (during the Jurassic?), and the strike of the Paleozoic
near San Juan, coupled with the lines of the Huri-
cangana hills, would imply that the structure continues inland at least 50 kms., if not very much
more. Does it represent an ancient structure pushed
down by the (drifting?) South American continent?
If this ridge once stood above sea level, the Humboldt Current, insofar as it affects central and
northern Peru, must surely date from after its sub-
mersion, as the current has its present origins over
20° latitude further south. Further south, from
Lomas to Camana, the coastal strip virtually disappears in a grim line of cliff, but then gradually
widens to some 50 kms. in Tacna. The Continental
Divide retreats eastward in Arequipa to some 200
kms. from the coast, but returns near the frontier
to about 100 kms. There are some large rivers in
this area, the Majes and Tambo for example, and it
is hoped that the desert pampas will be irrigated
effectively in the near future.

THE SIERRA

The second topographical unit, the sierra, is
much less easily defined or described. Its western
limit may be taken as the Pacific slopes of the
Cordillera Occidental down to, say, the 1,000-meter
contour. But its eastern structure is much more
irregular, being eroded by the major rivers that
flow into the Amazon Basin. These rivers--Maranon,
Huallaga, Apurimac, Urubamba--have a tendency to
follow the direction of the Andean structure northward and then swing suddenly east, cutting through
the mountains in a series of rapids--the "pongos."
(An exception is the Madre de Dios Basin of south-

---

*Guyot, from the French, is a geological term
denoting a submarine table-top mountain.

east Peru, which drains directly northeast into the
Madeira.) Their countless tributaries, which rise
in the sierra, have pushed back the Continental Divide ever further westward by their continuous erosion. A second general feature of the sierra is
that its western limit, the Cordillera Occidental,
is largely formed of Tertiary volcanic rocks, while
on the east, the Cordilleras Central and Oriental,
where they exist, are predominantly Paleozoic and
metamorphosed sedimentary rocks.

Starting from the north, the sierra between
Ecuador and Cajamarca at once forms an exception.
A large area of the Paleozoic is found here in the
Cordillera Occidental, which is something of an anom-
aly. This part of the cordillera is also noticeably
lower than in the rest of Peru, with very few peaks
over 4,000 meters and much lower passes--the road
east from Olmos crosses at 2,300 meters. The fertile
Cajamarca department is one of the areas where the
Cretaceous is most fully developed in the country.

The next area south extends to north of Cerro
de Pasco. The general altitude rises, and from not
far south of Cajamarca it is possible to walk to
Chile without dropping below 4,000 meters. On the
coastal flank, the great batholithic intrusions start,
and south of Chimbote the structure is formed by
three great ranges. On the west, the Cordillera
Negra (volcanic) shelters the magnificent Cordillera
Blanca, across the Santa Valley, from the moist winds
of the Pacific, thus maintaining the great snowfields
and glaciers that cover this range containing Peru's'
highest mountain, Huascaran (6,768 meters). Further
eastward, across various major faults that run along
the Maranon Valley, the Cordillera Central rises
again to heights over 4,000 meters. The Cordillera
Blanca is a batholithic intrusion, while across the
Maranon the bedrock of the Paleozoic appears.

The next area south, from Cerro de Pasco to
Huancavelica, is the heart of Peru's mining industry.
Most of the mines lie on the eastern flank of the
Cordillera Occidental, and between it and the
Cordillera Central lie two large basins--that of the

lake of Junin and the rich valley of the Mantaro,
between Jauja and Huancayo. The Cordillera Occidental is at its highest here, rising in gigantic ram-
parts from immediately behind Lima. Unfortunately,
the roads that climb over the passes, which are all
about 4,500 meters high, go up such narrow and steep
valleys that the ordinary traveler does not really
appreciate it. To get some idea of the scale of the
mountains, some of the roads further south, e.g.,
Nazca-Puquio, are really more rewarding. Further
southward and eastward, through the departments of
Ayacucho and Apurimac to Cuzco, lies some of the
wildest and most broken territory in Peru. To the
west, the great puna* erosion surface (which can be
traced over almost the entire length of Peru) is
well-displayed (for example, northeast of Puquio),
while eastward the Apurimac River and its tributaries
have gouged out deep gorges that are tropical at the
bottom and edged with snowy peaks above. The terrain is extremely accidented but a general eastern
trend is discernible. This area corresponds to the
Nazca Ridge of the coast, and it may be wondered
whether the clashing of two distinct structures is
not responsible for the nature of the landscape.

North and east of Cuzco, the Cordillera Oriental
appears from vestigial remains in the eastern jungle,
and where the Cordilleras Vilcabamba (through which
the Urubamba cuts), Carabaya and Real extend into
Bolivia is a series of peaks, many over 6,000 meters.
Illimani, in Bolivia, is nearly 7,000 meters. A
branch, the Cordillera Vilcanota, runs southward and
separates the Cuzco and Titicaca Basins. To the
southwest of the Cordillera Oriental lies the great
altiplano, at some 4,000 meters. Geologically, it
is a complex area obscured by Mesozoic and Tertiary
vulcanism and Tertiary/Quaternary alluvial deposits.
Lake Titicaca was formerly much more extensive, and
it is thought, on the basis of biological studies,
that it could be a former arm of the sea cut off and
lifted to its present altitude during the general
lifting of the Andes. To the southwest, the puna

----

*Puna is the high, cold, arid plateau of the Andes.

extends to the Continental Divide, a wide bleak land
that nevertheless supports very large flocks of sheep,
llamas and alpacas. The coastal limit of the sierra
in this region is the desert, which reaches considerably inland toward Arequipa. There is a line of
active volcanos to the west of the Continental Divide
(Chachani, Misti, Ubinas, Tutupaca, etc.) that provide living evidence of the volcanism that seems to
have characterized this area on and off since Jurassic times.

THE JUNGLE

The third topographical unit is the jungle.
This vast area is very little known even today. The
lower eastern slopes of the Andes, between 500 and
1,500 meters, are gradually being colonized and opened
up with roads. This applies particularly to the
lower Maranon, the Huallaga Valley from Tingo Maria
to Tarapoto, the Parene, Apurimac and Urubamba Valleys, and parts of the Madre de Dios Basin. These
areas largely correspond to the Mesozoic sediments
east of the Paleozoic, that is to say a shallow but
extensive eastern basin associated with the main
Andean geosyncline. Below 500 meters, the rivers
have still some 4,000 kms. to flow before they reach
the Atlantic. With such a slight incline, there are
naturally innumerable meanders and silted backwaters,
and the whole area is liable to flooding. Forest
and Quaternary deposits obscure what structure there
might be to see, and, indeed, it is thought that this
huge flat area is no more than the remains of a large
inland sea. A few towns on the river banks, Iquitos
being the largest, together with some forest exploitation and considerable petroleum exploration--in a
part of the department of Loreto that is claimed by
Ecuador--represent all the human activities in the
northeast of Peru (while the jungle that adjoins the
Acre Territory of Brazil appears unknown, at any rate
to the outside world). In this alluvial land, no
metal-mining occurs, of course, but the rivers of
the eastern slopes are all gold-bearing, and panning
goes on in virtually all of them. This is a seasonal
activity after the rains of the sierra, which last

from November to April in the south and somewhat
longer in the north.

THE STRATIGRAPHY OF THE ROCKS

The geology of Peru is by no means fully mapped
and still less fully understood, but, nevertheless,
what is known is of considerable interest and helps
to throw some light on the location and origin of
Peru's very extensive mineral resources. The oldest
rocks are to be found in the Cordillera de la Costa,
the Cordillera Oriental and along the upper Maranon
River, but their age is not yet known. They are
certainly pre-Triassic, and it is possible that they
are Cambrian or pre-Cambrian. Gneiss and other met-
amorphic rocks exist in coastal Arequipa (e.g.,
near Atico), and the Lomas complex near San Juan--
heavily folded and metamorphosed--bears evidence to
the landward continuation of the Nazca Ridge. In
the Maranon Valley and also near Cuzco in the Vilcabamba Range, similar rocks occur and, frequently,
schists as well (another area for schists being the
Piura/Cajamarca border). Several of these old outcrops are associated with intrusives, which are
thought to be Paleozoic. Some of these intrusives
are very extensive and are probably associated with
periods of orogeny (mountain-forming) which certainly
took place in the Paleozoic. (An easily visited
example of these intrusives lies between San Ramon
and the Perene Valley, due east of Lima.) Corresponding to Ordovician/Silurian times, there exist
widespread shale and sandstone facies in the central
part of the eastern Andes. The later Devonian is
then missing and the next formation is continental,
the Ambo group of the lower Carboniferous. After
this lifting, the sea seems to have transgressed
again during the Pennsylvanian era as more shale formations are found. The next formation, known as the
Mitu, is continental (red sandstones, conglomerates)
and occurs well beyond Peru's frontiers, even into
Argentina. It is very conspicuous (the tourist may
see it between Cuzco and Pisac), not least on account of its marked discordancy with all earlier
deposits. The Mitu corresponds to the Permian, and

since the lower Triassic is absent in all Peru (and
other Andean republics), and since the subsequent
marine formations lie largely concordantly on it and
continue throughout the Mesozoic, it is considered
to represent a period following fairly major orogeny
that defined the form of the Andean geosyncline, a
shallow basin bound on the east and west by the
Paleozoic.

During the Mesozoic, the geosyncline, with its
accompanying basin to the east, became fully developed. It never seems to have been very deep as continental and shallow water facies appear sporadically,
but in the Cajamarca region it apparently extended
well eastward into what is now the Amazon Basin. In
Triassic times, a conspicuous series of limestones
(the Pucara series) was laid down, which are best
seen running from east of Cerro de Pasco to south of
Huancayo. Such limestone deposits are generally
well into the Jurassic, although submarine volcanic
sediments start appearing in the south, and the
Pucara also has volcanic facies in the north. Between the Jurassic and early Cretaceous, there are
certain discordancies and remnants of continental
formations in northern Peru that suggest a minor
orogeny and emergence. This period is then followed
by another prominent formation, the Goyllarisquizga,
which is of shales, quartzite and sandstone, often
contains low-grade coal and is very widespread.

With the Cretaceous, the geosyncline is most
fully developed. Near Lima, the characteristic
barren headlands of regular stratification, often
with volcanic dikes, belong to this period, as do
the limestone and sandstones of the Santa Valley
and, slightly later, the white limestone near La
Oroya. The later formations are well developed in
Cajamarca (limestones, shales and marls) and Titicaca
(sandstones), and in the far south, in Moquegua and
Tacna, there are further volcanic deposits that become more and more extensive. Toward the end of
the Cretaceous (although some authorities would put
it later), the coastal batholith intruded. This
enormous block of varying, but predominantly granodiorite, composition extends from the department

of La Libertad in the north to Arequipa in the south,
with outlying intrusions particularly to the north.
The folding that accompanied this apparently raised
what is now the sierra above sea level, where it has
remained ever since. However, largely using biological evidence, it is generally agreed that it was
not much above sea level. The batholith of the
Cordillera Blanca probably intruded a little later
than that of the coast.

Throughout the Tertiary on the coast there are
extensive formations, particularly in Piura in the
north and Ica in the center. These formations are
relatively well-studied (on account of oil-prospec-
ting) and are separated by disconformities and
faulting, and there has obviously been a continuous
series of block-faults and local transgressions.
Indeed, there is another very widespread continental
formation similar to the Mitu. These red beds are
well-seen at Casapalca, east of Lima, and they are
often named after this mining camp. Following the
Casapalca group, discordantly, are a prodigious
series of volcanics, conglomerates, tuffs, etc. This
series, not properly studied, covers huge areas
along the line of the Cordillera Occidental, particularly in the Ayacucho/Apurimac/Arequipa area. The
strata are often multi-colored and very spectacular,
and correspond to the late Eocene and Oligocene.
Further folding was followed by a quiescent period
when the puna surface, so characteristic of the
southern sierra, was formed by erosion. This probably took place during the Miocene and at an altitude of less than 1,000 meters. Some time later
(early Pliocene?), there is renewed vulcanism, and
this is probably associated with the lifting of the
Andes to their present height. This event, which
lifted the puna surface to heights over 4,000 meters,
remains very obscure. The forces that produced the
titanic effect have yet to be explained, as the conventional geosynclinal theory apparently does not
fit the case of the Andes. Whatever the explanation,
it must surely involve the even more enormous trench
immediately west of the continental mass. There is
evidence that the lifting took place in two or more
stages, as various erosion surfaces are known.

The lifting was followed in the Pleistocene and Quaternary by various glaciations and probably other climatic changes; by extensive vulcanism in the south; by large unconsolidated Quaternary deposits, particularly in the jungle; and by minor faulting and earthquakes that continue to this day.

THE EARTH MOVEMENTS
IN PERU'S GEOLOGICAL HISTORY

The tectonic (land structure) history of Peru, insofar as it can be deciphered at all, can be read between the lines of the sedimentary history. The various Paleozoic discordancies have caused authors to attempt to correlate them with orogenies in Europe or elsewhere. Thus, the breaks in the Ordovician to Devonian sequences are seen as Caledonian and Acadian orogenies; hence, the subsequent continental deposits of the Ambo group. Even Assyntian orogenic effects are postulated. It seems clear, however, that the first reliable (Appalachian?) orogeny is that preceding the Mitu. Thereafter, throughout the Jurassic, the geosyncline developed, rising and sinking, with few other effects except a possible disturbance at the end of the Jurassic. The Cordillera de la Costa, which formed the western edge of the geosyncline, must have been continually eroded during this period. With the batholithic intrusion, the first important folding occurs, coupled with the start of the block-faulting process on the coast. After the continental Casapalca deposits, the next (and major?) folding took place. The final folding followed after the big volcanic deposits and before the puna formation.

With these three major Tertiary folding movements, numerous faults were developed. East of the Continental Divide (e.g., north and south of the snowpeak La Viuda above Canta or east of Celedin in Cajamarca), there are major trust faults at the base of the Cretaceous. Massive longitudinal faults occur in the eastern ranges (east of Junin, the Maranon faults) and in the central sierra--e.g., the famous

fault of Cerro de Pasco. It is thought that similar
faults or fissures in the Cordillera Occidental gave
rise to the very prominent volcanic deposits--not
from any identifiable conventional volcano. An example of this sort could be the Cordillera Negra,
and it is striking how the volcanics lie along the
line of the Continental Divide, a kind of hinge line.
It is somewhat surprising, then, to find that virtually every mine of importance in the Cordillera
Occidental of central Peru is associated with transverse faults (and a neighboring intrusion). Do
these transverse faults, which are never long, nevertheless correspond to some profound feature of the
basal structure that also shows itself in the block-
faulting of the coast?

The Tertiary intrusives mentioned above are a
very common feature of the central sierra. They are
never very large and seem randomly scattered but are
almost always associated with a mineral deposit and
a mine and vice versa--so much so that to prospect
for minerals in this area without looking for suitable intrusives would be regarded as folly by any
mining geologist. They occur, too, in the southern
sierra, but the big copper fields are connected with
longitudinal faults and vulcanism.

MINERALIZED AREAS

In very general terms, it is possible to outline the main known mineralized areas in Peru.
Apart from the big copper deposits already mentioned
toward the Chilean frontier, copper is found all the
way up the coast to Lima, in low-grade but fairly
easily workable quantities. Many of the lead/zinc
mines of the central sierra (Ayacucho to Cajamarca)
have also older(?) copper ores. Copper also occurs
with iron associated with the batholithic intrusion
in Apurimac and at Marcona on the coast. The major
mines exploit disseminated ore bodies, but copper
veins are also mined, particularly when they occur
with other minerals.

Lead/zinc ores of the sierra are very often
associated with valuable quantities of silver. The

main area is the Cordillera Occidental, the mineral
being found in the transverse faults already mentioned, frequently in andesitic rock. Further east,
moving onto the limestones of the Jurassic and
Cretaceous, replacement ore bodies are found. There
are innumerable small mines in the south in Puno,
but it appears that the absence of a suitable rock
for replacement (limestone being rare) has prevented
the formation of any major lead/zinc deposits. The
Cordillera Negra is another important center for
small lead/zinc mines.

Of the precious metals, silver is the most widespread. With the exception of Cerro de Pasco itself
(for over 400 years a major silver mine), the "silver belt" seems to lie along the western edge of
the Continental Divide, being found particularly in
the volcanic rocks of the Tertiary. Gold, however,
is not found in large quantities in this area. Most
of the gold is mined as a by-product, but the few
active gold mines per se are either in Arequipa or
associated with the Paleozoic of the Cordillera
Oriental. Carabaya, Sandia and the Maranon Valley--
all extremely inaccessible--are good examples.

Iron is widespread in Peru but is only economically interesting on the coast. Various unworked
deposits are known from the northern frontier to
the field near San Juan, which is exploited on a
large scale. These deposits appear, from their probable age and location, to be associated with the
coastal batholith. Some small deposits further
south near Mollendo may be much older. The sierra
iron fields are isolated and not properly surveyed,
but it is possible that there are considerable quantities in the area of the Apurimac batholith.

Considering the economically less-interesting
metals, the first of importance is mercury. The
famous mines of Huancavelica were once the world's
largest producer and they are still active. The
mineralized zone is in the immediate neighborhood
of the capital of that department. Tungsten, apparently related to the batholith of the Cordillera
Blanca, is found to the north of that range in La

Libertad, as well as east of Lima and in Puno. Also
associated with the Cordillera Blanca is a small tin
mine at its southern limit, and the great Bolivian
tin fields may reach further into Peru than is commonly thought. Some manganese is also found in the
central and southern sierra, while molybdenum is exploited with the coastal copper deposits and at one
isolated mine in Piura.

The rarer metals, such as bismuth, antimony,
selenium, tellurium, cadmium and vanadium, are nearly
all by-products of the lead/zinc mines of the central
sierra. In some cases, the quantities are sufficient
to maintain an otherwise doubtful mine in healthy
economic state (cadmium is such an example), while
in the department of Pasco there is a unique bismuth
mine--Peru being the world's largest bismuth producer. Puno is an important source of antimony.

A final group of metals is the nickel, cobalt
and chromium of the Paleozoic of the Cordillera
Oriental, often associated with gold or iron. These
metals are scarcely exploited.

TRANSPORT AND COMMUNICATIONS

All mines depend fundamentally on transport and
communications, not only for bringing supplies to
them but especially for removing the mineral from
them. When it is remembered that, for example, typical zinc ores are 5 to 8 per cent zinc metal and
production is some 300,000 tons per annum it will be
seen that mining it involves moving 4 to 5 million
tons a year (more, in fact, if allowance is made for
losses and shifting of sterile rock). Of course this
ore is virtually always concentrated at the mine before further transport, but even then some 600,000
tons of, say, 50 per cent zinc concentrate are being
carried about the country from concentrator plant to
smelter, deposit or port, as the case may be. Most
of this movement is from the sierra to the coastal
ports, which is, at any rate, downhill, but 4,000-
meter descents in heavy trucks on ungraded roads are
still an arduous under-taking.

Rail transport in Peru is limited but much-used by the mining industry. The line from Lima across the Andes to La Oroya, which branches north to Cerro de Pasco and south to Huancayo and Huancavelica, has been in use since the beginning of this century. Not only does it serve to bring concentrates to the coast but also to feed them to the refinery of the Cerro de Pasco Corporation at La Oroya and then to transport the refined products to Lima. The other railway system in the south (Mollendo-Arequipa-Puno-Cuzco) is less important because the area served contains fewer mines. Some minor railways also serve the industry in other parts; for example, the Ilo-Toquepala line is the main transport system of the gigantic Toquepala copper mine.

Important as the railways are, the bulk of transport is by road. In the first place, very few mines have a railway directly to them (and in some cases where there was one, it was found uneconomical), and second, many mines are not even in an area with a railway at all, near or far. The coast of Peru is well served by roads with the asphalted Panamerican Highway running its entire length. Mines on the coast have easy transport to the various ports, and every coastal valley has a road going up it well into the sierra, if not across the Continental Divide. The main roads that do cross the Divide are from north to south as follows:

1.   Olmos-Bagua. A new road passing through a district of little mining importance, probably owing to its lack of exploration since it is well-vegetated.
2.   Pacasmayo-Cajamarca. There are other passes in Cajamarca (the mountains being relatively low), and it is possible to continue by road to the upper Maranon and the Chachapoyas area.
3.   Trujillo-Maranon. This passes by the Northern Peru Mining Company at Quiruvilca. Trujillo is served by the important port of Salaverry.
4.   Casma-Huaraz. Serves the Santa Valley and the mines of the Cordillera Negra, linking them with the modern port at Chimbote.

5. <u>Pativilca-Huarez</u>. A branch now runs past a new lead/zinc/copper mine to Huanuco. From Huanuco, one can travel right down the center of the Andes to Bolivia, and all the passes further south connect with this road. From Huanuco, one can also travel northeast to Pucallpa in the jungle.

6. <u>Huacho-Ambo</u>. This road is not yet open but will serve an important mining area when it is.

7. <u>Lima-Canta-Cerro de Pasco</u>. Passes some of the largest lead/zinc mines.

8. <u>Lima-La Oroya</u>. The most important pass of all (4,818 meters). It is the only tarred road a-cross the Andes—and even it is not tarred at the summit. From La Oroya, excellent roads run south to Huancayo and east to Tarma, but beyond those places there is no more asphalt. Two further roads connect Huancayo to the coast further south.

9. <u>Pisco-Huancavelica</u>. A branch will run from Castrovirreyna to Ayacucho. To give an idea of the distances, it can be added that this run is reckoned at 12 hours in a car.

10. <u>Nazca-Abancay</u>. This is the main road from the coast to Cuzco.

There are no further road passes until those that run east from Arequipa to Puno, and even here the Panamerican Highway to La Paz is ungraded.

11. <u>Moquegua-Puno</u>. Very long and bad.
12. <u>Tacna-Ilave</u>. Very long and bad.

Driving in the sierra, one averages 25 to 30 kms. per hour. Dirt roads are divided into two main categories: <u>afirmado</u>, i.e., steam-rollered, or <u>sin afirmado</u>. The latter often form tremendous corruga-tions. The afirmado roads are usually good, but the terrain is frequently dangerous and roads are always lined with crosses where trucks and buses have gone into ravines. Heavy truck-driving in the Andes is an endurance test, but, nevertheless, many mines rely exclusively on the skill of these drivers for the shipment of their products to the major buying cen-ters.

Many of the larger sierra towns have airports, and this mode of transport is much used by mine executives. Cuzco, for example, has air transport as its normal link with the capital, and business people fly to Arequipa or even San Juan. Air transport is, however, largely for passengers.

Turning to communications, all sizable mines have a private short-wave radio link with their head office, normally in Lima. These links are customarily used twice daily at fixed hours. The ordinary post is slow and a traveler will frequently find himself asked to act as postman if he is going the right way. The public telephone service, even in the capital, is very bad and it is almost non-existent elsewhere.

The greater part of Peru's metals production (whether in the form of concentrates or of refined metal) is exported. The coast is well-served, with the ports at Callao being the largest. Callao handles a total of 4.5 million tons a year, and new mineral handling facilities are being built. Matarani and Mollendo serve Arequipa, the former being new and to be further enlarged, while a big deep-water facility is being built at Paracas to provide an outlet for the Huancavelica-Ayacucho region. (This is part of the same project as the Castrovirreyna-Ayacucho road). North of Callao, there are several ports--the largest being Chimbote, Salaverry, Pacasmayo, Paita and Tumbes. The biggest companies have built their own harbors, e.g., Southern Peru Copper Corporation at Ilo, Marcona Mining Company at San Nicolas and SOGESA (the state steel works) at Chimbote. The various ports on the Amazon are not used for mineral transport.

SUMMARY

Peru is richly endowed with mineral wealth, the bulk of which is associated with Tertiary mineralization and the formation of the Andes. Thus, the very source of wealth is at the same time the biggest impediment to its exploitation. In the high Andes,

not only is transport to anywhere else difficult and
dangerous, not only are communications tenuous and
the ordinary comforts of life few, but the very altitude makes life harder. A strong and healthy man
finds work above 4,000 meters exhausting, and rapid
changes in altitude are usually accompanied by head-
aches, sickness and lethargy. The cold at night is
bitter and resistance is lowered to the common ill-
nesses of pneumonia and tuberculosis. Nevertheless,
many wives and families accompany the miners to these
remote spots and there are obligatory schools and
hospitals at all mining camps. Those miners lucky
enough to work on the coast have another problem--
water shortage. The Humboldt Current, which fills
the sea with fish, makes the land a desert, and as
mines use considerable quantities of water in the
drills, concentrator plants and for consumption they
often have to bring it in long pipe lines from the
sierra. Peru is a rugged and wild country, and the
exploitation of her mineral wealth never has been,
nor ever will be, easy.

2

**THE HISTORY
OF MINING
IN PERU:
PRE-SPANISH
TO 1824**

PRE-SPANISH

From earliest times, there is evidence of mining
and metalworking in the sierra and west coast of South
America, but not until the Inca period are there any
records other than archaeological. All the major pre-
Inca cultures have produced metal ornaments and small
tools that are largely made of gold, silver and copper. Thus, the Paracas culture of the start of our
era furnishes metal fishhooks and the Chancay necrop-
olis some thousand years later has yielded many gold,
silver and coral necklaces. There is evidence of much
earlier copper mining in Chuquicamata in northern
Chile, and one can also infer the existence of metal
tools for the elaborate stonework and carving of sites
such as Chavin of the first millenium B.C. However,
how far into the past the knowledge and use of metals
in the area is to be traced is as yet unknown.

In the period corresponding to the rise of the
Incas in the Cuzco Valley, there was a flourishing
metal industry on the northern coast. Great quantities of beautiful gold ornaments are known from the
Chimu culture in particular, and it must be supposed
that the metal was extracted from the Cajamarca-
Maranon area. Among the ornaments are found some

21

articles of platinum, also encountered in Ecuador and
Colombia. Since platinum has an exceptionally high
point of fusion (1,755°C.), its use is somewhat enig-
matical, but it is thought that it was fused together
from small grains by means of gold/silver solders.
(Platinum was first "discovered" in this area in the
early 18th century by the Spaniards who gave it this
name on account of its similarity to silver [plata].)
The techniques used in making these ornaments are
varied and include casting, soldering, repousse and
different forms of gilding, among which mercury gilding is thought to have been employed. Examples of
tinning have also been found. A wide variety of cop-
per/gold/silver alloys are known.

     With the Inca conquest of all Peru in the 15th
century, the metal industry, like everything else,
seems to have been placed on a centralized basis.
Gold and silver in enormous quantities were used for
decorating the temples and ornamenting the royal house-
holds, becoming apparently a royal prerogative. The
Incas introduced bronze for tools that had previously
been made from copper, perhaps hardened by accidental
impurities. The bronze was relatively low in tin (2
to 4 per cent), and there seems to be considerable
doubt as to whether this quantity was controlled at
all, or whether the alloy was formed from mixed ores
instead of isolated copper and tin. Bronze objects,
of course, predominated over copper ones in the areas
centered on the Bolivian tin fields, whereas further
north the absence of local tin meant a relative scarcity of bronze tools. Strangely enough, the use of
iron before the arrival of the Spaniards was unknown,
and how the Incas managed to cut stone with such in-
comparable precision using copper or bronze is the
origin of many strange legends. (They are supposed
to have had a secret method of tempering metal, while
others maintain that the stones were not cut with
tools but worked by rubbing with the leaves of a plant
whose juices had the property of dissolving stone--
what it did to the stonemason's hands is not recorded.)

     The arrival of the Spaniards provides written
evidence of the state of the metal industry in Peru.
The fabulous quantities of gold and silver collected

for Atahualpa's ransom in Cajamarca are agreed to be
only a small part of what was at Cusco before the
Spaniards arrived there and what was also concealed
both by Huascar, rightly fearing the outcome of civil
war with his half-brother, and by the Indians when
they heard of Atahualpa's murder. Historical evalu-
ation of plunder is always difficult, but if Atahualpa's ransom is added to the figures for the booty
taken in Cuzco, the quantity of gold is 1.91 million
pesos de oro and that of silver, 267 thousand marcos.*
This makes, at current prices, some 58 million Swiss
francs or 14 million U.S. dollars. The quantity was,
in fact, considerably greater due partly to other
hoards, partly to the fact that not all booty was declared, thus avoiding paying the royal fifths (quintos reales) in tax. Needless to say, the vast
quantities of money had their resultant inflationary
effect. An egg would easily cost a silver peso ensayado and a horse can seldom have been so valuable
as in the early days of the conquest. One changed
hands at 3,000 pesos de oro, roughly equivalent to
14 kilos of gold--perhaps not quite the price Richard
III of England put on the same animal.

     In their greed for plunder and with the civil
wars that followed, the conquerors gave little thought
to locating the source of the Inca wealth and by the
time they turned their attention to it in the 1550's
it was almost too late. With the exception of the
silver of Porco in Bolivia and some Inca gold mines
known in Carabaya, very few of the colonial mines
were continuations of Inca workings. The mines had
all been deliberately hidden by the Indians. Nevertheless, the chroniclers and the absence of the discovery of any large workings seem to agree that Inca
mining was superficial even if a lot of people were
employed in it. Gold was found probably from wash-
ing--indeed water courses were built for this pur-
pose--and from readily available veins. Silver was
extracted from the oxidized parts of the veins, and
there were only rudimentary tunnels and galleries.
No doubt much of the Inca wealth was itself acquired

_____

     *For an explanation of monetary units, see Ap-
pendix A.

as booty during their conquests, and may well have
come from far afield. In a well-known passage, Cieza
de Leon states the annual production in Inca times
to have once reached 15,000 and 50,000 <u>arrobas</u> (11
kilos) for gold and silver, respectively, or some
172,000 kilos of gold and 575,000 kilos of silver
per year.* If we discount as exceptional the abso-
lute values of the figures and consider only their
ratio (less than 1:4) and compare that with modern
figures for Peru (4,000 kilos per year of gold and
well over 1 million kilos per year of silver, a ratio
greater than 1:250), the decline in gold production
is very noticeable. The decline dates from the first
years of the conquest, despite a steadily improving
gold/silver price ratio from 10:1 in the 16th century to 20:1 today. Allowance being made for the
exhaustion of gold mines, especially placer deposits,
and the fact that the Incas were not subject to market forces in their mining policy, the figures still
give credence to the legends about the concealing of
the gold mines by the Indians.

The method of smelting the ore was in small port-
able earthenware furnaces (<u>guayras</u>) shaped like a
tumbler, a meter high, some 30 centimeters (cms.) in
diameter at the base and 50 at the mouth. (Some had
a square cross section.) The walls were pierced with
holes through which the air passed, previously heated
by pieces of burning charcoal in small receptacles in
front of each hole. The furnace was filled with
charcoal and covered with the mineral. Despite their
primitiveness (there was no method of forced draft
and the operator had to go up and down the hills
looking for a spot with suitable wind conditions),
these furnaces continued into colonial times, proving
initially more efficient than Spanish furnaces
equipped with bellows. Silver, particularly, was
smelted in this way and it appears that copper was,
too, on occasions. The silver was then refined in
furnaces known as <u>tocochimbos</u>. These were large
hemispheres with a big doorway, the floor being
carefully prepared with ashes, etc., as for

_____

*Cieza de Leon, <u>La Cronica del Peru</u>, Part II
(Madrid: Austral Edition, 1945), Chapter 18.

cupellation.   Inside was placed a smaller hemisphere
(pierced with innumerable small holes) with an entrance passage, or _mufla_, like an igloo that projected
out via the big doorway.   The space between the door
and the mufla was sealed with mud.   The lesser hemisphere contained the crude silver for refining, and the
space between the outside of it and the inside of the
larger one was filled with charcoal from a hole at the
top.   Once lit, the draught to the charcoal could be
regulated by a door at the end of the mufla, through
which the progress of the operation could also be
watched and controlled.   The point was that the metal
for refining and the fuel were separated, the heating
being indirect.   Padre Alonso Barba described the
tocochimbos in his El Arte de los Metales, and most
of the early chroniclers refer to the guayras.

Copper, besides being smelted and refined in
guayras (an analysis made on a find in Chuquicamata,
Chile, showed that 99 per cent purity was achieved
from ores of 17 per cent copper oxides, perhaps 2 per
cent copper), was normally treated in a hole in the
ground filled with _ichu_ (the coarse Andean grass),
firewood and the mineral.   This was made on a hillside
so that a tunnel could be dug to drain off the metal
once founded.   The objective must have been to con-
serve heat as much as possible in view of the high
point of fusion of copper (1,083°C.).   Refining consisted of leaving the melted copper in the furnace
until all impurities were thought to have been burnt
off, or alternatively removing a sort of copper matte
or _crudio_ and starting again with it.   The process was
not very successful with sulphide ores, so oxides were
normally the only ones used, and the oxidized zones of
nearly all modern Peruvian copper mines show evidence
of previous working, some of which is pre-Spanish.

If, despite the great quantities of metal extracted because of the extreme richness of the deposits and the amount of labor employed, all evidence
points to the fact that the Indians as miners and
metallurgists were not particularly advanced, when
it comes to metalworking there is no doubt of their
skill and artistic sense.   The famous golden garden
at Cuzco was melted down by the Spaniards and, indeed,

they spent a year and a half at the destruction of
works of art; but, nevertheless, enough has survived
to show clearly the high levels attained in metalworking. The Museo de Oro in Lima contains a staggering collection of ceremonial and decorative objects,
largely from the Chimu culture, and the conquerors
recorded, if they did not preserve, some of the Incas'
creations. It may be said that the Peruvian Indians
really had developed metals for ornamentation, concentrating, above all, on gold and silver. The serious
business of their existence was agriculture and they
had not fully appreciated the practical uses of
metallurgy.

THE VICEROYALTY:
THE FIRST 100 YEARS

"Capitulo grandioso de la obra colonizadora es
el relativo a la metalurgia." ["A magnificent chapter
in the effort of colonization is that of metallurgy."]
With these words, Rey Pastor opens his chapter on
mining and metallurgy in La Ciencia y la Técnica en el
Descubrimiento de América, and it is hard to disagree
with him. Between 1532, when Francisco Pizarro cap-
tured Atahualpa, and 1634, when the Inquisition inves-
tigated the activities of a large colony of Portuguese
in Peru (and from which date various authors have
traced the decay of the mining industry), a series of
astonishing discoveries, inventions and publications
testifies to the vigor with which the industry was
developed in the most difficult terrain imaginable.
If there were errors and abuses--as most certainly
there were--there were also outspoken critics to de-
nounce them, and the period can best be described by
comparing it to the Industrial Revolution in Europe
two centuries later, with all its triumphs and fail-
ures.

Although it was not until 1548, with the defeat
of Gonzalo Pizarro by the astute Pedro de la Gasca,
that Peru may be said to be tolerably at peace, the
first major event dates from three years earlier. In
1545, the world's most famous silver mine was discovered in what was then Alto Peru. The story goes that

an Indian following a deer climbed the hill of Potosi
and came across a lump of native silver when a bush
he was pulling himself up on came away. He managed
to keep his secret for a time, but eventually another
Indian who had entered into partnership with him,
thinking the part of the mine he had been allotted
was inferior, gave the secret away to his encomendero
(sponsor), a Spaniard called Villarroel, who "denounced" the mine jointly with him. Situated only
slightly to the east of Porco, the minerals were
transported there for treatment during the first few
years, despite the fact that the town of Potosi was
founded almost at once. Soon, however, Potosi grew
to be the most important mining center in South America, and from it prospectors sallied forth through
the Andes looking for new mines. Cieza de Leon, who
traveled the area at this date, scarcely passes
through a province without mentioning its mines, citing as silver zones Cajamarca (Hualgayoc?), Huanuco
(Huallanca?), the area north of Huamanga, and Tarapaca (Huantajaya?) in what is now Chile. Gold-mining
areas were east of Loja in Ecuador, Chachapoyas, Con-
cepcion north of Cuzco, Carabaya and Sandia, down the
eastern side of the Cordillera Real where Gonzalo
Pizarro's followers were said to have fled from justice. Although the Spaniards were aware of the presence of other metals (they could hardly not be), such
as lead, zinc, copper, iron, tin and antimony, the
main interest was in gold and especially silver, because of its greater abundance, and more discoveries
followed in Lipes, Castrovirreyna (1590), Oruro
(1595, now better-known for tin), San Antonio de Esquilache (1619), Caylloma and Huancapeti (Ticapampa,
Ancash, 1620's) and Cerro de Pasco (1630). These
places all lie in bleak puna areas at or over 4,000
meters altitude. Perhaps the single most important
discovery was that of the mercury deposits of Huancavelica. Much of the credit for this must go to
the Portuguese Enrique Garces who had been conducting
a systematic search through the Andes for mercury,
finally exploiting a small mine north of Huancavelica;
but the famous Santa Barbara mine itself was actually
denounced by a certain Amador Cabrera on January 1,
1564, in the city of Huamanga. He appears to have
been told of its existence by a local curaca, or
chieftain.

The importance of the mercury was its use in
extracting silver by the amalgamation process. This
process, which became the standard one for treating
silver ores throughout the world until the later 19th
century, was invented by Bartolome de Medina in Mexico,
probably in 1554. The fact that gold can unite with
mercury to form an amalgam has been known since antiquity and used by metalworkers in gilding, and it may
be that they were aware that silver could be similarly
amalgamated, but there seems little doubt that Medina
was the first to think of applying these properties to
extracting the metal from the ores. Once Huancavelica
was discovered, it became obvious that the new invention should be applied in Peru, and the Viceroy Toledo
had an experienced practitioner, Fernandez de Velasco,
brought from Mexico to Potosi in 1571 to demonstrate
the method. Its great virtue was its efficacy with
relatively low-grade ores, and Potosi, which Cieza de
Leon refers to as being in decay only five years after
its discovery because of a fall in the grade of ore,
was resuscitated for a further 250 years. To Toledo
also goes the credit of officially establishing the
mining industry. He founded the city of Huancavelica,
promulgated the first legislation, transferred the
mint from Lima to Potosi (in 1575, after a brief and
abortive few months in Chuquisaca) and established
the system of Indian labor or _mita_, the source of so
many controversies. These two centers, Potosi and
Huancavelica, effectively dominate the history of
viceregal mining and metallurgy, and the techniques
used can best be discussed with reference to them.

THE MINES

With the exception of Cerro de Pasco, nearly all
viceregal silver mines exploited fairly well-defined
veins that ran between walls of sterile rock--the
cajas (singular: _cajon_). The minerals sought were
varied. The surface oxides were usually the highest
in silver content and were known collectively as _pacos_.
The rich sulphide argentite was called _tacana_ and when
mixed with copper or iron pyrites, _negrillo_. Tacana
in fine-grained form, often mingled with _panizo_
(crushed calcite and gangue), was also called

polvorilla. Ores that were half oxide, half sulphide
were known as mulatos. These sulphides, except, particularly, in Cerro de Pasco and Potosi itself, were
rather rare, and a more common silver mineral was
rosicler--a name applied to proustite and pyrargyrite,
which frequently appears in Peru as a reddish metallic
hardened paste smeared on the surface of fissures.
Argentiferous lead was also a major source of silver
and as it was easily treated was prized higher than
its grade would warrant, being used as a flux in
smelting where its silver content acted as a bonus.
It was known as soroche. Finally, the silver-bearing
varieties of tetrahedrite (e.g., freibergite) were
recognized and called pavonados.

     Potosi itself contained most of the minerals and
was typical in its form if not in its richness. The
deposit consisted of four main veins--Rica, Diego
Centeno, Estano (tin) and Mendieta--running more or
less south to north vertically on the eastern flank
of the famous mountain. According to Padre Jose de
Acosta, the vein first discovered--Rica--ran like a
crest along the ground for 300 pies (89 meters)* with
a width of 13 pies (3.6 meters). Its grade was almost
50 per cent silver and persisted thus to a depth of 67
estados (some 130 meters). When Acosta visited Potosi
with the Viceroy Toledo in 1574, the workings were already nearly 200 estados (390 meters) deep. The veins
varied in width from 6 pies (1.65 meters) to 1 palmo
(21 cms.), and the grade was reckoned to be rich at 30
to 50 pesos (these pesos are to be taken as pesos
ensayados) per quintal (i.e., 6 to 10 marcos per quintal or 30 to 50 kilos per metric ton) and poor at 2 to
6 pesos per quintal (2 to 6 kilos per metric ton).**
A modern silver miner considers his vein rich at 600
grams per metric ton. These staggering grades, of
course, did not persist and by Barba's time, in the
1620's, 20 marcos per cajon is cited as an average,
not a poor, grade. If the calculations made in Appendix D are acceptable, when applied to Potosi where
mercury sold at some 100 pesos corrientes per quintal
and we assume three additional men for every man at

_____

     *For units of length, see Appendix B.

     **For weights, see Appendix C.

the face, the ore "paid" when the grade was better
than 7 marcos per cajon. (In the 1740's, Antonio de
Ulloa says the mineral "paid" in Potosi at 8 to 10
marcos per cajon). Thus, the miners were still working with a large profit margin of some 68 pesos per
cajon, allowance being made for increased mercury
consumption. A miner with 20 employees working 300
days per year could thus earn a personal income of
over 10,000 pesos per year, roughly a quarter of the
viceroy's salary.

The actual extraction of the ore from the vein
was done initially by a barretero, or man armed with
a 25-pound crowbar. Potosi was renowned for being
particularly hard rock. The ore was then carried to
the surface by the apires. Acosta says they went in
threes, the front man with a candle, and each carried
two arrobas, or 23 kilos. They climbed up through
the mine by a series of ladders made of three leather
ropes so that people could pass going up and coming
down. Each ladder was some 10 estados long (20 meters) and then there was a rest platform. There
might be anything up to 20 such ladders to the surface. At over 4,000 meters, this was very heavy work.
Why did the Spaniards exploit their mines in this
curious way, with an opening at the top and violent
descent inside? The reason was not stupidity, as
some authors have assumed, but rather the law that
controlled the size of the mine a man could own. The
maximum size (i.e., length of vein) was 80 varas and
the minimum, 4 (65 and 3.5 meters). Short of owning
a stretch of vein on an almost vertical hillside,
there was little ore that would remain above a gallery dug in horizontally from the lowest part of the
surface concession; the mine had to work downward,
and very steeply, too. The Rica vein, for example,
contained 78 mines and the congestion inside must
have been dreadful. The obvious conclusions were
drawn and various miners joined together, or sometimes an outside contractor offered, to dig a socavon—a horizontal crosscut that gave access to several mines and also served to drain them. Such an
operation required capital and planning, as the first
socavon showed. It was started in 1556 and finished
in 1585, was 250 varas long, 8 pies wide and one

estado high.   It met the main vein 135 estados (some
260 meters) below the surface.   The owner closed it
with a locked door and charged all users of it one
fifth of the mineral they extracted by it.   Acosta
says there were some 9 socavones and more being constructed when he wrote his Historia Natural y Moral
de las Indias.   In Potosi, there seems to have been
no need to refill the veins where the metal was extracted or to prop the walls apart.   Many of the silver mines in Peru were blessed this way with rigid,
almost vertical, cajas, and the cuts in hillsides
where veins have been completely removed can be seen
frequently--for example in Caylloma and Morococha.

What was the production of the mine?   This question is not easily answered.   Acosta states that
300,000 quintales were treated by amalgamation yearly
and indicates that this yielded perhaps 30 per cent
of the refined silver production.   As the richer ores
were smelted and refined in the furnaces, this figure
may perhaps be doubled to give total production from
the mine.   Six hundred thousand quintales is not incompatible with an effective mita of some 2,000 Indians and the assumptions of Appendix D.   The figure
is equivalent to 92 metric tons daily if we assume,
as was customary, that the year contained 300 working
days.   Once extracted from the mine, the mineral was
normally dumped in a cancha outside the entrance
where it was hand picked by pallaqueros to separate
ore from obvious gangue.   It was then transported on
llamas down the hillside to beneficiating plants situated on the streams near the town.   Allowing for the
distances involved and the small load a llama can
carry (2 to 3 arrobas), there must have been well
over 1,000 llamas employed in this transport.   So
necessary indeed were the llamas that later, when the
Indians found they could get a better price for them
as meat rather than as beasts of burden, legislation
had to be introduced to control their slaughter.   A
juez del hierro was created, an official who had a
branding iron with which all animals no longer fit
for this work were to be marked as available for
slaughter.   With true criollo initiative, this official was, in the 1680's, hiring out the iron to
would-be butchers at 30 pesos a week!

Such, then, was the mine of the famous Villa Imperial de Potosi in the late 16th century, less than half a century after its discovery. The brute figures referring to extraction place it in the class of a modern mine working with all mechanical aids, pneumatic drills in particular. Other silver mines were similar, if on a much smaller scale. Nevertheless, Caylloma has colonial workings over 100 meters deep and Cerro de Pasco, in much more difficult circumstances, went down to 70 meters, although at a later date. Three fears beset the silver miners: first, that the grade would drop or they would "lose the vein" (this expression presumably referred to faults that had displaced it); second, that they would encounter water; and third, that they would not be able to get labor. (In contrast with Huancavelica, the silver mines were not famous for collapses, Cerro de Pasco excepted, and in most of them no such accidents are recorded.) As the years passed, progressively lower grades were worked, and Antonio de Ulloa, in the 1740's, says that 5 marcos per cajon "paid" in Tarma (Cerro de Pasco?), while Demetrio O'Higgins, referring to San Juan de Lucanas in 1804, implies that the limit had been reached at 2.5 marcos per cajon (250 grams or 8 ounces per ton--very near the modern cutoff). Flooding of the mine implied socavones, pumps being a later introduction, and the history of some mines (e.g., Cerro de Pasco) is a history of their drainage tunnels, expensive long-term projects needing a stable political climate. The third problem, that of labor, will be discussed shortly.

The other famous mine of Peru was Huancavelica, which maintained the silver-mining industry and even at times supplied Mexico with mercury. Famous, or perhaps better infamous, the mine had a long history of disasters, litigation and debt and was popularly known as la mina de la muerte--the mine of death. Its importance was recognized very early and the Viceroy Toledo "nationalized" it, buying out the mine denounced by Cabrera for 250,000 ducados in 1572. However, there were over 40 other mines in the same area and it would appear that the Crown did not have exclusive control of the mineralized zone until well into the 17th century. Cabrera very soon decided that

he had been swindled and opened a lawsuit against the
State.   Whether this was the cause of his being jailed
in Huamanga is unknown, but when the contracts for
operating the mine were renewed in 1618--in which, by
a gentlemen's agreement, the contractors were the
original owners of the mine--the unfortunate Cabrera
was excluded on the grounds that he was under sentence
of death.   These contracts are worthy of some examination.   The general basis was that the miners operated the mine for the Crown and were obliged to
deliver a certain quantity of refined mercury per
year.   One fifth of this mercury was taken as quintos
reales and the rest was bought at an agreed price,
any surplus production being treated similarly.   The
miners were authorized a mita with which to work the
mine, and in later contracts the amount of mercury
they were obliged to produce was tied to the number
of mita Indians they were allocated.   The details of
the early contracts are obscure.   Acosta states that
Potosi was using 6,000 to 7,000 quintales of mercury
a year, so presumably the miners were obliged to supply approximately this quantity.   In 1596, however,
a new contract was made reducing the obligatory production to 1,000 quintales, and in 1600 this was renewed for another six years.   The price the Crown
paid for mercury was 40 pesos ensayados per quintal.
Apparently, at the time of the contract there were
large mercury reserves in the royal stores.   Moreover, the pernicious effects of the mine were becoming visible in the appalling mortality of the Indians,
and one is tempted to think that there was almost a
deliberate policy to run down the mine on the part of
the Viceroy Velasco.   However, by 1605 the new vice-
roy--the Conde de Monterrey--alarmed by the shortage
of mercury, raised the price to 47 pesos ensayados,
increased the mita, contracted for 4,600 quintales
and sent a certain Dr. Arias to reorganize the mine.
The viceroy died very soon after and his successor--
the Marques de Montesclaros--who actually spent six
weeks in Huancavelica, acted even more vigorously,
lifting production to 8,200 quintales annually.   He
complained bitterly that his predecessors had left
the mine in chaos and that the miners owed the Crown
300,000 pesos in advances made to pay the mitayos
(the Indians of the mita).

Behind these <u>volte-faces</u> in policy lay the lamentable story of the mine itself. According to early accounts, it is clear that the original deposit consisted of a very rich vein of cinnabar (llimpi), which was finally lost in 1645--all that is left now being disseminations in sandstone. This mine had been worked in pre-Inca times for cinnabar, which was used as a cosmetic, if not for mercury gilding as suggested earlier. The Indians were aware of the dangers of mercury and the Incas actually prohibited the use of the mine except with royal authority on these grounds. The Spaniards, it seems, were not so well aware, or were careless, and by Acosta's time the mine was already 70 estados (136 meters) deep. If Montesinos is to be believed, the grade was some 10 per cent.* Once at these depths and with these grades, the mercury dust became lethal with the lack of ventilation. The obviously scientific way of exploiting the mine with galleries and crosscuts was prohibited for this reason in 1600 by the Viceroy Velasco, who recommended working down from the surface in the manner of an open pit. In 1603, a priest by the name of Padre Agia descended 150 estados (nearly 300 meters) into the mine and stated that to work there even a few months was certain death. Ghastly stories of Indians who when they cut themselves bled mercury as well as blood and the dreadful effects of mercury on the lungs caused the Conde de Monterrey to close the principal socavon, and Dr. Arias began digging ventilation shafts and small open pits from the surface. This started a dispute that lasted until 1681 when the mine collapsed in one of the richest parts, San Jacinto, owing, said the miners, to rain and water entering via these workings of Dr. Arias. Those in favor of the socavon seemed to have got their way again in 1609 with the Marques de Montesclaros' productivity drive that involved starting a gallery three varas wide and three-and-one-half varas high, finally finished in 1642 (in the construction of which occurs the first reference to the use of

---

*Fernando Montesinos is the author of <u>Memorias Antiguas Historiales del Perú</u>. The book was written long after the Conquest and is not considered to be too reliable a source.

explosives in a Peruvian mine, 1635).   The next viceroy (the Principe de Esquilache) signed yet another
contract, this time for 6,600 quintales per year, and
supported the socavoneros against another expert who
took Dr. Arias' part.   This viceroy in his memoir implies that his predecessors' high production was owing
to pulling out all the props and supports in the mine,
which had to be rebuilt with stones brought in for
the purpose, and remarks on the general difficulty of
it all as the mine was now 200 estados (390 meters)
deep.

So it goes on.   The issue involved was a very
real one.   The mine was unsafe whatever was done to
it with the techniques available at the time--only a
huge open pit on modern lines could have solved the
problem, but this was impossible at the end of the
16th century.   On the other hand, if Peru was to continue to produce silver--and the Spanish Empire depended on it--the mine was indispensable.   The series
of compromises and changes of policy led to an irrational exploitation, and the ever-present financial
difficulties tempted the miners every so often to
remove the supports of rich ore.   The end was clear;
Dr. Arias' well-intentioned ventilation shafts let
in the weather and, aided by earthquakes, the mine
experienced a series of horrific collapses throughout
the 17th and 18th centuries, with 200 lives lost in
the final disaster of 1786.

The mine itself was only half the headache.   The
refined mercury was required almost entirely in the
Potosi area.   It was carried in leather bags by llamas
and mules to Chincha, then by boat to Arica, then by
mule to Potosi and Oruro.   The contracts with carriers
were an endless source of argument, particularly the
part by sea, and the cost was some 19 pesos ensayados.
Add this to the 47 that the Crown paid for a quintal
in Huancavelica and it totals 66.   Since mercury sold
in Potosi at 70 pesos ensayados (116 pesos corrientes),
the profit margin was small, as the Principe de
Esquilache pointed out.   This was assuming free shipment to Arica in the boats of the Navy.   (In fact, he
was being somewhat disingenuous as the cost of mercury
to the Crown was four fifths of 47 pesos ensayados,
the remaining 50 being the royal fifth, and the price

in Potosi was subsequently lowered to some 100 pesos
corrientes.) In Potosi--and elsewhere--the mercury
was sold on credit, one libra being delivered for
every marco of silver expected from the harinas, or
milled ore ready for amalgamation. The product of
the amalgamation was to be used to pay the debt. Of
course, the debts were often not paid and were 1.3
million pesos at the time of the Marques de Montesclaros. The offices from which the mercury was sold
were known as the cajas reales. Here the royal fifths
were collected, the amount of mercury bought serving
as an indication of what might be expected in the way
of quintos from the buyer. Here, too, was the ensayador who assayed and stamped the silver bars to certify
that the taxes had been paid and that the silver could
be generally sold. The major mining centers each had
a caja real. It is interesting to note the consumption of mercury in the various zones at this time (the
late 1610's): Potosi, 5,000 quintales; Oruro, 700
quintales; Castrovirreyna, 200 quintales; others (including the gold mine at Zaruma, near Loja, Ecuador),
100 quintales.

LABOR FOR THE MINES

The first reference to the way in which labor
was procured for the mines is in Cieza de Leon's account of Potosi. It is worth quoting the passage in
full: "Pues tomada posesión (de la mina) por los es-
pañoles, comenzaron a sacar plata desta manera: que
al que tenía mina le daban los indios que en ella en-
traba un marco, y si era muy rica, dos cada semana;
y si no tenía mina, a los señores comenderos de indios les daban medio marco cada semana." ["Then, once
the Spaniards had taken possession of the mine they
began to extract silver in this manner: to a mine
owner the Indians who entered the mine gave a marco
per week, or two marcos if the mine was very rich;
but if he (and here is a difficulty, who is this he?)
did not own a mine, the Indians paid half a marco
weekly to their encomendero."]* The passage is not

_____

*Cieza de Leon, La Cronica del Perú, Part I
(Madrid: Austral Edition, 1945), Chapter 109.

completely explicit but some implications seem clear.
First, the Indians paid to enter the mine, so presumably all they could extract over and above the fee
for entry was their own.   On the basis of Appendix D,
it seems probable that a group of seven Indians working together could extract a cajon a week fairly
easily.   If the grade was "poor," they would pay 7
marcos to the mine owner.   Poor grades, according to
Acosta, were from 20 to 60 marcos per cajon, so if we
assume a grade of 40, each Indian should readily make
4 to 5 marcos profit per week, or nearly 1,000 pesos
ensayados yearly, tax paid.   No wonder, as Cieza de
Leon says later, Indians came from far and wide to
work in the mine.   Second, it seems that those Indians
whose encomenderos were not mine owners would get permission to work in the mine at a fee of half a marco.
(The encomienda system allocated to the Spaniards
various regions plus their inhabitants from whom they
were allowed to extract the Crown taxes and in return
for which they were expected to provide the public
services, magistrates, priests etc.   The system was
very soon abused as the encomenderos tended to look
on the Indians for which they were responsible as
their private employees, if not positively slaves.)
Thus, initially it appears that Indians were so keen
to work in the mine that they not only paid to enter
them, but also paid to be relieved from other duties
or allegiances.   As Cieza de Leon goes on to say, the
mine was only part of the incentive, the other being
the refining by guayras--the only method applicable
in Potosi before the introduction of amalgamation.
This refining was done entirely by the Indians, who
climbed the hillsides with the furnaces to catch the
wind.   When they were refining someone else's mineral,
it was impossible to check if some was not stolen,
and with their own minerals evasion of paying the
quintos was easy.   Thus, there is no evidence that
the Indians regarded the Potosi mine, and by analogy
any other silver mine, with dread.   If later they
were to flee from the mita, it must have been because
they were badly treated, under paid or over worked--
not because the mine itself was uninhabitable.

    When Viceroy Toledo visited Potosi in 1574, he
decided to establish the mita.   What his reasons were

for doing so are unknown, other than the desire of a
tidy and orderly mind to set up the mining industry
on an organized footing. Was there a labor shortage?
If there was it must have been difficult to appreciate
its extent as the whole mine was in decay until the
introduction of the amalgamation process, which occurred almost at the same date. The system was one of
forced labor for the Indians. The surrounding country
was divided into districts, the number of able-bodied
men in each district determined (men between the ages
of 18 and 50), this number being divided into seven
groups so that each group would serve once every seven
years. Each group was, in turn, divided by three so
that the mita, or spell of forced labor (mita in
Quechua, the Indian language of Peru, means "time")
lasted four months. Instructions were given that the
mitayos, the Indian laborers affected, be moved around
weekly during their four-month spell so that one man,
for example, did not spend all the time under-ground
while another worked driving llamas. Systems of
forced labor of this sort had frequently been used by
the Incas for public works and it was not a novelty
to the Indians. The towns, in particular Potosi itself, were exempt from the mita, which was extended
to most, but not all, of the major mining centers.
The initial number of Indians affected in the Potosi
region was some 80,000, giving a mita of about 3,800.

There are two ways of viewing the mita. One
point of view was that adopted by many priests and
more half-heartedly by some of the viceroys: that it
was iniquitous. That Indians who were nominally free
men should be forceably removed from their homes and
made to work in those terrible mines from which they
seldom returned was a sin in itself. Add to this the
abuses: the fact that some mine owners tried to make
them work day and night, and indeed live, underground;
the attempts to link their wages to the grade extracted (independent of the richness of the part of
the mine they were put to work in); the non-payment
of journey money from and to their homes--up to 150
leguas* distant; the non-observance of certain public

---

*For units of length, see Appendix B.

holidays and saints' days; these and innumerable
other forms of exploitation horrified well-thinking
contemporaries. Acosta, in his De Procuranda Indorum
Salute, after citing what St. Crisostom thought of
mines, continues (author's translation):

> . . . but all this is pure shadow and smoke
> of what we see now: perpetual and horren-
> dous night, thick subterranean air, the de-
> scent difficult and perilous, exhausting
> battle against the living rock, to stand
> still is dangerous, if your foot slips it's
> the end, the back-breaking burden on the
> shoulders, the ascent by steep and unsafe
> gradients, and other things which cause
> terror merely to think of them: on top of
> this, since the silver veins are in broken
> and inaccessible places, in uninhabitable
> districts, to work them one has to abandon
> one's native lands, changing air and soil,
> so that one easily falls sick. And then
> what about the mercury mines, whose vapors
> once inhaled produce death?

Acosta had entered Potosi and suffered from soroche,
or altitude sickness. He can only conclude, somewhat
jesuitically, that the ways of God are inscrutable--
for without the silver the Spaniards would not have
come to Peru, and without that the Indians would be
still living in darkness and idolatry. To the Jesuits' credit they attacked the mita, at least one
priest being summoned before the Inquisition by Viceroy Toledo for a book along the lines of those of the
famous Bartolome de las Casas. This put Acosta, who
was a member of the Inquisition and provincial of the
Company, in a difficult spot--a false move and Toledo
would expel the Company from Peru, an event that
would have been a misfortune by any standard as the
Company was, and remained until its final eviction,
the Indians' greatest single defense. Acosta was so
cautious, he was blamed by his fellow Jesuits at the
time, but later they recognized his tact and diplomacy.

      Another view of the mita was expressed a century
later by the Viceroy/Archbishop don Melchor de Linan y

Cisneros.* He said that since an Indian would be
affected only four or five times in his lifetime, and
only for four-month spells, the mita could hardly be
regarded as overly burdensome. The faults lay in its
abuse and this must be controlled rigorously, and he
proceeded to list some common perversions of the
original scheme. He mentioned the pay that was 4
reales per day, less half a real that went to support
a wealth of officials (including an interpreter) whose
job was to look after the Indians' rights. If we take
the mita as 75 working days, the mitayo earned some 33
pesos, a sum better than the total annual agricultural
wage in the 18th century according to Ulloa. Added to
this, the Indians used their non-working spells for
acting as palladores, people who wandered around the
mountain picking up what they could find and selling
it—a process known as rescate. Most of the chunks of
mineral were, of course, stolen from the mines and not
found loose at all, and it was determined to turn a
blind eye to these activities as, after all, the Crown
got its quintos. The case is argued by the Marques de
Montesclaros in the early 17th century, who actually
opened a market for this trading in stolen metal to
"shame the Indians into stopping it" he says, but more
likely to make sure that the Crown could keep an eye
on it and collect its taxes. The Archbishop, in his
turn, pointed out that voluntary laborers, mingados,
also worked in the mine, at 6 or more reales daily.
If the mine was uninhabitable, he argued, it should
have been shut to voluntary as well as to forced
labor. The presence of volunteers testified it was
not so dreadful and, besides, economically it was
out of the question to shut it. If it was to be
worked properly, however, the volunteers were not
sufficient; therefore, the mita was necessary. The
only point to assure was that the mita was not abused.

A third point of view of the mita has often been
adopted by foreign authors, particularly British ones
just after the Latin American wars of independence.
This view was that the cruelties of the mita were just
a symptom of Spanish colonial savagery, backwardness

---

*See M.A. Fuentes, ed., Memorias de los Virreyes
(Madrid, 1959).

and incompetence and that if only the countries were
governed by the British all would be well. Apart from
the hypocrisy of this from a country that was still
running a slave trade, one may, perhaps, not unfairly
suspect these and other authors of enlightened self-
interest. It is worth remarking that the principle of
forced labor is regarded as acceptable today in most
countries of the world, whether it be military service
in France or sugar harvesting in Cuba, and the real
point at issue is the conditions.

The most general characteristic of the mitas of
all the Peruvian mines was that they never achieved
their theoretical full strength. One reason, undoubtedly, was the natural disinclination of anyone
to forced labor, coupled with a dislike for the
mines--a dislike that might stem from past horrific
experiences or could simply be claustrophobia or an
objection to any work whatever. A second reason was
the way in which the mita was recruited by areas,
where by moving into the next area where he was not
registered an Indian could escape the mita with very
little trouble. If he was once brought to Potosi,
then he often did not go home. Sometimes, the journey was very long and if he was not paid the _pririna_
(which seems to have been 2 reales for every 5 leguas
of journey) and was a bachelor, the incentive for
return was small, particularly as he was exempt from
the mita living in Potosi and could seek employment
in the mine at a much higher wage as a free man.
Regular Indian suburbs grew up this way; 14 Indian
parishes existed in 1620. The priests in charge of
them said that the mitayos never had anything to con-
fess to them, whereas these Indians who settled in
Potosi were up to every kind of wickedness. However,
the viceroy says at the same time that even mitayos
who were supposed to work a six-day week starting on
Monday frequently only came to work on Tuesday morn-
ing because of weekend drunkenness! Perhaps the most
common way of avoiding the mita was to buy oneself
off. This could be done in two ways. The first way,
much denounced by the authorities, consisted of paying the local _cacique_ (chief) or _corregidor_ a sum of
money (up to 180 pesos) who then avoided registering
the Indian or wrote him as dead, missing, etc. This

method was favored by the chiefs, of course, who
sometimes accepted payment in the form of a sort of
voluntary slavery contract. Indeed, they were accused of getting people off the mita this way without even asking their consent, thus furnishing themselves with labor and potential labor in the form of
debtors. Another way was to pay the miner directly.
This was popular with the miners, who received an income without the bother of having to operate a mine,
but very unpopular with those who were trying to
collect the royal fifths. One way or another, the
effective mita was continually dropping from the
nominal 4,000 or so to below 2,000 and continually
being revived by the authorities who, faced with a
decreasing rural population, could do no other than
increase the frequency, so that in the 1610's the
mita fell once every three, not every seven, years.
Moreover, the decline in grade in the mine naturally
drove the owners to strive for a higher mineral production, but with fewer workers to achieve it.
These extra burdens, of course, fell on the men least
able to bear them: the fathers of rural families who
could not move because they were living off their
little piece of land. Some viceroys attributed this
decay in the population to the responsibility of establishing and maintaining an ordinary family having
grown too much for the average Indian who preferred
a nomadic, bachelor life.

Such was the mita in Potosi and it was similar,
if on a smaller scale, in most other silver mines.
In his 1614 memoir, the outgoing viceroy, the Conde
de Montesclaros, lists the following silver mines as
being established centers with mitas: Potosi, Pasco,
Vilcabamba, Castrovirreyna and Nuevo Potosi.* Oruro
did not have a mita as voluntary labor was easily recruited from the populous surrounding country. Gold

---

*Pasco and Nuevo Potosi. It may be conjectured
that Pasco refers to Colquijirca since this reference
is before the discovery of Cerro de Pasco. Nuevo
Potosi, also known as San Mateo de Huanchos, is a
mystery. It and Huanuco are later said to lie in the
province of Pasco, which might imply that it was

mines with mitas were Zaruma and Carabaya, a gold-
washing area that gives the impression of being somewhat outside royal control.   In 1612, a famous gold
mine was discovered near Cotahuasi (Arequipa) and
called Montesclaros in honor of the viceroy.   Montesclaros' successor states that in Nuevo Potosi, the
mita was 200 Indians, and in Castrovirreyna, 1,400.
Both these mines paid diezmos (tenths) instead of
fifths and the apparent prosperity of the latter was
largely due to extraneous silver being brought there
to pay the lesser tax.   When Caylloma opened, it was
allocated a mita of 480, but Cerro de Pasco apparently had none.   Besides the regular miners, the
country was full of undesirable vagabonds known as
"soldiers," since many of them were deserters who had
got a free passage to Peru by enlisting.   These people were a great nuisance to the authorities as they
were always demanding Indians as servants in one form
or another.   It was generally agreed that something
should be done about them because it would be improper
to let them starve and, besides, they were very fond
of disorders and insurrections.   Their only virtue
seemed to be that they went prospecting for mines in
the hope of getting rich quick--their only aim in
coming to America--and so, occasionally, they were
allocated mitas to work their discoveries.   These
mitas were restricted to 200 Indians, and it is perhaps these Indians who were to be pitied most among
the mitayos.

Vinchos, but both Pasco and Nuevo Potosi had cajas
reales, which seems unlikely if the two places were
a mere 50 kms. apart.   Elsewhere, Nuevo Potosi is
referred to as the nearest caja to Lima.   Llano Zapata, in a confused reference to Colquipocro in Ancash, says it lies between Jauja and the lake of
Junin.   Could it be Morococha?

     The author has no idea where the mine was in
Vilcabamba, but it is possible that it was one of
the molybdenum prospects that exist there and that
the Spanish had not yet discovered their mistake.
There are almost no later references to it, which
would support this view, although Llano Zapata men-
tions a silver production of 50 barras yearly.

It remains to discuss the mita for Huancavelica.
Until 1643, the number of Indians employed was something over 2,000. These worked for two months, when
another 2,000 arrived and so on for four 2-month periods. The remaining two 2-month periods had a mita
of some 1,000 Indians and corresponded to winter in
Huancavelica (the sierra winter being the actual sum-
mer, i.e., December to March when the rains occur).
It is not clear what the frequency was from the early
account, but much later a 7-year cycle is indicated,
so some 70,000 Indians were affected by the mita.
The Viceroy Montesclaros determined by experiment
that 1 mitayo could produce 2 quintales of mercury
yearly, and the contractual obligation of the miners
was drawn up accordingly. It is strange that this
officially approved production would not even cover
the mitayo's wage--1 man-year being worth some 150
pesos corrientes, while 2 quintales (quintos paid)
valued 75 pesos ensayados or some 124 pesos corrientes. The next viceroy put the figure at 3 quintales
per Indian. In view of the dangers of the mine, the
Crown maintained a hospital in Huancavelica (from
before 1608), which counted 120 beds, but since mercury poisoning was incurable it cannot have been of
very much use, notwithstanding remedies that consisted of swallowing powdered gold, which was supposed to collect the mercury to be later expelled as
an amalgam and, no doubt, recovered. With regard to
the dangers, it is surprising to note that the Viceroy Montesclaros, who actually visited Huancavelica
only five years after Padre Agia, made very light of
them. True, a socavon had been closed and perhaps,
too, Dr. Arias' ventilation shafts had some effect,
but it suggests that the dangerous areas might have
been fairly localized and that most of the mine was
not lethal. Certainly, in later years the disasters
recorded are nearly all collapses, not poisoning, but
this may be because of the drop in grade when the
main vein was lost in 1645. Huancavelica is full of
mysteries, not least the fact that the mita dropped
to a nominal 620 in 1643 and an actual 350 by 1680
but, despite this and the loss of the vein, production increased toward an average of 6,000 quintales
per year. If this was due, as seems likely, to the
introduction of explosives (first used 1635) and to
Lope de Saavedra's improved furnace for extracting

mercury (1633), it is a striking example of the effects of technology.

METALLURGY

The field in which technology was most noticeably
successful was that of metallurgy, and as the most
important metallurgical process was mercury amalgamation it is interesting to follow it through--from the
refining of mercury to the final release on the market
of plata ensayada (assayed silver) and coins--noting
the various technical improvements that were introduced.

The basis of mercury production from cinnabar
ores was, and still is, the heating of the milled ore
to drive off mercury vapors that are then condensed
and collected as liquid mercury. For obvious reasons,
this should be done in some sort of closed container
and, thus, the original equipment used at Huancavelica
consisted of little more than an eartherware pot full
of ore with another inverted pot on top of it. Where
the two met, the join was sealed with mud and the
whole was heated by building a fire up around it.
When all the mercury was thought to be driven off,
the fire was extinguished, the pot left to cool and,
once it was certain that all the rich (and lethal)
vapor had condensed, the inverted top was removed
and the mercury was found sticking to the inside of
it. The deficiencies of the process were the fuel
consumed; its "batch" nature, which always involved
a long waiting time while the pots cooled; and the
large losses because of the mercury falling back into
the gangue in the lower pot where it was difficult
to recover. To overcome this latter problem, the
top pot occasionally was modified by the addition of
a sort of spout that terminated under the surface
level of water in a third vessel, the vapor driven
off condensing in the water. Perhaps the biggest
drawback was the small scale of the process. When
production was aimed at some 6,000 quintales annually,
and even if we assume grades of 10 per cent, it would
be necessary to treat 60,000 quintales of mineral.
If the lower pot contained one quintal--a plausible
figure--and we assume two charges per pot per day and
300 days in the year, it is clear that some 100 such

small condensers would be working continually. Once
the grade dropped, as later it did to some four libras
per _carga_ (just over 1 per cent), this number would
have risen to 1,000 without some changes in the process.

The first and obvious improvement was to have a
common furnace in which all the pots stood, or sometimes were buried in the ground. Such would appear
to be the design of the _javeca_ introduced in the late
16th century or, more likely, it was the furnace described by Barba, which had a vaulted roof with holes
in it in which were set small pots with the mineral,
covered with an inch or two of well-pressed ash. The
vessels for collecting the mercury were then set up-
side-down on top of these, so that the lower pot projected into the furnace to get the heat from the fire,
whereas the upper one was in the open air so as to
cool it and condense the mercury. Any mercury that
fell down instead of sticking to the inside of the
upper pot was easily collected from the ash bed.
Whatever their exact form, the javecas were regarded
as a great innovation as also was the use of _ichu_
(Andean grass) as fuel. It should be emphasized that
throughout the high Andes wood is extremely scarce,
even after the introduction of the ubiquitous eucalyp-
tus in the 1860's. The process still suffered from
its "batch" nature, although clearly the fire could
be kept going and one pair of pots replaced by another. The pots were allowed to cool naturally as
the peril of a fracture if they were cooled with water
was too great. A furnace charge, according to Montesinos, was 15 arrobas.

In 1633, Lope de Saavedra, a doctor living in
Huancavelica, presented a new design of furnace that
became popularly called the _busconil_, since its devel-
oper was nicknamed _el buscon_ (the seeker). Unfortunately, contemporary details of its construction do
not seem to exist, but Mariano de Rivero states that
it consisted of a hearth with a grill 2.5 or 3 varas
above it and a conical roof 3 varas above the grill
(in all, some 6 meters high). The mineral sat on the
grill with the fire below it, and the furnace was
heated for 3 to 5 hours, when all ventilation to it
was stopped. Near the top of the cone there were four
holes pierced, through which passed eight tubes leading

down the outside to condensation vessels filled with
straw or water where the mercury collected. The tubes
were occasionally cooled with water to help condensation. A charge was 50 quintales and it appears that
it could handle one charge daily. (Jose Antonio
Becerra, in 1792, states that one furnace would produce 20 to 30 quintales of mercury a year, which would
agree with this figure using grades slightly under
10 libras per cajon.) The invention was reckoned such
an improvement in its saving of labor and fuel and
its ability to treat low-grade ores that Saavedra
(together with his heirs) was awarded a pension of
2 per cent of the value of the mercury production at
Huancavelica. He was later drowned with his son at
sea, and the Crown appropriated the 2 per cent for
the upkeep of Huancavelica hospital. Once refined,
the mercury was sold to the caja real in Huancavelica
at the agreed price (in the 1620's, 47 pesos ensayados), less the 2 per cent, less the quintos, and
transported to the various silver- and gold-mining
regions. (A further method for extracting mercury
from cinnabar was that invented by Capellin in Mexico
in the 1570's and named after him. It is described
by Francisco Javier de Gamboa. Apparently, it was
not used in Peru; probably, it was only suitable on
a small scale.)

The amalgamation process in which the mercury
was used was current in Peru and throughout many parts
of the world for over 300 years from its invention
in 1554, and it is not to be supposed that it remained
unchanged over such a period of time when applied to
a wide variety of ores. What follows is, therefore,
a description of the general principles based on
Acosta, Barba, Gamboa (who described the process as
used in Mexico, where the quantities seem to have
been somewhat different) and, couched in more modern
terminology, Mariano de Rivero, Johann Jacob von
Tschudi and Antonio Raimondi in their interesting
descriptions of Cerro de Pasco in the 19th century.

The first stage in treating the ores was, of
course, milling. According to Acosta, already in the
16th century various elaborate water mills were in use
in Potosi coupled with seven artificial lakes of over
1 million cubic meters capacity each to tide the plant

over the dry season. The milling was done by hammers
falling on the ore, or by a wheel that rolled around
on top of it. (The wheel had a horizontal axle fixed
to a vertical one attached to a horizontal water wheel
under the floor of the building--a method much criticized, inexplicably, by Zachariah Helms in the
1790's.) Mills were also powered by horses and, occasionally, by men who rocked a half-moon stone from
the opposing ends of a bar across the diameter. The
crushed ore was then sieved through wire sieves to
make it as fine as possible so that the mercury could
contact and embrace the silver. The silver ore was
placed in the <u>patios</u>, which were normally round but
sometimes rectangular, and salt and mercury added.
A charge for a patio could be anything from 20 to
600 quintales. The amount of mercury added was approximately four to five times the amount of silver
expected and this went to form the amalgam, plus one
third of the weight of this expected amalgam to ensure
a sufficient surplus for traces of silver still in
the ore. Thus, one cajon of ore estimated to contain
20 marcos required some 56 to 70 libras of mercury.
Clearly, a previous estimate of the grade was necessary and this properly was done by the smelting and
cupellation of a sample. Often, however, a small
amalgamation was performed that was not too accurate.
The amount of salt, or salt water, added depended on
the state of the mineral, enough being supplied to
"ungrease" it, that is to stop it sticking together.
The salt could be 10 per cent of the total charge to
the patio.

Once the mercury was added, and this was done by
squeezing it through a cloth over the patio so as to
ensure it was evenly and finely scattered, the amalgamation as such could start. To aid the process, the
contents of the patio were stirred from time to time
and often violently, by walking horses around on top
of it. If all went well between stirring and leaving
it to work on its own, the amalgamation might be complete in anywhere from 5 to 20 days. This was judged
by inspecting the mixture for any unamalgamated silver
or, better, by adding the mercury slowly so that there
was never a mercury surplus, and when the necessary
quantity had all been supplied the silver could be
judged all "incorporated" and the final mercury additions made to clean up the remnants. Unfortunately,

the process did not always go so smoothly. Two major
ills could affect it--"heating" or "cooling." "Heating" referred to when the mercury showed little sign
of amalgamating the silver but remained brilliant and
often became divided into minute lis (finely divided
mercury). Iron filings and sometimes basic additives
such as lime and ashes were used as remedies. "Cooling" was when the mercury became dirty and sluggish.
It was revived with the famous magistrales, acid solutions of one sort or another, particularly copper sulphate and urine. Other problems also occurred, such
as the silver floating in fine dust on the surface.
Not only was the process affected by the additives but
also by the ambient conditions--particularly the temperature. In sunny weather, it was observed to go
much faster so that sometimes the patios were heated
artificially from below, although the practice was not
widespread because of the cost of fuel. These heated
amalgamation baths were known as buitrones, and Barba
actually developed a process that he claimed as in-
fallible. It consisted of boiling the mixture in
copper cauldrons on a sort of kitchen range. Despite
his analysis, which showed that his process easily
paid for the fuel costs in increased yield, it did
not seem to catch on except after his lifetime.

It was natural that, instead of curing the ills
of "heating" and "cooling" in the patio, some methods
should be developed to remove them beforehand. Thus,
"heating" was to be avoided by ensuring that the mixture had sufficient quantities of lead/tin/iron in it
before the mercury was added and by previously washing
the mineral to remove copper sulphate solutions, "cooling" occurring if the former materials were added in
excess. Soon, however, it was found that the process
could be extended to a wider class of minerals, namely
sulphides, if they were previously roasted. This had
to be done carefully so as not to lose silver in the
fumes or in any slag that might be formed if the mineral overheated, and after roasting it was then washed
and calcined floating silver recovered for smelting
and the copper sulphate solutions removed. Milling
would follow this, facilitated by roasting where the
silver lost in dust would be less than if it had been
roasted already milled. So a variety of improvements

were developed, many of which were claimed by "inventors"--for example, the addition of iron filings was attributed, in 1587, to a man named Corzo from Tarapay (just north of Potosi).

Once the silver was all incorporated by the mercury, the mixture was washed in a separate bath with water, aided by a small manual stirrer mounted vertically over it. The heavy amalgam remained at the bottom and the slimes, etc., over flowed. Here, of course, occurred the losses, both of silver and, more seriously, of mercury. One of the many reasons for this, as Barba interestingly remarks, was the higher specific gravity of salty water, causing minerals to float that would not in clear water. Great care had to be taken, using as many as six washings whose slimes were treated to recover the mercury, but, nevertheless, even the experts could not avoid losing one marco of mercury for every marco of silver produced. As has been seen, the common reckoning was double this figure. Acosta gives some interesting annual statistics that imply slightly higher mercury losses, but in his day the grades were also much higher. Nevertheless, he states that of the total annual "consumption" (i.e., losses) in Potosi, which was between 8,000 and 9,000 quintales of mercury, some 2,000 were recovered by treating slimes, for which purpose over 50 furnaces existed--in short, the problem of mercury losses was taken seriously. Silver recuperation was, according to Barba, something better than 85 per cent.

After washing, the pella that remained (four or five parts mercury to one part silver) was formed into a pina, a "pineapple," and heated in a small condenser system like those used in the extraction of mercury. The distilled mercury returned to the circuit and the spongy silver that remained was hammered into bars. Pinas weighing 200 pounds might yield one bar of 65 marcos. This silver was plata corriente and it was forbidden to trade in it as it had not paid taxes, but, nevertheless, it circulated, as the viceroy's memoirs testify. Correctly, it was brought to the ensayador who took a small sample and by cupellation tested its purity. Pure silver was reckoned at 2,400 maravedis (copper coins) per marco and most Potosi

silver reached 2,380, which was the highest figure
authorized. As the coinage was less pure, at 11 dineros, 4 _granos,_ the silver required alloying with
copper if it was to be minted.

The assayed silver (plata ensayada) paid a tax
of 1 per cent, known as the _derecho de Cobos_ (a man
to whom the Emperor Charles V rashly gave this present
together with the title of Master of the Mint--when
the wealth of Potosi became apparent, the gift was
appropriated by the Crown), plus the royal fifth.
Metal that then went on to be minted paid _senoraje_ (a
charge to the Crown as the only person with the right
to mint coins) and _braceaje_ (minting costs) of 1 and
2 reales per marco, respectively. The latter charge
was often appropriated by the mint officials, although
they also received salaries. Finally, the silver was
struck into coins of .25, .50, 1, 2, 4 and 8 reales,
67 reales in all being produced from one marco. Here,
too, frauds occurred, particularly in the late 17th
century, with under-weight and debased coins being
produced. Fraud was not confined to the mint officials. Coin shortage permitted trading in "worked"
silver (as well as plata ensayada), as it was assumed
that such silver in the form of plates or candlesticks
would already have paid tax. One of the viceroys
acidly remarked that any old lump of silver with a
couple of hammer blows was being passed off as
"worked" silver (_plata labrada_).

The amalgamation process was applied to gold as
well as to silver, but in what is now Peru it seems
that most of the gold was produced by washing. Some
gold was also extracted from the refined silver, and
Barba gives instructions as to how this was done.

Although the amalgamation process dominated colonial metallurgy, it must not be thought that all silver was produced this way. First, the three types
of Indian furnaces persisted for some time, as Acosta's account of Potosi shows. It is not clear what
date he refers to but if we assume the 1580's, then
some ten years after the introduction of mercury to
Potosi perhaps some 40 per cent of silver production
was still due to the guayras (furnaces). The tocochimbos and _pachamancas_ (the pits dug in the ground)

also continued in use, charcoal- and wood-fired, respectively. Moreover, the Spaniards introduced two
new main designs of furnace. The first, the castel-
lanos, were used very early on in Porco. They were
a sort of forerunner of the blast furnace--a vertical
structure up to 2 meters high filled with charcoal
and ore that moved slowly downward gaining in temperature and finally melting in the hearth. They were
operated with bellows applied just above the level of
the molten metal. Their main use was in producing
intense heat, and they were particularly applied to
ores with a high copper content and, indeed, were
used for refining copper itself. They never were
successful with the Potosi ores, probably because
they converted the silver too readily to dust and
slag. The most important furnace, however, was the
reverberatory, introduced some time in the early 17th
century. This was heated indirectly by the flame
from a wood fire lit in a neighboring vault with an
opening through which the heat passed to the hearth
and mineral. This furnace was used for a variety of
purposes from roasting to cupellation. Most commonly,
it was employed for smelting silver ores over a lead
"bath." Rich ores such as tacana or rosicler were
mixed with argentiferous lead in a proportion of 1:2
or 1:3, smelted, the slag removed and then the plomo
de obra drawn off, cooled and broken into small
pieces for cupellation. The cupellation was performed
in the same furnace by preparing it with a special
hearth of ashes and powdered bones. The furnace seems
to have been particularly popular in southern Bolivia,
but the basic method survived until the 20th century
in most of Peru. Its advantages are obvious in a
country well-endowed with lead, as its indirect heating permits inspection and control of what is going
on, the only drawback being the fuel consumption.

Whatever the method used to produce, it is worth
under-lining the final figures for refined silver production. According to Acosta, between 1545 and 1585
111 million pesos ensayados passed through the caja
real in Potosi alone, giving an annual production of
some 2.8 million, not counting tax evasions and the
production of other mines. In modern units, this is
some 129,000 kilos yearly, larger than the production

of any single modern silver mine in the country
equipped with all modern aids.   In the early 17th
century, if the mercury "consumption" is used as a
guide to the silver produced by amalgamation, the
production from that source alone can be estimated
at 2,500 to 3,000 quintales annually, or, very
roughly, the same figure of 130 metric tons per year.
We can perhaps put total Peruvian silver production
for the first 100 years of the viceroyalty (amalgamation, smelting and evasions included) at a yearly
average of between 150 and 200 metric tons.

Although, of course, silver, mercury and, to a
certain extent, gold dominated the mining industry,
other metals were extracted and refined--Barba again
giving instructions in his book on how to do so.   The
main source of copper was from Coquimbo in Chile, and
as early as the 1610's it was being brought to Lima
for founding canons (for beating off English priva-
teers).   Ulloa says that high-quality copper sold at
8 to 10 pesos the quintal--a silver/copper ratio of
200:1.   Tin was always readily available in Bolivia
and used for bronze alloys, but iron seems never to
have been exploited.   Even as late as the 18th century, Ulloa refers to iron being brought from Mexico,
while high-quality steel was, of course, Spanish.
Thus, Peru, despite its vast resources, was not self-
sufficient in metals, and the familiar colonial pattern of economic development was already being set--
huge production and export of one product (silver),
together with the absence of a fundamental industry
even in the same field (iron and steel).

PUBLICATIONS AND LEGISLATION

It remains to discuss briefly two important
fields.   The first is that of technical and other
books written about the mines.   It is perhaps not
surprising that the discovery of a new world, together
with its fabulous wealth, should have provoked those
who were witnesses to its discovery to write about it,
but what is surprising is to find these accounts so
informative and enlightening.   There is an excellent
general description of Potosi by Cieza de Leon, and

none of the viceroys whose memoirs have survived fail
to describe both it and Huancavelica--often with
graphic accounts of their less-desirable aspects.
Emboldened by the clear royal pronouncements that the
justification for the conquest was the evangelization
of the Indians, many persons, whether viceroys or
humble friars, did not hesitate to speak their minds
when they thought the Indians were receiving bad
treatment, and the mines, as has been seen, also came
in for some savage written attacks. On the technical
side, two authors stand out in particular. The first,
Padre Jose Acosta, hardly needs praise as his inquir-
ing brain, scientific eye and clear exposition have
already been eulogized by no less a man than Humboldt,
over 200 years after his death. His account of
Potosi is both descriptive and filled with sufficient
figures to be able to reconstruct the processes used
and their efficiency. The second, another priest,
Alonso Barba, was the author of El Arte de los Metales. This astonishing book starts with several
chapters of mineralogy, describing the nature of rocks
and ores, and proceeds to give comprehensive instructions for smelting and refining all the metals known
in Peru. These accounts include the design of furnaces and the method of assays, the preparation of
fluxes and ways of rectifying processes that go
wrong. Theory is complemented with details of experiments that may be performed to verify it. Although
a Spaniard by birth, Barba spent the greater part of
his life in the area of Titicaca south to Lipes and
may be considered justly as the founder of American
science.

        The second field is that of legislation.
Strangely enough for a country given to passing laws
controlling everything, Spain promulgated none to
regulate the mining industry in America until 50 years
after the conquest of Peru, when in 1584 the so-called
Ordenanzas del Nuevo Cuaderno appeared. Perhaps the
reason was to be found in the contracts that Emperor
Charles V had signed with Pizarro that established
the royal share of any precious metals found (or
seized) and left everything else to the discretion
of the conqueror. Whatever the cause, the Viceroy
Toledo found the absence of order not to his liking
and passed his own laws in 1574, which he was entitled

to do by a 1563 <u>real cedula</u>. Toledo's laws were approved in 1592 by Philip II and remained in force until the late 18th century with few modifications, the <u>Nuevo Cuaderno</u> legislation only being referred to where Toledo's was deficient. Toledo, as has been seen, nationalized Huancavelica and established the mita. Besides these two capital steps, he laid down the principles of mine ownership. Mines belonged to the Crown but vassals could exploit them (this affords a justification for nationalization if deemed necessary). "Vassals" included foreigners--but Gamboa, in his later commentaries, makes it quite plain that foreigners were those who were either naturalized or had special permission, no other foreigners indeed being allowed to come to the Indies. Dimensions of mines were fixed, with a maximum of 80 by 40 varas for the discoverer's and 60 by 30 for the others' (a discovery had to be over one legua distant from the nearest existing mine), and the need for marking them out with small landmarks at the four corners, together with the procedure for doing so, was established. The ownership of a mine was conditional on its being worked. For a 60-vara mine "worked" meant no less than eight Indians employed, and a break of four months implied loss of possession--a time-lapse later increased to one year and one day in the 1590's. No excuses of labor shortages were allowed--war, pestilence and famine alone being acceptable. The legislation continued with rulings for trespass between mines, exploitation of tips, the sale of mines, litigation (which was not to stop work), etc. Also, the right of freedom to prospect anywhere was made clear. These basic rulings, particularly those referring to possession, throw considerable light on modern legislation and popular feeling toward certain aspects of the operation of foreign companies in Peru. The standard taxes were the quintos and the derecho de Cobos, but new mines might have tax concessions, e.g., pay tenths. Surprisingly, although mines were treated in detail, together with safety regulations for them, there was virtually no mention or rulings about beneficiating plants. Gamboa was to comment succinctly on this in his <u>Comentarios a las Ordenanzas de Minas</u>: "To refine sugar one has to pay a fortune for a good <u>maestro,</u> and to refine silver one is to confide in a great idiot?" (author's translation). Indeed, no

control whatever was exercised over the technical
competence of the <u>azoqueros</u> or plant owners.

THE INDUSTRY ESTABLISHED

By 1632, 100 years after the capture of Cajamarca,
the mining industry was firmly established in Peru.
Although new discoveries, inventions, publications
and legislation lay ahead, all the fundamental ones
had already been made. The norms and even the tra-
ditions of Peruvian mining were laid and many present-
day attitudes and feelings can be better understood
with a knowledge of what happened during these first
100 years. One final event is particularly illumina-
ting.

In 1633 and 1634, Lima's most famous Inquisition
trial began. Although final judgment was not passed
until 1639 (when remarkably few people were actually
convicted), in these two years a veritable witch hunt
against the Portuguese in Peru developed. Of course,
by law no Portuguese were allowed into the country
without special permission, but many seem to have got
this and those who had not were tacitly ignored, particularly since the Crowns of Spain and Portugal had
been united since 1580. Soon, the Portuguese seem to
have made themselves busy in the field of commerce and
it was not long before they were accused of monopoliz-
ing trading and controlling a large number of mines
as well. In 1620, the Viceroy Principe de Esquilache
was even to accuse them of tax evasion by sending silver from Lipes (in southern Bolivia) to Portugal via
Buenos Aires. The formal charge brought against some
of them, however, was that of being secret proselytiz-
ing Jews, but a charge so difficult to establish led
to widespread denouncements, information and ven-
geances against any unfortunate Portuguese one might
have a grudge against. Soon, the jails were full and
panic was sown in the foreign community. By force or
by fear, the Portuguese mine owners are said to have
been evicted from their mines, many of which were not
worked again until the late 19th century. This is the
tradition supported by authors as reputable as Tschudi,
who cites the Morococha and Yauli regions as having

been abandoned at this date. There seems little
doubt that the gold mine of Cochasayhuas in Apurimac
was similarly affected, but conclusive evidence of
these supposed abandonments is absent.* Perhaps it
is the tradition itself that is most informative.
On the one hand, the Peruvians feared that their mines
were getting under foreign control and rose and threw
out the foreigners; on the other hand, various foreign
authors have chosen to cite this as an example of
Peruvian xenophobia leading to economic decay. What
the truth really was is uncertain, but the attitudes
are all too familiar.

It remains to ask, was the mining industry as it
became established a desirable addition to the economy
or not? Was all this tremendous effort, both physical
and intellectual, that went to produce silver and gold
out of some of the bleakest and most uninhabitable
regions of the earth worth it? What was all the silver for? The truth was that most of the silver was
for export. Certainly, the domestic economy required
currency, whether in coin or bars, but this it had to
excess--more silver than goods on which to spend it.
Unfortunately, the produce of the mines was singularly
acceptable outside Peru, and apart from what the Crown
shipped home to Spain (over and above its large local
expenditure), tons of silver left Peru annually in
payment for imported materials and even agricultural
products such as wine and olive oil. It was an open
part of Spanish policy to maintain Peru, and her other
colonies, in a condition in which they would be
obliged to import in this way, paying heavily for
goods that were cheap at home; after all, the costs
and risks of crossing the Atlantic had to be covered.
As long as the fiction that Spain and Peru were one
and the same country could be maintained, this setup
might be justified, but when Peru gained her independence it was to find herself without other industries. Internationally, Peru could always pay her

---

*Ricardo Palma, the famous 19th century Peruvian
author, stated that he had seen the order expelling
the Portuguese from the mines in the Biblioteca Nacional, Lima, before the Chileans sacked it in 1881.

way, and still does, handsomely, with the product of
her mines, but domestically--as David Barry, the ed-
itor of Jorge Juan and Antonio de Ulloa's Noticias
Secretas de América, trenchantly points out--poverty
and under-development became the background to the
superficial wealth of the Indies. The effects of di-
verting the energies of the strongest arms and best
brains in the country into sending silver overseas is
still being felt, and it is not without its present-
day parallel.

THE NEXT 150 YEARS:
1634-1783

The period that follows the first 100 years is
hard to characterize. Apart from the constant official interest in Huancavelica, the mines, as a subject of viceregal pre-occupation, gradually gave place
to more pressing matters such as pirates, smuggling,
earthquakes and, above all, the administrative and
financial problems of running what was now a large
bureaucratic empire. References are relatively rare
to the industry as a whole, and it is clear that technically it was fairly stagnant. However, there were
undoubtedly many more discoveries of mines, the first
of which were in the Puno area. The most famous of
these Puno discoveries was that of Laicacota (1657),
which was to yield as much as 7.5 million pesos in
one year (some 330 tons of pure silver if we assume
they were pesos ensayados). The mine was even more
famous for disorders. Rival factions developed between the immigrant Spaniards and the criollos, headed
by the Salcedo brothers who were the main mine owners.
Throughout the 1660's, the riots raged, spreading at
times to La Paz, and the corregidor's house was burned
down and innumerable people killed. In 1668, the
newly arrived viceroy, the Conde de Lemos, decided
matters had gone far enough and paid a surprise visit
to Laicacota. There, he ordered the hanging of Jose
de Salcedo and 24 others without worrying much about
the legal preliminaries, and moved the town one league
to the north to present-day Puno. The viceroy's be-
havior was condemned by contemporaries, but historians
seem to agree that he was justified. Salcedo is said

to have sealed, flooded and hidden the mine before
his death so that it was never worked again, and even
in the 19th century miners in the same area were still
hoping they would strike Salcedo's lost vein.

In the latter part of the 17th century, Caylloma
developed into a major center, and no doubt from it
interest spread away from Alto Peru more northward
and to the coast. Thus, in 1670, Otoca was discovered,
and the various silver and gold mines from Condesuyos
to Parinacochas are thought to date from the latter
half of the 17th and first part of the 18th centuries.
San Juan de Lucanas was active during the same period.
There were discoveries also in Carabaya (silver,
1709); in Chanca (Cajatambo, 1712); a new vein in
Huantajaya (1718) that produced the famous lumps of
silver, the papas, and that was followed by many more
finds in the area; a gold mine in Guamachuco (1721,
Milluachaqui?); the famous silver vein of Huallanca
(1712); Queropalca (1736); and a mercury prospect in
Chonta (also in Huanuco, 1756). These dated discoveries, however, are only a very small number of those
actually made. Llano Zapato in 1759 lists some 50
mining zones, some of them, albeit, imprecisely.
However, it is clear that by that date all the mountains behind Lima were being exploited, or at any rate
known of, from Cajatambo to Castrovirreyna. The Quichas area is referred to (Rauma--is it Raura?) as are
Canta, San Mateo, Huarochiri and Yauyos. Other major zones that he lists are Lucanas, Cotabambas and
all the Southern Apurimac/Ayacucho area, while specific mines mentioned are Condoroma, Lampa and Julcani,
to cite only three well-known today. By this date,
there are beginning to be references to abandoned and
unworked mines, references also to be found in the
famous works of Jorge Juan and Antonio de Ulloa.
These authors' Noticias Secretas de América, which
forms the most damning comment on administration in
Peru during the first half of the 18th century, is
more interesting for what it does not say about the
mines than for what it does, which is surprisingly
little considering Ulloa was later to be governor of
Huancavelica for some six years. The industry is only
slightly touched on and there is no comment whatever
on the mita for the mines, although the institution

is savagely attacked in connection with other industries. One is tempted to conclude, with Ruben Vargas
Ugarte, that the mita for the mines was by this date
relatively inoffensive and probably so ineffective as
not to merit much attention. In short, by the middle
of the 18th century, despite new discoveries, the
mines were in a state that was often called decadent.

A study of the two main centers, Potosi and
Huancavelica, during this period confirms the deca-
dence. Potosi was suffering from falling grades and
high costs. Mercury sold at over 97 pesos the quintal in the 1670's, compared with 85 pesos in Otoca
and some 87 pesos in Caylloma. By the 1680's, there
were fierce discussions about the price of silver--
an extremely confusing concept when it is remembered
that silver was money. Adjustments to the price of
the pina, to the various charges and taxes (in particular, the derecho de Cobos) were proposed and
sometimes made, and even such items as the cost of
iron for tools (imported via Buenos Aires) were considered by the viceroys in the 1720's. Irregularities
occurred in the mint. Tests made under Viceroy Marques de Castel Fuerte showed that 1,000 pesos, which
should weigh over 119 marcos, actually weighed some
115 (35 pesos missing), and that their grade, which
should be 11 dineros 4 granos, was only 11 (i.e., a
further 1.5-per-cent theft to add to the former 3.5
per cent). Although the same viceroy talks of the
need for improving the techniques of metallurgy and
cites the beneficient influence of learned and scientific societies in Europe, little seems to have been
done in this way. In 1676, a man named Corro had
claimed to invent a new method of amalgamation, but
tests proved that it was neither original nor successful, and a book published by Felipe de la Torre, owner
of San Juan de Lucanas, on the same theme in 1738 had
small effect. This book is cited by Gamboa, and its
author was a recognized authority, but the experiments
performed at his mine, which still contains a number
of exotic and rare silver minerals, may not have been
applicable elsewhere. Despite all, Potosi continued
averaging some 400,000 pesos annually for the Crown
in quintos in the late 17th century, which represents
a total production of 55 tons. This corresponded to

a mercury consumption of 3,000 quintales, 138 tons.
Ulloa states that in the 1740's, Potosi "paid" with
grades of 8 to 10 marcos per cajon.   It would appear
that many of the grades did not pay as the Viceroy
Castel Fuerte says that many miners were bankrupt and
owed large sums to the Crown for mercury.

The miners blamed the inoperation of the mita
for their state, but the authorities held the miners
responsible--in particular, for not wroking the mines.
The bishop elect of Potosi, Fray Francisco, claimed
in 1661 that the miners were receiving 600,000 pesos
yearly from Indians who were buying themselves off
the mita, and when he attempted to restore a just and
equitable scheme he was found dead in his bed--prob-
ably poisoned.   The Conde de Lemos (who quelled Laicacota) came to the conclusion that the mita ought
to be abolished as it was so abused.   In a letter to
the King he says, "I did not come to the Indies to
risk my salvation but rather to serve Your Majesty,
and to unite Your Royal service with that of God."
The mita was not abolished.   By the 1670's, it was
down to 1,700 and by the 1680's, to 1,400--from Toledo's original 4,000.   The Viceroy Duque de la Palata
(1681-1689) tried to reform it and caused further
resentment.   In 1697, six basic rules for operating
the mita were drawn up, the most important of which
were that mitayos and voluntary labor should receive
equal pay, that journey money (leguaje) should be
paid and that pay should be by the day and not by
the work done.   An attempt to enforce this in 1728
led to a three-day strike organized by the mine owners.   The miners said that the provision for equal
pay would have meant doubling the mitayos' wage.   The
authorities had to give in for fear the mine would
shut.   They also had to consider themselves content
if the mita reached 1,000 Indians.

Huancavelica was an even greater worry.   The
Viceroy Mancera's contract with the miners, made in
1643, had set the mine on an orderly footing.   A
mita of 620 Indians was provided, the miners had to
supply 11 quintales annually per mitayo (instead of
3), and a liquidation price (taxes, etc., paid) of
some 59 pesos per quintal was agreed upon.   An expert

was sent to plan the exploitation, a Portuguese(!)
called Vasconcelos. Mancera's contract was necessary
as there was such a shortage of mercury that he himself had come from Spain on his appointment as viceroy with 4,000 quintales from Almaden. However, the
miners picked squabbles with the expert, the mita soon
fell below strength and had to be reinforced from Cas-
trovirreyna--now in decay--and an earthquake in 1647
damaged the mine. By 1660, the Crown owed the miners
400,000 pesos and the memoirs of the Viceroy Conde de
Castellar (1674-1678) give a picture of complete financial chaos with innumerable incomprehensible and
contradictory debts. This unfortunate man had been
removed from his post and his memoirs read as those
of someone slightly mentally unbalanced, but it is
clear that Huancavelica was in a bad way. In Conde
de Castellar's viceroyalty, the shipments of mercury
to Mexico started, the first being of 3,500 quintales.
His successor, Viceroy/Archbishop don Melchor de Linan
y Cisneros, in an attempt to understand the economics
of the mercury business, analyzed costs of transport
to Potosi but, more important, made an investigation
of the mine reserves in considerable detail. (In
this investigation, "prohibited" parts of the mine
are referred to, i.e., parts shut off as dangerous.)
Grades were averaging some 4 libras per carga (over
10 kilos per ton). The effective mita had dropped
to 350.

The Duque de la Palata succeeded the Archbishop
(who had left him debts of 600,000 pesos) and decided
to restore financial order with another detailed contract. His arrival coincided with a major collapse,
that of San Jacinto, and provision was made for its
repair, which took six years and cost 270,000 pesos.
Attempts were made to control two abuses. The first
was the working of the mine by sub-contractors instead of the officially authorized miners. The sub-
contractors had no interest in the future of the mine
and were accused of removing the supports of rich ore
and causing the collapses. In the future, sub-contractors were prohibited. The second abuse was the
"sale" of mitayos. The original miners having died,
their heirs were often women who could not work the
mine, but who nevertheless had mitayos allocated to

them for that purpose.   These mitayos they hired out
or sold almost as slaves--a practice condemned severely by the viceroy.   The Crown, in its turn, prom-
ised to pay cash for the mercury produced and to maintain a balance of 40,000 pesos in Huancavelica for
that purpose--although this would not even pay for two
months' production.   In fact, the Crown was very soon
in debt again as pirates diverted funds to the defense
of the realm, and a further shipment of 9,000 quintales to Mexico was not paid for.   These shipments
were sent on orders from Spain and more times than not
the Mexicans did not pay.   Nine thousand quintales
represented at least 18 months' production and was
worth over half a million pesos--a very severe financial burden when it is realized that this was worth
almost the entire royal earnings in Potosi for a
similar period.   An earthquake again damaged the mine
in 1687.

The general proposal to abolish the mita, first
raised officially by the Conde de Lemos, was rejected
by Philip V in 1720, except for Huancavelica.   He
went so far as to order the then viceroy to travel
there on purpose to finish with it.   The Marques de
Castel Fuerte could not comply.   Mitayos earned 3.5
reales daily and voluntary laborers, 7 to 8.   The
proposal was impossible without a rise in the cost
of mercury.   Instead, he proposed running down production to a level compatible with the mitayos that
remained and pointed out that the low level of silver
production did not require more than 3,500 quintales
yearly.   Eighty piqueros (men at the face) by day and
80 by night were sufficient for this, as from sunrise
to sunset, with a two-hour lunch break, a piquero
could mine 1.4 cargas, some 250 kilos.   The viceroy
also refused to obey a royal order to reduce the
price the Crown paid for mercury, saying it would
close the mine.   He also sadly pointed out that the
miners were chronically insolvent, this time the
Crown being the creditor of over 1.5 million pesos,
a sum that dated from advances made to the miners to
repair the collapses.   Only 14 miners (i.e., those
contracted with the Crown) were left by 1727.

The cause of this general decay of the mines
was largely the crisis through which Spain passed at

the end of the 17th century with the war of the Spanish succession. Lack of money caused high mercury
prices and financial disorder in Huancavelica. A
high price of mercury hit the silver producers. The
drop in silver production reduced the royal income
even further. Hence, the attempts to reduce the
price of mercury by law (Mancera had even tried this
in the 1630's) and hence, too, Philip V's next move,
the reduction of the quintos on silver to diezmos,
10 per cent, in 1735. In the same year, he also appointed the first governor to Huancavelica, a man
responsible to the Consejo de las Indias in Spain and
not to the viceroys as had been the custom previously
Clearly, the Crown realized that the industry was not
to be revived without some temporary sacrifices. The
new governors set to work with a will. The most famous, Geronimo de Sola, raised production again to
5,500 quintales annually, exploited the tailings and
dumps of former years, prohibited the use of gunpowder
in the mine (he said the dust was the cause of the
poisonings), tried to control corruption and built
the fine portal to the socavon Belen, which can be
seen to this day. Grades worked were now 30 libras
per cajon, dropping to even 8 (6 to 1.6 kilos per
ton). Later, Antonio de Ulloa was to plan an even
more ambitious socavon from the city of Huancavelica
itself, but he fell out with the Viceroy Amat who
tried to get 12,000 pesos out of him--no doubt the
appointment direct from Spain did the viceroy out of
some useful pocket money--and resigned.

Improved management of Huancavelica did not,
however, reduce the price of mercury. The next royal
proposal was to close the mine altogether and import
mercury from Spain, and an experiment was performed
to show that mercury from Almaden shipped via Buenos
Aires could sell in Potosi at only 70 pesos--25 per
cent below the normal price. Needless to say, the
proposal upset the viceroy and did little for the
morale of the Huancavelica miners. However, collapses in Almaden put a stop to the suggestion and once
again the viceroy was forced to supply Mexico and
Guatemala from Huancavelica with at least 5,000, and
probably 9,000, quintales of mercury (1756-1761).
The viceroy had to put out 469,000 pesos in partial

cash advances to the miners and in freight charges
for these shipments, and only the Guatemalans showed
the slightest intention of paying, with a contribution of 20,000 pesos (although their 1,000 quintales
valued 94,000). Under these circumstances, it is
hard to see how Huancavelica could be expected to
operate satisfactorily.

The crises of the mines was both result and
cause of a general financial crisis of the Spanish
Empire. From 1761 to 1774, the mints of Potosi and
Lima produced over 100 million pesos, of which 67
million were sent to Spain, 33 million to Buenos
Aires, Quito, etc., and a mere 266,000 remained in Peru
to stimulate the economy. The economy was in need of
stimulation. The Viceroy Amat, in view of the falling royal earnings from the mine, had increased taxes
in other fields, increases that fell particularly
heavily on the rural populations. Behind the luxurious facade of Lima the country was rapidly being
ground into poverty. It is to the credit of one or
two enlightened men that they realized that something must be done. One of these men was Francisco
Javier de Gamboa, an Oidor (the highest ranking ju-
dicial figure in the colonial hierarchy) of Mexico,
who published his famous commentary on mining legislation in 1761. The book is not merely a legal trea-
tise (both Mexican and Peruvian law are analyzed) but
also contains instructions and illustrated examples
on subterranean geometry, trigonometrical tables,
discussions of metallurgical processes and many useful references to other authors. Among the subjects
discussed is the touchy one of the royal mercury
monopoly. Apparently, mercury mines had been closed
in Mexico to avoid competition with Almaden and Huancavelica. Ulloa states that the mine at Azogues in
Ecudor, which supplied Cajamarca, had been similarly
closed. Gamboa joins those in favor of reducing the
price of mercury while Ulloa urges a reopening of
closed mines. Gamboa's book was dedicated to that
other enlightened man, King Charles III, who approved
highly of it and used it extensively in producing the
Nuevas Ordenanzas de México, the new legislation that,
modified for Peru, was to herald in the final era of
colonial mining in 1783. Besides tackling legislation,

Charles III was also responsible for a major reform
of Potosi mint, introducing new machinery and erect-
ing the fine (and extremely costly) building that
still faces on to the plaza.

This new scientific and enlightened spirit
coupled with the (re-?)discovery of Haulgayoc in
1771 by Rodrigo de Ocana and a rapid development of
Cerro de Pasco, two mines that dominate the late
18th century, might be supposed to have reversed the
trend and placed the mining industry once more on a
sound base, but in the same decade as the Nuevas Ordenanzas de México were promulgated two other events
showed how far the decay had gone. The first was the
great revolt of Tupac Amaru, which was so savagely
repressed and avenged. The revolt, according to its
author, was largely caused by the insufferable burden
of extortion and taxation that fell on the Indians of
the sierra. Long-endured (cf. Noticias Secretas de
América), the burden had become intolerable with the
newest taxes introduced precisely because of the falling income from the mines. By the time the revolt was
over, the whole of the Puno/Cuzco area was in ruins
and the Indian population cowed but still smouldering
with hatred. Needless to say, many of the mines of
this rich area were abandoned, a state from which
they have never properly recovered. The second disaster was the terrible 1786 collapse in Huancavelica.
An overzealous and criminally irresponsible adminis-
trator, by the name of Marroquin, in his efforts to
raise production removed the supports. Two hundred
were killed and Marroquin died in prison. Both these
disasters further under-lined the need for reforms,
and the last few decades of the viceroyalty witness
the attempts by the Crown to implement some.

THE END OF THE VICEROYALTY:
1784-1824

Peruvian mining legislation had been drawn up by
Toledo in 1574, modified at times by the viceroys and
finally compiled by Dr. Tomas Ballesteros in a book
entitled Las Ordenanzas del Perú, which was published
in 1685 with viceregal approval. The legislation

treated ownership, disputes, etc., and was more concerned with controlling than fomenting the industry.
The Nuevas Ordenanzas de México were inspired by a
different spirit. In the preface signed by King
Charles III, the king states that in 1771 he had been
asked by the viceroy of Mexico to approve the formation of a Cuerpo de la Mineria--a sort of professional
body. In 1774, the miners extended their request to
the establishment of a mining bank (to be financed by
a tax on the product of the mines) and a college of
metallurgy, both of which requests were granted by
the king. The Nuevas Ordenanzas de México formalized
these institutions and the new law was extended to
Peru in 1786 by the visitador (special emissary from
the king), Jorge Escobedo, formerly in charge of
Potosi mint, who appended a series of 56 "declara-
tions" (comments/amendments).

The interests of the industry were embodied in
a Tribunal de Mineria, composed of deputies elected
by the miners of the various regions,* two per region
for a three-year period. Over these deputies presided two diputados generales, a director and an ad-
ministrator. The Tribunal was to look after the
welfare of the industry in general, in particular by
advancing money to the miners and by giving technical
assistance, but, also, it was to examine the competence of miners and plant owners and to inspect their
operations at least once a year. It was financed by
a tax of 1 real on every marco of silver produced,
which was estimated to yield 45,000 pesos per year.
(Peru's production was somewhat under 400,000 marcos
yearly, Potosi and Oruro now belonging to the recently
created viceroyalty of La Plata.) A mining college
was also to be established with free education for 25
youths, and more if they paid, who would then be obliged to complete their studies by 3 years in the
mines. The Tribunal would cost 18,000 and the college,

---

*The mining regions in Mexico were fairly compact
and well-defined. In Peru, they were more diffuse.
Initially, they were ten: Huarochiri, Pasco, Huamanga,
Lucanas, Huancavelica, Castrovirreyna, Curahuasi
(Apurimac), Caylloma, Huantajaya and Haulgayoc. In
1787, a request was made to add Huallanca.

15,000 pesos yearly--which would leave only 12,000
for financing the mines.

The Mexicans had requested the new laws but the
Peruvians had them imposed on them. It is true that
in Potosi in 1752 the gremio (association) of miners
had formed a bank to buy silver from the miners at a
reasonable price and that this bank had been made
official and incorporated to the Crown by the same
Jorge Escobedo in 1779. But elsewhere in Peru, the
miners were not sufficiently sophisticated for the
new legislation. The legislation fomented the formation of mining companies, controlled avios (advances of cash against the mine production) and mortgages (maximum interest, 5 per cent), but where were
the capitalists of Peru? Peruvian terrain being what
it is, the miner labored on in the remoteness of the
mountains alone, and if a traveling buyer of silver
came near him he was only too glad to sell his product for what he could get, i.e., heavily discounted.
How was he to carry his silver to the official centers? What would happen to the mine in his absence?
It should be emphasized that the legislation was a
success in Mexico and that the level of scientific
and technical education there was, in Humboldt's opinion, higher than that of the United States, so that
its ineffectiveness in Peru must have been due to a
relative backwardness of the Peruvians as well as to
the awesome nature of their territory. Whatever the
reasons, the Tribunal de Mineria did not live up to
expectations in Peru, and the college never got off
the ground. As for the Banco de Rescate, only one
is known to have been set up in Peru. It functioned
in Lucanas in the early 1790's, starting with a capital of 25,000 pesos and buying a marco of silver at
7 pesos. As there were now 68 reales to the marco--
subtracting 10 per cent tax, 1.5 per cent derecho de
Cobos and 3 reales minting charges--the minted marco
was worth 57 reales, or 7 pesos 1 real, so that the
bank was charging less than 2 per cent for its services. Demetrio O'Higgins, nephew of the Irish viceroy and Intendente (a local administrative official)
of Huamanga, indicates that production in Lucanas at
the time was some 40,000 marcos yearly valuing, at
7 pesos, 280,000 pesos, so it is clear that the bank's

capital was woefully insufficient for the task as-
signed to it.   Consequently, the experiment was a
failure, the bank was closed in 1794 and no others
were formed in Peru.

The new legislation, besides detailing measures
designed to promote the mining industry, changed the
size of concessions.   A holding was now 200 varas
along the vein and up to 200 on the dipping side, 100
on the other.   A discoverer could have three contig-
uous holdings, a company was allowed four--a very
significant increase on previous law, but old claims
were not affected.   The prohibition on foreigners as
owners, except with special royal permission, still
held.   If the promotionary aspects were not very successful, these other clauses of the Nuevas Ordenanzas
de México were to remain in force until 1877.

The most positive thing that the Tribunal did
was to engage the group of German experts that came
to Peru at the end of the century.   Even here, the
contracting was done by a Mexican, don Fausto de
Elhuyar, director of the Tribunal of that country who
was in Germany on a visit.   He was asked to do this
by the Viceroy Croix (who came from Lille, France),
former viceroy of Mexico.   The contract was signed
in 1787, two years after the signing of another contract with Germany to supply Potosi, via Buenos
Aires, with 10,000 to 12,000 quintales yearly of
mercury--good foresight considering the collapse that
took place in Huancavelica in 1786.

The German expedition is a perfect example of
mutual non-comprehension between visiting "experts"
and the inhabitants of an "under-developed country,"
which they were supposed to be helping, so it is worth
going into it in some detail.   The Germans were from
Saxony and apart from bringing their general knowledge
of mining--in particular, mining machinery--they were
to demonstrate the method of amalgamation as practiced
in Freiberg, invented (or, rather, introduced there
some 200 years after its invention in Mexico) by Baron
Born of Vienna.   The team was led by the Baron von
Nordenflicht, a Swede aged 31, and was comprised of
Daniel Weber, Francisco Mothe, Francisco Kuhn (sometimes written Quinn), Zachariah Helms and two ordinary

laborers named Fleischer and Griespach. Helms left
Peru--"a land morally and physically pernicious to
me"--in 1792, long before the others, and wrote embittered memoirs that received much popularity in
Europe.

Initially, the visiting experts were anxiously
and eagerly awaited, and when they were delayed in
Potosi on their journey from Buenos Aires popular
excitement was only further whetted by the notices
of their technical successes that appeared in the
Mercurio Peruano in Lima. In Potosi, they stopped
work on a misdirected socavon and started another;
Weber installed some pumps and Helms gave domonstra-
tions of the Freiberg amalgamation. Soon, however,
they came upon one of the difficulties of Potosi--
the lack of timber, a shortage hard for a German to
envisage. Nevertheless, the Potosi miners were im-
pressed by the amalgamation in wooden barrels, even
if they thought the machine driven by a water wheel
rather costly. Von Nordenflicht remained in Potosi,
where the socavon was taking longer than planned, and
the rest came via Huancavelica to Lima. In 1790,
Helms returned to Huancavelica to build and operate
furnaces for extracting mercury as used in Idria--
now in northern Italy. He never achieved his object.
He became ill and claimed that the governor, Pedro
de Tagle, was obstructing him. As de Tagle was the
man who had successfully put in new machinery in the
Potosi mint and had been especially appointed to
Huancavelica as a trustworthy person to restore the
1786 collapse by the Viceroy Croix, universally accepted as honest and conscientious, it is hard to
believe Helms' accusations against him. Helms then
went with Kuhn to Pasco where he remarked on the
richness of the deposit and the incompetence of the
miners, but they maintained that he suggested no
improvements. Kuhn's pumps were said to have been
pulled out of Colquijirca by angry workers. Helms
also went to Chanca, near Oyon. By this time, he
was, according to his own account, being accused of
being a German Jew, a heretic, plotting to put men
out of work, etc., and he left Peru in disgust on the
grounds of ill health.

Meanwhile, von Nordenflicht had arrived in Lima and set about establishing a laboratory and college of metallurgy in line with the Nuevas Ordenanzas de México. He overspent his 15,000-peso budget by 27,000 pesos and, soon, doubts were expressed as to the utility of the Freiberg amalgamation method. The Peruvians claimed that the Germans did not have a standard practice that they could follow and, finally, the viceroy, now Francisco Gil y Lemos, organized comparative tests. Two experiments showed that the Freiberg method, which added the huge quantity of 40 per cent mercury to the amount of ore to be refined, produced no more silver and lost perhaps four times the amount of mercury. The experiments are detailed in the viceroy's memoirs and there is no reason for doubting their veracity--it was in everybody's interests to adopt a new method if it was really better. The laboratory did not prosper and the college never came into existence, the viceroy refusing to spend any more money on the Germans' plans that had already proved extremely expensive. In 1795, Francisco Mothe, a subterranean geometer, went to Hualgayoc where he probably had a hand in the famous socavon real--although a contemporary picture shows it existed at least in part in 1785--and where he proved sufficiently popular for the miners to request his stay to be extended; but, in general, the public was disillusioned with the Germans. They had spent a lot of money and done very little. The viceroy remarked that perhaps the most useful thing they could have taught was the method by which the Germans raised capital for their mines, issuing shares of relatively small nominal value, but he felt that their technology was not adaptable to Peru.

Rivero gives an account of the Freiberg amalgamation method and comparing it with the Peruvian one there are three essential differences. First, a much greater amount of mercury was added to the ore; second, the ore was previously mixed to produce a silver grade of 22 to 25 marcos per cajon; third, barrels and, in general, wooden machinery were used instead of stone-lined vats and manpower. In view of the, by now, chronic situation of mercury supplies in Peru (production dropped to below 2,000 quintales in the

early 1790's), the first item was sufficient cause
for objections. The mixing of ore would be practical
only with fairly regular grades from the mine; it
would be too much to expect in remote areas as it
pre-supposed various samples and tests. A single
test such as Barba suggested, with the mercury added
in proportion to the silver expected instead of the
ore treated, seems more sensible. The third item,
the barrels, must surely have been an improvement on
the often crudely made vats. Nevertheless, the problem of wood and the lack of direct evidence of increased yield did not encourage the Peruvians to adopt
them.

In 1807, the Germans' commission was withdrawn
but von Nordenflicht did not leave Peru until 1812,
since he wished to secure his pension in Spain, at
the time under Napoleon's domination. He had been to
Huancavelica in 1794 to build a storehouse for mercury
and to Cerro de Pasco in 1799 to inspect the socavon
of Yanacancha, a northern branch to San Judas, but it
is not recorded that he or his companions did anything
else of use. Indeed, the Tribunal, whose money was
being spent, reported unfavorably on them, and although Helms says that its members were devoid of any
mineralogical knowledge this may be doubted. Its
first director was a Frenchman, Coquette, who was an
experienced miner, and it is unlikely in a mining
country such as Peru, and in view of the stipulations
in the Nuevas Ordenanzas de México about the qualifications for posts on the Tribunal, that ignorant men
would be appointed or elected by the miners. In
short, the Germans' visit was a failure--it did not
help Peru, cost a lot of money and embittered the
Germans. Perhaps, more than any technical reasons,
the cause of the failure may be sought in the differences of temperament and education: the superior,
inflexible, protestant German trying to instruct pa-
ternally the undisciplined, but courageous, Catholic
Peruvian of the Andes in a skill that he had practiced for centuries and, in certain cases (amalgamation), virtually invented.

THE MINES

Huancavelica was now a disaster. From 1793 to
1796, the mine was closed and production only maintained by permitting anyone to go through the tips and
dumps, which yielded some 36,000 quintales over ten
years--sure evidence of former waste. An interesting
account of the furnaces, costs and comparisons with
Almaden is given by Becerra in 1792. Becerra was
accountant at Huancavelica and in his time grades
(much of the ore coming from tips and not from the
mine) were just over 1 per cent and the mercury was
costing nearly 100 pesos per quintal to produce.
Helms states that it cost 166 pesos in de Tagle's day,
but it is clear that this included the exceptional
costs of repairs to the mine. If we accept Becerra's
figures, mercury should have sold at well over 100
pesos in the silver-mining centers. For large-scale
production, grades in the mine seem to have been
nearer .50 per cent, if not lower (Humboldt), and the
price of mercury per quintal should really have been
about 200 pesos. This, in fact, is the real cause of
Huancavelica's end--mercury being under-priced. If
the Crown's efforts in the past had not succeeded in
lowering the price, they had, at any rate, prevented
it rising. The miners under contract had received 58
pesos (tax paid), whereas a just price was now three
to four times that amount. Almaden, according to Becerra, was working grades of 6 per cent--Huancavelica,
1 per cent and below.

In 1797, a new manager, Pedro Subiela, was appointed. His caustic comments on the mine make amus-
ing reading. In 1799, the Crown finally agreed to
raise the price it paid for mercury, but only to 85
pesos from 73. In 1804, it was openly receiving cash
payments instead of mitayos from the area designated
for the mita. Finally, in 1806 an order was given to
destroy the mine, an order that was not obeyed. In
effect, the Crown had washed its hands of it and left
it to the mercy of small miners who continued producing some 2,500 quintales yearly until 1813. Among
Helms' more useful comments on Huancavelica is one
stating that a large number of people had died in the

past from treating arsenic ores in the furnaces in
mistake for mercury. This would agree with other
authors who suggest that the peril of poisoning was
not so much in the mine as in the treatment plants.
Whatever the cause, there can be little doubt that
"the precious jewel of the royal crown," the magnificent, legendary and mysterious mercury mine of Huancavelica, in its 250 years' existence, had well earned
its title "la mina de la muerte."

Two other mines are worth mentioning. Hualgayoc,
although not living up to expectations, was averaging
70,000 marcos yearly (16 tons). Discovered before the
new legislation, there were, and still are to this
day, too many small uneconomic concessions with the
result that only some 16 mines of the 185 denounced
were really active. The miners also suffered from
labor and capital shortages and proposed setting up
a bank with 400,000 pesos capital, but apparently it
did not materialize. Nevertheless, some communal
socavones had been under-taken, the famous socavon real
being 530 varas (450 meters) long with a 3-by-3-vara
cross section. It goes right through the center of
the hill at the lowest level possible below the town,
and cost 130,000 pesos--the value of three months'
production. Humboldt visited Hualgayoc in 1802.

More important was Cerro de Pasco, which raised
production from some 70,000 to over 300,000 marcos
between 1780 and 1805. This was undoubtedly due to
the socavon San Judas, started in 1780 and finished
in 1800, although extensions, e.g., to Yanacancha,
continued until 1807. This drainage tunnel entered
from the southwest, 400 varas in a cutting and 1,400
underground (1.2 kms.) and cost 100,000 pesos. The
mines were worked below its level, water being lifted
to it by hand pumps or buckets from a collecting well
some 30 meters further down. This was by no means
the first drainage tunnel in Cerro de Pasco that had
known various previous bonanzas, sufficient to attract
the Salcedos from Laicacota to it, but it was the
start of the mine's really major expansion. In 1806,
yet another socavon was started, that of Quiulacocha,
designed to enter the mineralized zone 32 varas (27
meters) below San Judas.

In 1790, the viceroy made a census of mines that
showed there were 784 silver and 69 gold mines in Peru
(not including placer deposits). There were also
nearly 400 treatment plants for silver and some 70 for
gold. More than 720 miners, i.e., owners, produced
412,000 marcos yearly, a figure that rose to some
500,000 in 1800 and 550,000 in 1805 (125 tons), thanks
to Cerro de Pasco. The price of mercury was now virtually uncontrolled and was over 150 pesos per quintal
at the mines, but all the same this period saw a final
flourishing of the mining industry. Virtually all the
known zones in Peru, except mines with no silver content at all, were in exploitation at this date, and
although many were suffering from financial problems,
from buying mercury on credit against future deliveries of silver, the industry had not been so active for
almost 200 years.

THE MINES AND THE ECONOMY

It has been said already that mercury was under-
priced, the basic cause of the ruin of Huancavelica,
and as mercury represented some 15 per cent of the
costs of production of silver, a rise in its price
was bound to increase that cost noticeably and thereby
affect the minimum silver grades that "paid." One is
tempted to question, was silver really being mined at
artificially low grades? Did silver have an artificially high value? On the basis of Appendix A, it
is possible to put modern prices on other commodities,
using silver as the standard. With that assumption
the prices (in soles, $, the currency now in use in
Peru) of wheat, mercury and copper in the late 18th
century were $0.80 per bushel, $145 per flask, $350
per ton, respectively--one half to one quarter of
modern prices in terms of silver. A skilled miner's
daily wage was some 60 soles, against perhaps 120
soles today. It seems clear that silver, even allowing for the very approximate nature of the calculations, was valued relatively much higher than today,
obviously because of its use in coinage. A century
later, 1897, the moment of truth was to come when
world silver prices became established on the basis
of silver's utility rather than its prestige, and the
final blow was dealt to traditional mining in Peru.

At the time, however, silver was still very acceptable overseas and the Viceroy Gil y Lemos' accounts show that exports of all commodities were running at some 2.8 million pesos yearly, of which 2.4 million were in metals (85 per cent, today 50 per cent). This was nearly 70 per cent of production, today over 90 per cent. The budget was 4 million pesos, the value of the production of the mines 3.5 million (87 per cent of the budget, today 40 per cent). Total exports were 70 per cent of the budget, today they are 85 per cent. These rough figures show that at the end of the viceroyalty Peru was even more of a mining country than it is today, both in the influence in the domestic economy and in exports. Nevertheless, a higher proportion of the mines' production remained for domestic use--cash--and the incidence of imports and exports, although much higher than in earlier centuries, was less marked in the economy than today.

If these facts are put in modern jargon, Peru in late viceregal times was more of a monocultural country than today--metal-mining dominating exports--but less colonial in the sense that total exports of raw materials in exchange for manufactured goods were proportionally smaller and a higher proportion of metal products were for domestic consumption. This is not to say that Peru was not being run economically as a colony; it was, as the intellectual movements that gave rise to the wars of independence recognized. In fact, the above figures are largely compiled from data collected by the Mercurio Peruano, an enlightened publication of the time that was questioning Peru's status. What the fighters for independence were not to know was that the fruit of their struggle was to be 50 years of economic stagnation, ending in a disastrous military defeat, followed by the growth of an economy even more colonial than the old one.

If an attempt is made to assess the progress of the mining industry under Spanish rule, it is important to bear in mind the situation of Peru, its terrain, the technology available at the time and the nature of its inhabitants. In extremely difficult circumstances, the Crown managed to foster and develop

a very impressive mining and metallurgical industry
in the first 100 years. Furthermore, every effort
was made to ensure justice for and prevent exploitation
of the Indians, who comprised, to put it bluntly, a
conquered race. The difficulties of communication
and the number of undesirable adventurers who came to
seek their fortunes (by any means they could) hindered
this task, but it is not until the start of the 18th
century that it appears the viceroys were beginning
to give up the effort of administrating the sierra
and were confining themselves to the artificial and
sophisticated life of Lima. The Noticias Secretas de
América in the 1740's, then, give a shocking picture
of extortion and corruption in the administration,
and it is this period that corresponds to the nadir
of the mining industry. It is also this period that
sees the rise of a frivolous and decadent way of life
in the capital, deliberately modeled on the ancien
regime of France and later encouraged by the Viceroy
Amat, in particular, whose reign is often seen as the
zenith or the "golden age," when, economically, it
was exactly the contrary. Various Indian revolts,
culminating in that of Tupac Amaru, are sufficient
proof of the state to which the sierra had been reduced by negligence. The Viceroys Croix and Gil attempted to rectify the situation, in particular by
spreading European enlightenment as embodied in the
new legislation and the German mission--neither of
which, unfortunately, were really successful, as the
miners of the sierra from long isolation had now become invincibly conservative, not to say suspicious.
The next viceroy, the Irish Demetrio O'Higgins, was
to launch a frontal attack on decadent Lima itself--
for which he was, of course, much criticized.

     To this general picture of vigorous growth, fol-
lowed by decay, followed by a final flowering of the
economy and the mining industry (almost one and the
same thing) Huancavelica provides an exception. Both
the dangers of mercury mining and the key position
mercury held in metallurgy caused the exploitation
of Huancavelica to be irrational, inconsistent and
constantly subject to Crown interference--the Crown
being, after all, the owner. Some writers (Rivero)
claim that Huancavelica should never have been

nationalized, but left to private capital. It is impossible to argue this case objectively, but the role
of private capital in the mining industry as a whole
is worth a mention. The Peruvian miner was prepared
to work extremely hard, to travel and live in remote
places, often oblivious of physical hardships and
dangers, but he was seldom prepared to risk capital,
either directly or indirectly, in mining. The association of Potosi requested that their bank be incorporated to the Crown (i.e., the Crown put up the
money). Even the more progressive Mexicans sought
royal approval and direction in their projects. In
Peru, for better or for worse, the importance of central authority was always greater than that of private initiative when it came to any organized under-
taking, as opposed to small-scale prospecting and
exploitation. The Anglo-Saxon concept of capital
was, in short, largely non-existent.

These two characteristics, the confusion of Lima
splendor with real wealth and the inborn conviction
that the initiative for any major enterprise must
come from the State (Crown) rather than from private
individuals, were to have a profound effect in the
19th century. The characteristics may be said to
be not only Peruvian but Latin American. While the
wealthier Peruvians squabbled among themselves as to
who was to be president, the foreigners moved in,
first in the area of the non-metals, guano and nitrates, later to the mines of the sierra--they did
not waste their time in Lima. When it became rich
and powerful, the Peruvian oligarchy was forced to
admit the efficacy of the foreigners' system, of
which it then became, and still is, a fervent sup-
porter. But if it preached capitalism, it did not
practice it and resolutely refused to risk its money
in mining, except very occasionally or as a minor
shareholder in foreign-owned and -managed concerns.
By over indulgence in politics and, later, by direct
propaganda, the authority of the State was dis-
credited, but hardly any private enterprise, still
less a civic conscience, was put in its place. The
vacuum left by the Crown was inevitably to be filled
by the new holders of economic power, among which the
foreign mining companies were to feature prominently.

The Spanish Empire had many defects and many wrongs
were committed by it in Peru, but the Crown existed,
at least in theory, for the wise government and welfare of its subjects. The maximum profit of foreign
shareholders is, by comparison, a much less noble
aim. So, too, were the results. Peru, once synonymous with wealth, was to become a relatively insignificant nation in a generally under-developed sub-
continent.

CHAPTER

3

THE HISTORY
OF MINING
IN PERU:
1824 TO TODAY

With the end of the viceroyalty, mining in Peru
enters a very different era. The Spanish Crown may
have taken various mistaken measures in its attempts
to direct the mining industry, but it can never be
accused of being simply uninterested. Insofar as the
metal-mining industry was concerned, this was, unfortunately, the case for the first 50 years of independence, when the republican authorities ignored
the mines. They did, however, get heavily involved
in two non-metals, guano and nitrates, to the great
detriment of their country. When, in the 1870's,
official interest in metals was again revived, it was
to herald 25 years of disaster in that field. A
series of outside events (the Chilean War) and pos-
sibly well-intentioned but mistaken measures (the 1877
mining law and the 1897 suspension of silver minting)
meant that at the start of the 20th century Peru's
enormous mineral wealth had not been merely disre-
garded but actually had been handed over very largely
to foreign interests. Since then, those interests
have been consolidated progressively, with the monopoly of smelting and refining established in 1924 by
the Cerro de Pasco Corporation. The prostration of
the industry as a whole in the 1930's was a result of
events quite beyond its control; the progressive in-
doctrination of the population in the need for dollars
with its consequent emphasis on exports and export

industries, the resultant Mining Code of 1950 giving
the foreign investor preferential treatment and the
arrival of two more giant U.S. companies in the next
decade. Thus, one sees 50 years of inaction, 25 of
confusion and surrender, 70 of economic colonization.

THE FIRST 50 YEARS
OF INDEPENDENCE

During the wars of independence, mine production
was, of course, seriously interrupted, particularly
during the final phase when the fight was carried to
the central sierra, and from 1821-1825 silver production dropped to some 150,000 marcos yearly. Although
it was not to rise again for decades to the viceregal
levels of over 500,000 (since many mines had been definitely abandoned and, rumor said, deliberately destroyed by their former Spanish owners), a respectable
increase was registered after the wars to some 430,000
marcos yearly from 1826-1850. After 1850, it lapsed
to 300,000. This initial recovery was probably in no
small way due to Mariano de Rivero, Director General
of Mining in the late 1820's.

Mariano de Rivero is one of those eminent Peruvians almost unknown to his compatriots. Born in
Arequipa in 1798, he was rapidly distinguished for
his intellectual ability and sent to study in Europe,
first at Highgate School in London, then the Royal
School of Mines in Paris and, finally, to Freiberg in
Saxony, where he studied first hand the amalgamation
in wooded barrels that had caused such polemics when
brought to Peru by von Nordenflicht and his German
team. He wrote a detailed article on this method in
the magazine Memorial de Ciencias Naturales y de Industria Nacional y Extranjera, which he edited in
Lima together with another distinguished Arequipeno,
Nicolas de Pierola, and in which appeared many other
articles of considerable interest. One of these
articles is a very thorough description of Cerro de
Pasco in the year 1828. In fact, Rivero had been
specifically sent there to restart work on the
Quiulacocha socavon that had begun in 1806. The wars
had interrupted its progress and immediately afterward

a dubious English company appeared, called Pasco
Peruana, that undertook to complete it. At the same
time, they started a more ambitious one--Rumiallana,
even lower down--but they were grossly extravagant
and went bankrupt in three years, leaving the syndicate of miners with their mines flooded and a legal
action pending. Rivero re-initiated the project, financed by the government, by the Tribunal de Mineria
and by a special contribution from the miners themselves, and although he did not stay to see it finished, it reached a satisfactory conclusion not long
after. Besides drainage tunnels, steam pumps had been
introduced to Cerro de Pasco (by Pedro Abadia in 1816)
to lift water from the bottom of the mines to the San
Judas socavon. In 1828, only one was working, maintained by a Cornishman named Trewithick, and it drew
water from 36 feet down. This water itself was raised
from further down by hand pumps. One June 18, 1828,
the boiler burst and the mines were once again flooded
in the absence of the pump. These pumps, despite
vicissitudes, were a great innovation and for the
first time allowed the exploitation of sulphide ores.

    Rivero discusses the working of the mine, about
which he is fairly uncomplimentary. It was very unsafe and disorderly, and he puts the blame largely on
the arrangement whereby the miners received a fixed
wage (4 to 6 reales plus coca and candles daily) when
the grade was poor but got 50 per cent of the ore when
it was rich--when there was a boya (a bonanza, or very
rich find). Thus, when a boya occurred, the mine was
ransacked without any regard for safety, and all the
laborers of neighboring properties abandoned them and
came and joined in. In Cerro de Pasco itself, there
were 558 mines and another 1,000 small excavations.
The grade exploited was 10 to 12 marcos per cajon
(equaling 62.5 quintales, not 50 as elsewhere), and
accounts are given to show that this scarcely paid.
Rivero waged a long and eventually successful campaign to reduce the diezmos and Cobos taxes so that
the large quantities of lower-grade ore could be
mined economically. These lower grades were some 8
marcos per cajon, or 20 ounces per ton. The costs of
beneficiation were also high, mercury having once
reached nearly 200 pesos per quintal and being at the

time around 150, while the amalgamation process seemed
excessively slow in Pasco, with the ore lying in the
patio for up to three months.

Apart from this, the process was standard. Sulphide ores were previously roasted, oxides were not.
Mercury losses were 1 libra per marco of silver and
much more if the grade was high. There were about
130 different beneficiating plants around Cerro de
Pasco, and to this day their ruins can be seen--e.g.,
on the way to La Quinua. Production exceeded 200,000
marcos per year.

In his description of Cerro de Pasco, Rivero also
includes a geological map (the first ever made in
Peru?), while the magazine contains other articles on
Puno (1826) and Hualgayoc (1827). In 1826, apparently
all the zones known today in Puno were being worked
(Santa Lucia, Crucero, San Antonio de Esquilache--
even the gold morrains of Pampa Blanca), but wages
were low and methods primitive. Unlike in Pasco,
both amalgamation and smelting were used, the latter
with a primitive reverberatory furnace, while Rivero
himself did some experiments on amalgamation in barrels made of iron. The famous Pomasi mines are discussed in the magazine, and from this article come
the prints of miners in 19th century costumes that
are on the walls of every mining company's Lima office. A mercury mine at Arapa is cited. Some 20,000
marcos were officially assayed yearly in Puno, but
contraband and tax evasion were rife. The same goes
for Hualgayoc, where Jose Modesta de la Vega maintains that virtually nobody paid taxes in the remote
caja of Trujillo, which, nevertheless, registered
some 15,000 marcos yearly. It was extremely short-
sighted of the government not to have sent someone
of Rivero's caliber to Hualgayoc, both to direct the
exploitation and supervise tax collection. As it
was, Hualgayoc gradually sank into decay, although
its mines are far from exhausted to this day, and
Rivero himself was apparently exiled--at least nothing is heard of him until after the mid-1840's.
Peru, of course, was torn with factions and civil
war during the intervening period.

In 1837, Rivero's collaborator, Nicolas de
Pierola, attempted, without success, to revive the
famous Montesclaros gold mine near Cotahuasi, which
had been destroyed by a landslide in 1783.

In the middle of this disturbed period, another
famous author wrote about the mines--Johann Jacob von
Tschudi, a Swiss naturalist who traveled in Peru from
1838-1842. Tschudi has left interesting descriptions
of Morococha and Cerro de Pasco. At that time, Carlos
Pflucker was already established at Morococha, where
he was exploiting copper--this is the first reference
to a regular copper mine, as opposed to casual extraction, in what is now Peru. The mines were in the hill
known as Nuevo Potosi on the north side of Morococha.
Centered on Yauli and Huaypacha (on the Mantaro above
La Oroya) were some other silver mines worked by the
Indians. The method consisted of collecting some 60
llama loads (a cajon, more or less) of argentiferous
lead and then smelting it in a small reverberatory
furnace, very like the one described over 200 years
earlier by Barba, built especially for the purpose
in a suitable spot. Tschudi maintains that this
primitive furnace was more effective than expensive
European designs, although it was only fired with
taquia (llama dung). The operation took 20 to 40
hours, grades paid above 12 marcos per cajon and the
Indians sold the silver at the heavily discounted
price of 5 or 6 pesos the marco. Tschudi also cites
silver mines above Casapalca and a former large amalgamation plant, built by an English company, at Pachachaca, that was closed because of flooding in the
mines. Later, Pachachaca became a source of acen-
drada, the basic composition used to floor a cupel,
and to this day it has important lime kilns.

The description of Cerro de Pasco is extremely
fascinating. The town then counted up to 18,000
inhabitants and the disorders, drunkenness and riot-
ing were famous. Invariably, one mine was enjoying
a bonanza at any given time, so the hilarity never
ceased. The workings were, as Rivero maintained,
very unsafe and quite unplanned. Mine entrances were
frequently inside people's houses, no doubt to guard
them. However, the large-scale drainage projects
were still going on, one fifth of the metal extracted

being used to pay the pumps, while from the refined
silver some 2.5 per cent was deducted, 1 real per
marco to pay for the construction of socavones, one
half for the Tribunal and one fourth for foundry
costs (as all central government taxes were now abolished). Silver sold at between 7 and 8 pesos the
marco, the mint price in Lima being 8.5, so the difference was pocketed by a large number of merchants
who traded silver against tools, brandy, etc. Many
of these merchants were foreigners (Tschudi cites
Italians as running the pernicious boliches, or small-
scale amalgamation plants where the mercury was mixed
by human feet, thereby causing much poisoning of
Indians), while the mine owners were Peruvian-Span-
iards, the laborers, of course, being the long-suffer-
ing Indians. The mine owners worked largely on credit,
and if they ever accumulated capital it was spent not
on improvements to an existing mine but on reckless
exploration for new ones, hence the unscientific and
unsafe exploitation. (Cerro de Pasco has a spot
called Matagente, meaning kill people, where a collapse once eliminated 300.) Production was between
200,000 and 300,000 marcos yearly plus large-scale
contraband (85,000 marcos were caught in 1838). In
addition, this exotic boom town at 13,700 feet was
further enlivened by being ringed with bandits waiting for silver-laden travelers.

     With the arrival, in 1845, of Ramon Castilla to
the presidency, Peruvian life became more orderly.
In the same year, Rivero became prefect of Junin, a
department that included Cerro de Pasco in those days,
and he has left further accounts of it and of the
mercury mines at Chonta, Huanuco. Nine mines at
Chonta produced in one year 24,000 pounds of mercury,
not much by Huancavelica's old standards or by Cerro
de Pasco's needs, but, nevertheless, a relative boom.
In fact, most mercury was now being imported from
Spain in 75-pound flasks that sold at a minimum price
of 60 pesos and a maximum of 140 pesos (i.e., 80 to
185 pesos per quintal). Rivero wrote an important
account of Huancavelica itself in 1848 urging the
government to lease the mine only to a company with
sufficient capital to exploit it. Indeed, Flores y
Compania had taken it in 1846 but after some fruitless

efforts they transferred their attentions to the silver mine of Julcani at Lircay.   Rivero criticized the
furnaces at Huancavelica, comparing them unfavorably
with those at Almaden in Spain, but there seems no
doubt that the latter were also based on Lope de
Saavedra's famous invention of 200 years earlier.
The furnaces in Spain, however, had known improvements, while the Huancavelica ones had suffered the
opposite.   Grades in Huancavelica were still around
1 per cent.

    While the metal mines were carrying on as best
they could, much was changing on the coast.   Although
in 1804 Humboldt had sent guano to Paris to be analyzed and the details of this remarkable fertilizer
had been made public in Europe, and although Rivero
returned to the theme in Peru in 1828, no large-scale
exploitation began until the 1840's.   The Peruvians,
of course, had always used the accumulated bird-
droppings of the coastal islands on their fields but
the export possibilities were not at first appreciated.
It might have been wiser if they had never been and
if the guano had remained exclusively for national
use, but, as it was, it began to be exported, as did
that other fertilizer caliche--the nitrates of Tarapaca.   Guano production by the birds of Peru can be
put very approximately at 250,000 to 300,000 tons
yearly if they are not disturbed, marauded, etc.--
i.e., if the exploitation is done with care, that
amount of guano can be removed annually.   In the 19th
century, the islands were pillaged, the birds slaugh-
tered, even their eggs exported.   Between 1851 and
1872, it is estimated that over 10 million tons were
removed from the Chincha Islands alone.   It was clear
that the guano was not "inexhaustible"--the favorite
adjective--but quite the contrary.   The nitrates
brought another problem.   In the decade 1830 to 1840,
exports were at 1 million quintales, from 1850 to
1860 they were 9 million, and from 1870 to 1880, 50
million.   The Atacama desert where they came from lay
very near Bolivia and Chile, and the wealth the nitrates produced was one of the causes of the Chilean
War.

Such easily accessible wealth attracted foreigners and government policy deliberately favored immi-
gration. Most of the immigrants came from Europe,
particularly Italy, and even Garibaldi once commanded
a coasting boat ferrying guano. It has already been
seen that there were Englishmen, Germans and Italians
in the sierra mining centers for many years, but their
numbers were rapidly to increase. Such an influx was
essentially beneficial as the majority of the foreigners were genuine immigrants who contributed to the
country not only with their skills but also by set-
tling there; that is, they did not export their profits. With them came new techniques. From 1848 to
1854, a Frenchman, Pedro Hugon, operated a leaching
plant for silver--using the Agustin process (sodium
chloride), albeit not very successfully--in Algamarca,
while in the same period Remy, Davelouis and Bonafon
experimented with the same process, supplemented with
a foundry at Bellavista, above Oyon. The ruins are
still to be seen where they treated the ores from
Chanca. Among the most illustrious of these immigrants was the Italian Antonio Raimondi, who arrived
in 1850 and died in Peru in 1890.

Raimondi taught in Lima but his real occupation
was travel. He set himself the task of writing a
geography of Peru and to that end he pursued an almost incredible series of journeys up and down the
country. No corner was left uncovered. He inspected
gold mines at Chachapoyas or Sandia and silver in
Apurimac, Tarapaca, Hualgayoc or Cerro de Pasco. He
mapped ruins in Huanuco or Chavin or Urubamba. He
collected Indian dialects in the Chanchamayo, canoed
down the Maranon, Huallaga and Ucayali Rivers as far
as Iquitos, or examined rare birds in Chota and Tingo
Maria. To this day, if one wants information on any
remote corner of Peru, the first thing to do is to
look it up in Raimondi, and, indeed, the Cerro de
Pasco company has done much of its successful exploration for minerals just that way. Raimondi was
a mineralogist and for a knowledge of deposits in
Peru his works are invaluable. These journeys were
made essentially between 1853 and 1869 and it is impossible to detail them here, but a few salient points
about the mines at that time may be mentioned.

Among the famous mines Raimondi went to were
Huantajaya and, on two occasions, Hualgayoc, where
some very rich ore of 48 to 50 marcos per cajon was
still being found (1860).   In 1858, he was at Castrovirreyna where Carlos Pflucker was now working the
Quispisisa mine, with a modern mill and amalgamation
plant at San Jose.   (A plant built at La Virreyna by
Crosnier had proved unsuccessful.)   The Pataz and
Parcoy gold mines were in exploitation (1860) and a
new entrance was being dug at Pataz, while those of
the upper Inambari, Apuroma and Challuma, had apparently known a gold rush in 1849--so much so that a
Frenchman called Larrieu had christened a village of
this extremely remote area Versailles.

Foreigners were everywhere.   A Mr. Doyle unsuc-
cessfully worked a mercury mine near Caras, and a Mr.
Whitehouse, the silver mine of Santo Torribio at
Huaraz.   Those of Recuay (Huancapeti and Collaracra)
were, however, in Peruvian hands.   A suitably named
Dr. Plata exploited the orebodies of Huanta-Huallay,
while among the more exotic mines visited were the
nickel/cobalt ones of Rapi, Ayacucho and those of
Santo Tomas near Leimebamba, where 21-carat gold was
being extracted (1860) from ore with 14 to 115 grams
per ton by the most primitive amalgamation methods.
He also visited gold mines at Chinchao (Huanuco) and
Otoca.   Other mines described are at Conchucos (worked
by Torres de Lara, Taft and Smeeton), Huallanca,
Queropalca and Chonta (all much decayed), Quichas,
Parag (San Mateo), Yauricocha, Huancavelica, Julcani
(opencast), Posco, Caylloma Coris (he remarks on the
rich copper of what is now Cobriza), Aija, Colquipocro, Macate, Salpo and Pallasca.   In Chilete, where
the Murcielago vein was being worked, a certain Ramon
Babie had constructed a reverberatory furnace, a
water-jacket furnace and a cupel (pre-1868), and later, Malinowski, who was tracing the route of the
Pacasmayo-Chilete railway (he also was engineer for
the central railway), installed an ore-preparation
plant.   The list of mines is almost endless.

Apart from descriptions that appeared in the
first three volumes of El Perú (1858, 1876 and 1880)
or in the posthumous two volumes (1902, 1913) or in

his notebooks (published 1929 and 1945-1948), Raimondi
wrote some specialized articles. One was his "Minas
de Oro del Perú" (1887) and another was his catalogue
for an exhibition of Peruvian minerals at the Paris
Exhibition of 1878. He also issued a series of
1:500,000 maps of Peru (incomplete). Two detailed
studies of mining areas are particularly of interest--
Morococha and Cerro de Pasco. The Pflucker family
was still dominating the scene at Morococha with a
plant built at Pomacancha (above Casapalca), but by
1861 all the area was being exploited--Aguas Calientes, the region where Volcan Mines are today, Yauli,
Garahuacra, etc. The second study, Cerro de Pasco,
clearly indicates the growing complexity of the operations there. At this time, 1861, there was need for
another socavon and the miners were looking for a
contractor to complete the Rumiallana one begun in
1825. (Babinski, later of the Escuela de Minas,
helped trace its course and the contract eventually
fell to Henry Meiggs in 1877.) Raimondi reckoned the
mine should be exploited as an open pit and also
thought that the ore needed roasting before amalgamation, doubting it would pay the extra cost. (According to Rivero, this was done 30 years earlier.) A
very full description of the amalgamation process as
practiced in Cerro de Pasco is given, and in view of
its wastefulness compared with other mines one wonders why it was persisted with so stubbornly. Even
at nearby Morococha, furnaces were used. Besides
the mines at the town itself, it is clear that most
of the neighboring ones worked today were in exploitation then. Colquijirca, however, was on a small
scale and Huaron is referred to as essentially a
lead mine--Raimondi describes the Bosque de Piedras.

It is also clear that attention was being drawn
to the copper of Cerro de Pasco itself. This interest
in copper was also seen on the coast. Prices in the
early 1860's reached Ł125 per ton and caused mines in
the Nazca and Ica region to be developed, and later,
in the 1870's, exports of rich ores (25 per cent) were
made at the rate of 2,000 to 3,000 tons yearly. The
mine Canza was one of the most important and exported
from 1875 to 1884.

Thus, by the 1870's, there were considerable signs of development in the metal-mining industry. Old mines were being reopened, new metals were starting to be exploited and new techniques were gradually being introduced. For example, another water-jacket furnace, for smelting lead, was installed in Yauli. This was 3 meters high equipped, as the name implies, with a hollow wall in which water circulated for cooling, with a 30-cm.-high hearth below. The cross section was square and at the junction of hearth and superstructure were pipes for supplying a blast. Above, the furnace was equipped with a flue, while it was tapped into a small truck on rails that could be brought right up to the hearth. A 1.2-meter hearth could handle 50 to 60 tons daily. Amalgamation plants on German models were being built near Ambo (by the Durand family) and in Morococha (Tuctu) one such functioned from 1850 to 1895. Even the government seemed to be taking an interest. In 1829, a law had confirmed the Nuevas Ordenanzas de México as the mining legislation of the new Peruvian republic, and in subsequent years, due to Rivero's campaign, taxes had been reduced to stimulate the silver mines. In 1837, 1847, 1857, 1858 and 1862, discussions had taken place about a new mining code and various suggestions based on the Ordenanzas had been made, but nothing had been done (was there any need to change the Ordenanzas?). But in 1876, something was done in a field where it was badly needed--technical training. Although the Ordenanzas envisaged a mining college and although Rivero had attempted to establish one in Huanuco (it had had the name Colegio de Mineria since 1828 and Rivero bought 5,000 pesos worth of equipment for it in Europe in 1846, which arrived in 1857), there existed no technical training school for mining engineers. In 1876, the Escuela de Minas was founded under the direction of the Pole Eduardo de Habich, who had been preparing it since 1869. Thus, Peru could now, perhaps, look to a bright mining future even though one negative law had been made: the suppression of the Tribunal, which had proved ineffective in practice but which, properly organized, could have been made into a means of supervising the industry.

Where should the industry have gone from here?
Ideally, it would have continued growing and developing slowly, supplying the country with minerals other
than silver as industrialization proceeded, and improving its own techniques thanks to the efforts of
the newly graduated engineers. The government should
also have had enough experience with guano and nitrates to understand the dangers of exports. With
virtually no taxes on the metal-mining industry, what
was Peru supposed to gain in return for the exports?
Was there a need for foreign currency? Clearly, there
was some need but, equally clearly, such a need could
only be met by exploiting the mines under national
ownership--foreign companies would merely re-export
their profits, etc., at the rate of 80 per cent of
sales according to a study done later. Nevertheless,
in 1877 a law was passed, intended to be temporary
but which, thanks to the Chilean War, was to last
nearly a quarter of a century. This law established
a tax on concessions (30 soles per _pertenencia_ per
year, the sol having been introduced in 1863 and the
old peso valued at 80 centavos of a sol, while the
pertenencia was some 3 to 5 hectares according to the
Ordenanzas), the payment of which was sufficient to
maintain the concession--i.e., no obligation to work
it. It also established a Padron General, a registry
of concessions and a very positive step. But its
great fault was that it permitted foreigners to own
mines. It is clear that before 1877 foreigners did
own mines, either surreptitiously or, perhaps, in
partnership or they may have been naturalized. But
these foreigners were small operators who were, in
any case, rapidly becoming Peruvian citizens. What
the 1877 law permitted was the entry of international
capital to exploit the mines and remove the minerals
(leaving nothing in Peru except their small local
costs), or to buy mines and hold them without exploitation as pawns in their international operations.
In general, they would be able to do as they liked
in Peru where they would pay almost no taxes and have
no supervision, the Tribunal being suppressed. The
President who signed this law was Mariano Prado.

It may be that in normal circumstances the country could have survived the power of foreign capital,

particularly as the expansionist era of the United
States was still in its beginnings, but circumstances
were not normal. A brief political survey will not
come amiss. In 1866, Spain had already tried to make
trouble in Peru and had occupied the Chincha guano
islands. By defeating the Spaniards, or rather pre-
venting their landing at Callao, the then President
Mariano Prado, who had come to power by a coup, covered himself with glory. However, he was shortly
deposed as despotic. In 1868, Balta was elected
President and with him began a gigantic series of public works, including the Lima-La Oroya and Mollendo-
Puno railways. These works were to be paid for by
guano and nitrate exports and, to this end, the famous Dreyfus contract was signed with a French finance house. The French were to lend the government
money as advances against guano deliveries, the
Peruvian signatory being Nicolas de Pierola, the son
of the same-named friend of Rivero. Other money was
loaned from many sources (London), and the great increase in credit caused a rapid emission of notes by
private banks--an emission quite uncontrolled by the
law in any way whatever, and soon an inflationary
crisis was apparent. Moreover, guano production began to fall and Peru could not meet her foreign commitments. In the midst of this, one of the bloodiest
revolutions occurred when the Gutierrez brothers tried
to sieze power and assassinated the President. Once
the revolution was dealt with, Balta's successor
Manuel Pardo did a violent pruning of public expenditure (particularly bureaucratic, including the Tribunal), but he kept on the useful public works and,
indeed, inaugurated the Escuela de Minas. He handed
over office in 1876 to the returned Mariano Prado,
and was then murdered himself, in 1878. Mariano
Prado was to create further strife both with Nicolas
de Pierola and Manuel Pardo, while the latter was
still alive. One of the causes was a cutback on
the public works in favor of military functions, but
little seems to have been spent on military necessi-
ties and an unarmed Peru entered the Chilean War in
1879. Prado's subsequent defection from Peru is a
too well-known and shameful story to repeat here.

Thus, the background to the promising position

of the mines in the 1870's may be summarized as follows: The country went through a series of financial
crisis, particularly in 1875, and became bankrupt in
1879; of the three presidents of the period, the two
honorable ones were murdered; the stage had been set
for a complete sell-out to foreign financial interests
with the Dreyfus contract, the 1877 mining law and the
international debts; the war with Chile, much precipitated by the nitrate fields, was to lead to the prostration of Peru and the occupation of the capital
itself.

THE CHILEAN WAR TO 1902

The Chilean War was a military, economic and
moral disaster. The foreign troops left Lima in 1884,
and one of the many problems that faced the new government under President Iglesias was that of the foreign debt. Much of this debt was because of the
railway contracts. The Callao-La Oroya railway, designed by Malinowski, had been contracted to Henry
Meiggs by the Balta government. Meiggs, a gifted
entrepreneur who had come to Peru in 1868 as a result
of an undischarged bankruptcy in San Francisco, had
failed to complete it in the time scheduled largely
owing to non-payment by the State, and in 1877 a new
contract had been signed, this time referring to a
Callao-Cerro de Pasco railway and making Meiggs contractor for the Rumiallana socavon. Meiggs died in
the same year, his intests were inherited by the
Compania del Ferrocarril de la Oroya y Mineral de
Pasco and the railway remained incomplete at Chicla
(above San Mateo) throughout the war. The railway
debts were very largely owed to English financiers
but some were owed to Meiggs himself. In 1885, a
Michael Grace appeared in Peru as Meiggs' legatee.
Quite what his position was is uncertain but, presumably, he had bought a controlling interest in the
company left by Meiggs. In settlement of the debts
to Meiggs, a contract was signed that essentially
gave Grace the ownership of the railway (for 99
years), provided that he completed it from Chicla to
Cerro de Pasco. He was also given the ownership of
the Rumiallana socavon, provided that he built it and

that he also offered 20 per cent of the shares for sale in Peru. (The socavon was to be operated on the principles that (1) any undenounced mines encountered in its digging belonged to Grace, (2) mines drained by it paid 20 per cent of their minerals extracted to the company and (3) if the company extracted the minerals as sub-contractor for the miners, the company must pay them 25 per cent.) Armed with this formidable contract, which had converted Meiggs' part as a constructor into that of an owner, Grace contacted the London creditors, holders of Peruvian government bonds. He was empowered by them to negotiate a new contract that liquidated the bonds by handing over all the railways in Peru, offering options on important mining zones (Huancavelica, the petroleum of Piura and the coal of the Santa Valley) and promising further deliveries of guano. Excepted from this contract were the La Oroya-Cerro de Pasco stretch of railway and the Rumiallana socavon.

Grace had pulled off a very clever coup. He almost certainly did not have the money to complete the railway to La Oroya, indeed not even the Cerro de Pasco stretch, which he ceded to a Mr. Thorndike, but he owned the concessions and he could sell them. Even the Rumiallana socavon he sold in return for shares in the Cerro de Pasco Mining Company when that was formed in 1901, and the socavon was only restarted that year (16 years after the 1885 contract) to be finished in 1907. Indeed, it must have been Grace's prime objective to interest an outside company in Cerro de Pasco so that he could sell his concessions, and in that objective he was successful. As for the other railways, including the one to La Oroya, they went to what was to become, in 1890, the Peruvian Corporation, which was, of course, obliged by the contract to finish building some of them and do studies on others.

To their credit, some of the government's assessors repudiated these contracts. They failed to see why the debts could not be paid in time without handing over all this State property, but their views, though noted, were not upheld.

Meanwhile, the mining industry was showing some

signs of recovery. Even in the dark years of the war,
the Escuela de Minas had been working and, among other
activities, had produced some excellent publications,
the Anales. Articles by Raimondi, Delsol, Leonardo
Pflucker, Mauricio du Chatenet, Martinet, Babinski and
even the first graduate Pedro Remy (on Yauli) prove
the enthusiasm and seriousness with which the school
of mines faced its duties. But practical work was
also done and soon many metallurgical innovations
appeared in Peru. Thus, in 1881, a new foundry was
built in Algamarca; in 1888, Werthemann constructed
a water-jacket furnace in Tarica (Pallasca); in 1889,
the Huaraucaca plant was begun by Fernandini at Colquijirca; in 1885, the mine of Arapa, and associated
entrance, were initiated by Ricardo Mahr; and in 1890,
the Caylloma Silver Mining Company came into existence
with a group of English shareholders who built a special amalgamation plant at San Ignacio linked to the
mine by railway. Also in 1890, the most influential
innovation of the decade took place at Hualgayoc
where Heverling built a plant, completed in 1892, for
leaching silver by the Patera process.

The Patera process was invented in 1858 in Joa-
chimstal, Bohemia, but had various forerunners, such
as the Agustin one. By 1868, it was already in use
in Mexico on amalgamation tailings, but it was not
until the 1890's that it came, briefly, to Peru. The
process consisted of essentially five steps. First,
the milled ore was roasted to produce silver chlorides
and then it was washed with water to remove copper
(precipitated with iron if worthwhile.) A second
leaching, this time with hyposulphite, extracted the
silver--the basic reaction being: $2AgCl + 3Na_2S_2O_3 = Ag_2S_2O_3 + 2Na_2S_2O_3 + 2NaCl$. Next, the silver was
precipitated as a sulphide and the solution regenera-
ted by adding sodium sulphide: $Ag_2S_2O_3 + 2Na_2S_2O_3 + Na_2S = Ag_2S + 3Na_2S_2O_3$. If the ore contained much
lead and copper, unless removed by previous washing,
these metals were also precipitated, but the lead
itself was of use in the final stage, refining by
cupellation. The process had a more serious drawback
for rich ores, namely metallic silver was dissolved
and lost. However, the Patera process was a great
advance at the time and it was later introduced all

over Peru: Quichas (minerals from Raura) and San Jose
(from Castrovirreyna) in 1892, Quiruvilca, Algamarca
and Otuzco (1897), Pasco (1893), Ticapampa, etc.   Silver production rose from a yearly average of 130 tons
in the first half of the decade to 190 tons in the
second half.

Thus by the 1890's, it was clear that the industry was again on the move, and for those in favor of
foreign investment the advent of the English company
to Caylloma and Backus and Johnson to Casapalca (with
an important mechanical concentrator using jigs)
showed that the 1877 law had not gone ignored outside
Peru.   Why then did the government pass another law
in 1890 guaranteeing tax stability for 25 years?
Since the only existing tax was the 30 soles per pertenencia, a rough calculation shows that at that time
the whole of Cerro de Pasco, with an annual output
worth certainly 2 million soles, would pay, at most,
20,000 soles in tax.   Tax would be well below 1 per
cent of sales.

As if there were not already sufficient incentives for foreign investors, an international phenomenon now intervened.   The price of silver, which in
the 1860's had been 60 pennies the ounce (sterling),
fell to 50 in 1882, to about 40 in 1889, where it was
temporarily held by the Sherman Silver Act (a law
passed in the U.S. authorizing the treasury to buy
silver with notes), and finally to about 30 in 1895.
In Peru, it had always been the rule that any holder
of silver could bring it to the mint and turn it into
coin.   Since the value of the 90-per-cent-silver sol
was now falling with the metal (40 pennies in 1873
and 24 by the mid-1890's), it was decided by Nicolas
de Pierola in 1897, following a very minor further
fall, to suspend the liberty to mint silver.   This
extremely important decision has been much discussed
in the economic field, and an attempt will also be
made here to analyze its implications for the mining
industry--an industry whose aim for 350 years has been
the extraction of silver to turn into coin.

What worried the government and the public in the
1890's was not the fall in world silver prices (after

all, most of the silver was for internal use) so
much as the progressive devaluation of the sol in
terms of the pound sterling. The cause of this was
seen to be the uncontrolled minting of soles whereby
their international value was reduced to their metal
content, thus the sol fell with silver. There was
certainly some truth in this, but there were other
reasons also. The metal value of a currency is not
the only item that determines its value, as was seen
later when the sol, then with a very high backing in
gold and a nominal parity of 24 pennies, was to fluctuate between 17 and 29 pennies within a period of
only ten years. A second cause could be the balance
of imports and exports. In fact, from 1892 to 1896
Peru ran a trade surplus every year, the average being 4.6 million soles. Since deficits previously had
been the rule, the balance-of-payments situation was
clearly improving rather than worsening, and it should
be expected that this factor would strengthen the currency. (However, it is well known now that some countries can run deficits for years without devaluations,
i.e., the United States, while others have surpluses
but cannot avoid these crises.) Another cause for the
sol's decline could be a fall in its internal purchasing power. Unfortunately, there is no information
on this point for the 1890's, but it can be assumed
that if there was a fall it was not significant--cer-
tainly this was never cited as a cause of the problem.
(Purchasing power of a currency has remarkably little
to do with its international parity.) Thus, when
looked at, there appears to be a fourth reason for
the fall in value of the sol--speculation. Holders
of soles were buying sterling--a simultaneous currency
and metal speculation.

    To cure the malady, the government stopped the
minting of soles. They did not merely restrain it
by, say, just buying and minting such silver as the
economy needed, perhaps with a complementary gradual
issue of Peruvian gold coins; still less, of course,
was any legislation envisaged that might have controlled the inalienable right of the monied to spec-
ulate on the international exchanges. On April 9,
1897, the minting of soles was stopped for 17 years.
Two other measures were included: (1) the re-impor-

tation of soles was prohibited (unless delivered
straight to the mint for turning into silver bars)
and (2) the pound sterling was to be used for paying
fiscal debts, customs duties, etc.

What was the effect of these draconian measures
on the internal economy? The first consequence was
a tremendous liquidity shortage. From 1892 to 1896,
some 3.3 million soles had been put into circulation
yearly. Much of this money had of course disappeared
in the speculative buying of gold or sterling, but,
nevertheless, a proportion of it had been absorbed by
the economy without, apparently, any noticeable inflationary effects. As from 1897, no more money was
to be released. Such a program was impossible in
practice, and very shortly afterward Pierola put more
cash into the economy by the simple expedient of
allowing the pound sterling free circulation within
the country. At the same time, the mint started producing Libras Peruanas (LP) from melted-down sterling
as well as from gold from the mines (one Libra = 10
soles = ₤1) and issuing small silver coins (fractions
of a sol) from melted-down soles. The net effect
from 1897 to 1902 was a yearly issue of 2.9 million
soles of which half was sterling put directly into
circulation. When the unloading of internal hoarding,
admitted by Pierola himself to be very substantial,
is also added, it seems probable that the amount of
money put yearly into actual circulation after 1897
was greater than before. In short, the officially
diagnosed primary ill, the uncontrolled issue of
money, was actually increased by the 1897 law and
remained as uncontrolled as before, since there was
no limit to the amount of gold that could be imported
or minted. The 1897 law was confirmed in 1901 by the
definitive adoption of the gold standard.

The silver-based currency that had served Peru
and all Spanish America since the first days of the
conquest had been done away with overnight. It was
abolished as a result of a speculation on the relative prices of silver and gold, the real irony being
that silver had by 1897 already virtually reached its
lowest price (in terms of the pound sterling or the
dollar). If the sol's fall was because of the fall

of silver, the 1897 measure had, in fact, come too
late to be of any use.

It has been said that the 1897 law was a further
invitation to foreign investment in the mining industry. The first reason for this was the free access
of foreign capital. Not only was sterling legally
allowed to circulate, thus avoiding the troubles of
the exchange market and possible falls in its parity
should the demand for sterling be saturated, but it
was actively encouraged both by the government and,
of course, by a public that had been undergoing a
ferocious credit squeeze. Then, a severe blow had
been dealt to the mining industry. Pierola maintained that the industry was unaffected by a measure
closing a market that had previously absorbed two
thirds of its main product, but this was not the view
expressed by the miners. However, as has been said,
silver production increased during this period, very
largely owing to the new processes that were in no
small way responsible on the world scene for the
original fall in prices. One such process, called
Languasco, had been developed in Cerro de Pasco itself
(1896) and was used successfully in improving amalgamation. Silver was cheaper to produce and lower grade
ores could be worked economically. Now, however, the
Peruvian miner had to sell his silver for export. Indeed, the need for gold for the internal currency encouraged exports as never before and the commercial
surplus rose from 4.2 to 13.7 million soles in one
year (1897), in 1900 reaching over 21 million soles.
Superficially, the situation looked excellent, but
what really had happened was that the country had
been turned into an exporter of raw materials and had
opened its doors to a massive inflow of foreign capital, the reasons for coming to Peru being, of course,
to make money.

The situation was formally consecrated in 1900
with the arrival of the long-awaited Código de Minería,
which became law as from 1901. The new code, which
had been planned long before 1877 (but in a very different form), was projected again in various guises
from 1888 onward. In 1896, the government charged
the newly formed Sociedad Nacional de Mineria with

its preparation--an extraordinary procedure asking
the industry to invent the legislation governing its
own activities, and here, at least, the former Tribunal could have been of real service. Of the various
projects presented, that of the Sociedad was in fact
adopted. As could be expected, the legislation was
"liberal" in the extreme, and an ambiguous clause was
even taken to mean that the mines were no longer State
property. Otherwise, the 1877 law was confirmed and
some positive items were introduced, such as more
social and safety obligations than in the Ordenanzas
and a new definition of the concession (rectangular,
composed of 1 to 60 pertenencias, each 100 by 200
meters extending vertically), which got away from the
awkward law that tied concessions to the strike of
veins, while procedures for acquiring concessions,
trespass, lapsing, etc., were treated in detail. The
code was, in short, aimed at developing a more sophisticated, larger-scale industry with a frank invitation to foreign capital, and it was clear that
the days of the small miner in the big centers were
numbered.

Briefly, then, the mines throve with high silver
exports coupled with a new boom in copper, which
reached ₤70 per ton and caused an annual production
at the turn of the century of some 9,000 tons, much
of which came from Cerro de Pasco; but, in fact, confidence in the traditional mining industry was badly
shaken. The foreign capitalist stepped in. As far
back as 1887, a North American syndicate had attempted
to assess the copper reserves of Cerro de Pasco and
in 1901 the Cerro de Pasco Mining Company was established. Two thirds of the mines were bought out from
demoralized proprietors, paid with imported money,
and in 1902 the holding company in New York--the
Cerro de Pasco Investment Company--could look forward
to a rich future as concessionaire of one of the
world's famous mines, paying virtually no taxes, enjoying complete liberty in foreign exchange, in exports, in employment policy and in its capital movements. It was also holder of the La Oroya-Cerro de
Pasco railway and the Rumiallana socavon concessions,
thanks to Michael Grace who became a shareholder of
the New York company.

Thus, what had happened in 25 years was:

1.   In 1877, a law was passed allowing foreigners
to own mines, establishing derisory taxes and abolish-
ing the obligation to exploit concessions.

2.   In 1890, tax stability was guaranteed for 25
years, although there was no evidence of a need for
further incentives for mining investments.

3.   In 1897, the national currency was diagnosed
as being devalued owing to excessive circulation. As
a remedy, it was cut back so drastically that free
entry had to be given to a foreign currency--sterling.
A vicious domestic deflation was initiated for the
benefit of the foreign capitalist, who rapidly put
more of his own money into circulation than had been
taken out (between 1897 and 1902, 7 million soles in
sterling were added while 2.8 million soles of silver
coins were removed). The economy was completely re-
oriented toward exports, silver, in particular, no
longer having a domestic market. It must be under-
lined that the ultimate reason for the 1897 law lay
in the fall of the sol's international parity. Of
what importance was this parity to the vast majority
of the population? Less then than now; and even now,
the parity hardly affects the life of anyone outside
a few priviledged circles of the capital. A critical
date was 1897, when it was decided that the interests
of the holders of capital (in Lima or foreign) were
above the interests of the country at large. For 70
years, Peruvian financial and economic policy has
hardly changed.

4.   In 1900, a new mining code, confirming and
even going further than the 1877 act, was made public.
Drawn up by the powers of the mining industry, it
clearly was in favor of capital rather than in pro-
tecting the interests of the small miners or those of
the State.

5.   In 1901, the most important mine of all Peru
passed into the hands of a foreign company. The advent of this company must have owed much to the activities of Michael Grace, armed with the 1885

contract that made him owner of constructions for
which Meiggs was a simple contractor, who realized
that his fortune might be made if a large-scale exploitation was started at Cerro de Pasco.

THE 20TH CENTURY

The new century was entered with the mining
industry's future progress clearly mapped out. It
was back to its colonial position as an exporting
industry with all the disadvantages of dependence on
foreign demand, but this time the customer had no
responsibility for the welfare of Peru, as had Spain.
It was to be dominated by foreign mining companies
and the country was to become dependent on their investments. This state of affairs must be blamed
heavily on the Peruvian capitalist who in 1896 and
1897, for example, seemed to prefer to gamble his
money on the exchange rather than invest it in productive industry. But if in the long view the situation was depressing at the time, no one thought so.
The mines enjoyed an unparalleled boom until 1907.

In the main zone of central Peru, the railway
reached La Oroya in 1893 and Cerro de Pasco in 1904.
(According to Grace's contract of 1885, it should
have gotten to Cerro de Pasco three years after
reaching La Oroya, i.e., in 1896.) Similarly, the
Rumiallana socavon--planned since the 1820's, designed since 1861, contracted from 1877--was only
seriously begun in 1901. It is interesting to specu-
late what would have been the future of Cerro de Pasco
if these two capital works contracted to Meiggs and
Grace had actually been completed according to schedule. The miners certainly would have been in a position to exploit copper on a much grander scale when
the 1897 price rise came--perhaps they could have
even produced the 20 million soles that the North
American company was later to invest, an investment
ironically welcomed in a country where only five years
earlier an uncontrolled issuing of money had been
diagnosed as the cause of all ills. (As it was, the
two works were completed only in time to be of use to
the North American company.) Once Morococha and Yauli

were on the railway, these zones were rapidly developed. The Proano family opened a mine in 1894,
Miculisich started Puquiococha in 1897, Gildemeister
founded Alpamina in 1899 and other companies followed,
Santa Ines y Morococha (1898), Sacracancha (1902),
besides some long established ones that continued
through this period, e.g., Carahuacra. In 1905, the
Morococha Mining Company appeared and began buying
up a large number of the concessions. Who owned this
company, other than that they were North Americans,
is not clear, but it may be suspected that they were
some sort of "front" for Cerro de Pasco. Certainly,
in 1915, they both were united into the Cerro de Pasco
Copper Corporation.

Casapalca also knew a rapid, if slightly earlier,
development. Besides Backus and Johnson, there was
a Henry Garland working mines at Aguas Calientes,
while Pacococha (discovered 1886?) was bought by the
Proanos in 1906. It was they who built the foundry
at Tamboraque whose ruins still stand beside the central highway, and, indeed, this period saw a new
craze in smelter construction. The most famous of
these was the Casapalca one of Backus and Johnson.
Started in 1890, it went through innumerable modifications, but essentially the process consisted of
(1) a previous roasting or agglomeration of the ore,
(2) a smelting in a water-jacket or similar furnace
and (3) refining of silver by cupellation. With the
rise in copper prices, the smelter was rapidly developed to handle copper/silver instead of lead/silver
ores, and copper mattes were produced. Another large
smelter for copper matte existed at Rio Blanco for a
short while. In Yauli, there were at one time three
major metallurgical plants (Santa Barbara, Societe
des Minas de Yauli and La Victoria) plus several
small water jackets for lead/silver, while mechanical
concentrators were also being introduced both at
Morococha and at Mahr Tunnel (among the first, that
of Gluck Auf).

But the development of Morococha was small by
comparison with that of Cerro de Pasco. Mines being
worked included, in addition to the great center

itself, Vinchos, Chuquitambo (a company for exploiting
the gold was formed in London in 1902), Atacocha (W. C.
Dawson), Colquijirca, San Gregorio (for bismuth),
Minaragra (the famous vanadium deposit was discovered
in 1906) and Huayllay (two national companies bought
out by Huaron in 1912). The main Tinyahuarco plant
(of Cerro de Pasco) came into operation in 1905. This,
again, was based on three stages but, of course, was
designed from the outset for copper. First, the ore
was roasted or sintered, then it was reduced to matte
in a type of blast furnace or, alternatively, a reverberatory (these latter proved more satisfactory and
gradually superseded the other), and, finally, a 98-
to 99-per-cent copper was produced from Pierce-Smith
converters--which created a sensation on their first
introduction. The Huaraucaca smelter of Colquijirca
was similar, although it only went so far as to yield
copper matte. However, in later years (post-1914),
it had an interesting addition, namely bismuth leaching. The arsenate minerals were roasted and hence
oxidized, they were then leached with salt and sulphuric acid, precipitated in sulphide form with sodium
sulphide and then roasted again and founded as 90-per-
cent pure bismuth. These plants also produced their
own coke with coal from Goyllarisquizga, where the
railway had reached in 1907. There were, of course,
many other plants in the region, for leaching silver
by the Patera process, for amalgamation (e.g., in
Chuquitambo) and for producing plomo de obra for
later cupellation.

    It would be tedious to try to describe all the
mines, processes and allied constructions such as
hydroelectric plants and roads that began at this
time, and the reader is referred to C. E. Velarde's
excellent book La Minería en el Perú (1908) for
details. However, a very brief listing, taken from
that book, may be of interest. In northern Peru, the
figure of note was Fermin Malaga Santolalla of Cajamarca who was responsible for development in Hualgayoc, Sayapullo, Algamarca, Milluachaqui, Chilete
and Quiruvilca (where Gildemeister was also involved).
His most famous discovery was the tungsten of Pasto
Bueno, which he started producing in 1910. Fermin
Malaga Santolalla is certainly the most eminent of

the Peruvian miners of the time if not of the whole
20th century, a man of great action and initiative--
unfortunately, an almost solitary example, nearly all
the rest of the mining names being foreign. Other
mines of northern Peru were at Punre (Celendin), Otuzco, Pataz, etc. In Ancash, Magistral was awaiting
the arrival of the Chimbote railway; Patara (Macate),
Colquipocro and Italian-owned mines in Huari were ac-
tive--the latter with some small furnaces. The Anglo-
French Ticapampa was formed in 1896 and started Peru's
most important silver-leaching plant in 1904, while a
copper mine in Huinac (English-owned) was not so successful. Further south, Roque Durand was working near
Huallanca and Simon Dunstan exploited Raura (also
associated with Fermin Malaga Santolalla). In south-
central Peru, there was activity around Huancavelica
(Huachocolpa, Lircay and Castrovirreyna), and the
Picasso family already owned some mines there (Caude-
losa). In 1906, a company was formed to exploit the
nickel of Rapi, but never did so, while in 1899 there
had been copper produced in Tayacaja (presumably Cobriza). Further south in Apurimac, Puno and Arequipa, some notable developments took place.

    In 1893, the legendary Cochasayhuas gold mine
was rediscovered, sealed up, apparently, since the
Portuguese left it more than 250 years earlier. A
company was formed in 1903 for its exploitation and
eventually it was worked for a few years, but suffered
badly from its isolation. Another gold mine exploited
was in Andaray (1898), while explorations had been
done in Sandia (Apuroma) by Pflucker, and in 1905 a
dredging company had been formed in London for working
the Inambari. The most famous gold mine of all was at
Santo Domingo. Here, between 1896 and 1909, the Inca
Mining Company (North American) extracted £1.5 million,
which at the then-current price represented over ten
tons of gold. Both monitoring and dredging were being
used at Poto (Ananea), this enthusiasm for gold being,
of course, directly related to the monetary events of
1897. At Lampa, the English Lampa Mining Company had
been formed, while William Grundy was exploiting Berenguela with a foundry at Limon Verde. The Caylloma
Silver Mining Company had, however, gone bankrupt
(perhaps it led too luxurious a life--it was famous

for its tennis courts where ladies played in long
skirts, while gentlemen dressed even for lunch, somewhat incongruous at 4,200 meters). A Chilean-owned
society bought it (bankrupt in 1932), and another
company also entered the area at Cuchilladas in 1905.
Finally, it is worth adding that both Cerro Verde and
the Cuajone region were being exploited, albeit on a
small scale, for copper oxides.

In 1907, according to Velarde, the industry employed directly 10,000 people and some 2,000 as carriers. There were 21,000 pertenencias (mining concessions) denounced, not very much in fact, and
production for export was 8,912 tons of red copper
(98 or 99 per cent), 8,303 tons of copper matte, 144
tons of plomo de obra (i.e., with high silver content),
81 tons of silver precipitates, 521 tons of copper
cement (precipitate), 8,044 kilos of pure silver and
445 kilos of gold. In terms of metallic content,
total production was some 20,000 tons of copper, 5,500
of lead, 207 tons of silver, 28 of vanadium and 13 of
bismuth. There were also important non-metallic mines
for coal, petroleum, salt and borates, these latter
being extracted from the area inland of Arequipa where
Borax Consolidated had been operating since 1890. The
figures indicate that already, despite the plethora of
beneficiating plants of one sort or another, there was
a substantial export of semi-refined metals, although
the actual quantities may be taken with caution--what
happened to all that unexported lead?

In 1908, there was a severe recession and the
value of production fell by 20 per cent, largely
because of a fall in copper prices. The recession
made itself felt throughout the economy as a clear
demonstration of the dependence on exports. A recovery in 1912 (owing to developments at Morococha?) was
short lived and in 1914 the industry again suffered
a setback, not only with prices but also with production falling in all metals. At this point, a very
curious phenomenon occurred. With the outbreak of
World War I, a panic seized Lima and money disappeared
from circulation. Gold and silver coinage were
hoarded, bank deposits withdrawn and financial chaos
threatened. The situation was, indeed, somewhat

similar to that of 1897 when cash had become unobtainable because people were selling silver for gold
(which they held). This time, however, the exact opposite remedy was selected. Instead of stopping the
minting of soles (as was done in 1897), it was re-
sumed for the first time since then. Not only that,
paper money was put into circulation for the first
time since the Chilean War. Although the move was
successful in providing finance that helped the mines
to raise production (by 60 per cent in the case of
copper), domestically it was no more helpful in the
long term than the contrary measures of 1897.

At that time, the reduction of domestic currency
had allowed foreign capital to buy up the mines; this
time, an increase in domestic currency (bolstered by
huge trade surpluses as the war proceeded) merely
further financed exports (both mineral and agricultural). Even conservative economists have remarked
on the complete absence of industrial investment,
whose consequence was a very sharp rise in the cost-
of-living index from 104 in 1914 to 210 in 1920. In
1914, the trade surplus was 30 million soles and in
1919, 147 million, although it fell back to 114 million the following year. It is true that the sol (even
in paper) achieved a high premium over the pound sterling and the dollar, but the disadvantages of being a
country living on exports of primary products were becoming clear. Trade surpluses bring inflation (too
much money to spend on too few goods--unless they are
imported, which they could not be in wartime) while
trade deficits bring devaluation. This situation of
economic dependence, which was becoming evident, is
extremely complex and probably no thorough analysis
of its mechanisms will ever be made. It is sufficient
to say, however, that the fundamental cause is self-
evident. As long as the country is not using its
manpower and industrial and natural sources to satisfy
its own needs (if not completely, at any rate largely),
its economy is incapable of being controlled solely by
internal measures.

The war was, thus, a powerful stimulant to the
industry, tungsten in particular experiencing a boom,
but the country did not benefit much from it. In

1915, 25 years after the tax-stability law of 1890, this fact was realized and another cause for it was sought--foreign control of the mining industry. According to Alayza and Paz Soldan, in that period more than Ь40 million had been exported in minerals and four fifths of that value had gone with it in the form of profits, depreciation, imported machinery, salaries of foreign executives, etc. (This would be sufficient to annul over two thirds of the commercial surplus.) Over 80 per cent of the mining industry was, in 1915, controlled by capitalists who exported their profits. Moves were made to increase taxation and, in fact, an export tax, guaranteeing an intangible 110 per cent of costs, was to be introduced while a profits tax was planned.

Following the war, prices began to fall again, first copper and lead to some $0.18 and $0.06* per pound, respectively, while in the 1920's silver fell badly from $1.10 to $0.60 per troy ounce approximately. This was the opportunity for a further consolidation of Cerro de Pasco's hold on central Peru. As the holders of capital, they now invested in the La Oroya smelter (1923), which rapidly put every other surviving one out of business with the exception of San Jose (Huaron)--which, however, was to follow within a few years. This they could do thanks to the large supply of ore from their own mines with which they could under-pin the operation, while the introduction of flotation concentration (reducing transport costs) was a further disincentive to local smelting. Cerro de Pasco had bought out Casapalca in 1919 and was soon to buy the Empressa Desaguadora in Morococha. During the same period, the Northern Peru Mining Company established itself in Samne and Salpo. In 1922, the Direccion de Mineria was established, demonstrating the country's growing concern about the mining industry, and in 1924 a very comprehensive survey of the industry was published to mark the centenary of the battle of Ayacucho--the <u>Síntesis de la Minería Peruana</u>. Also in 1920, the new constitution

---

*Whenever the word "dollars" or the dollar sign ($) is used, it always refers to U.S. dollars.

cleared up the clause in the 1901 Mining Code, making
quite clear that mines belong to the State. Thus, on
the one hand a national conscience about the mines
was definitely forming, while on the other hand the
industry was slipping further into the control of
non-nationals.

Only a rough indication will be given of the
events until the present day. In 1931, metal prices
collapsed and economic troubles of all sorts beset
Peru, as they did the whole world. Despite the problems the U.S. suffered at the same time, despite a
commercial surplus of some 20 to 30 million soles
that persisted well into the 1940's, the sol began a
long slide that has accelerated rather than reduced.
In 1931, the dollar was worth 3.60 soles and it was
worth about 40 in 1970. World War II did little for
Peru's exports, unlike World War I, and by now Cerro
de Pasco had bought Yauricocha (1927), after litigation, and San Cristobal (1935). As before, even conservative economists were to remark that the commercial
surplus really signified very little when the ownership of the exporting industries was considered. However, too much cannot be blamed on the Cerro de Pasco
Corporation, which was only pursuing its own ends
within the law, when one major weakness lay in the law
itself (although one would like, sometimes, to hear an
explicit exposition of what the ends of this type of
company are, together with an ethical justification).
Why was taxation not higher? Another culprit was the
Peruvian capitalist who was prepared to sell out or
who never invested in the first place. This situation,
in fact, began to show some improvement in the 1930's
with the establishment of what is now Peru's largest,
and very impressive, national mine--Atacocha (1936).
Another positive step had been the foundation of the
Banco Minero in 1931. In the 1930's, for the first
time zinc begins to figure in the statistics.

The post-war years were brightened by price
rises (due to the Korean War, not rising internal
consumption, which did not take place), and the late
1940's and early 1950's saw the development of several
national mines devoted to silver, lead and zinc, metals that all rose 20 to 30 per cent in price between

1950 and 1951. Companies formed at this time were
Milpo, Pacococha, El Pilar, Santo Torribio, Buenaventura, all medium sized and nationally owned, but
this was counterbalanced by the arrival of Marcona
Mining Company and Hochschild (both discussed else-
where--see Chapter 5). In 1950, a new Mining Code
was introduced, which, with some modifications, was
still in vigor until 1971. In the late 1950's and
early 1960's, a few more national companies came into
being, together with some metal-fabricating plants
and SOGESA, as did the Southern Peru Copper Corporation, which caused copper production to jump from
some 50 to over 170 million tons yearly. At this
time, silver production was about 1,000 tons yearly;
lead, 120,000 tons; zinc, 200,000 tons; and iron,
over 3 million tons. A steady growth of the industry
characterized the 1960's.

THE PRESENT STRUCTURE OF
THE MINING INDUSTRY

There is little to say about the present state
of the mines that is not well-known or written elsewhere. The industry's economic importance is analyzed
in the final chapters while the mines that are func-
tioning are discussed individually in Part II. Of the
industry's production, put very roughly at $450 mil-
lion yearly, something over half can be attributed to
Southern Peru Copper Corporation and Cerro de Pasco
Corporation ($140 million and $110 million, respectively). Cerro de Pasco refines another $30 to $50
million worth of bought-in concentrates. Marcona
Mining Company produces over $70 million iron pellets
and concentrates, so these three U.S. companies can
be said to control three quarters of the metal-mining
industry. They are also the country's three largest
taxpayers, so their profitability is not in doubt.
After them come Atacocha, Huaron, Northern Peru Mining Company, Santander, Raura, Buenaventura, Milpo,
El Brocal, Corporacion Minera Castrovirreyna, Millotingo, Rio Pallanga and the Hochschild mines. Their
order in terms of value of production and that of
profitability are very different. In the late 1960's,
the silver mines of Millotingo and Castrovirreyna

proved far more lucrative than the more sober lead/
zinc ones. From the sales point of view, a further
10 per cent of the mining industry is foreign-owned
bringing the total percentage to 85. The situation
has not improved since attention was drawn to it in
1915. Another 10 per cent can be attributed to medium-sized national mines and the remainder, very
approximately, to small miners and the Banco Minero.

With regard to future prospects, however, there
is the possibility of radical change in the long term.
Major new ventures, particularly in copper, are likely
to have a high state participation, but these will not
be effective until the later 1970's. For the immediate future, the pattern set in 1902 will continue--
the great bulk of the industry foreign-owned, its
products exported (much in concentrated or semi-refined form), its economic effect inflationary in boom
times and disastrous in depressions.

4

THE MINES
OF
CENTRAL PERU

The departments of Pasco, Junin, Huancavelica and the sierra of Lima contain nearly all the major mines of Peru. With the exception of the copper fields in the south, Marcona, Raura and the mines of the Northern Peru Mining Company (of which only one is now active), all the mining companies of importance are concentrated in this zone, and even Raura belongs genetically to it although it is in the department of Huanuco. There is no doubt that the area is exceptionally rich in minerals, but much of its preferential development with respect to other parts of Peru is because of its nearness to Lima and to the existence of the mine at Cerro de Pasco, the cause and support of the central railway.

CERRO DE PASCO

Cerro de Pasco is one of the famous mines of the world. Its history has already been briefly traced from its discovery in 1630 to the 1780's when a major expansion in production began. Throughout the 19th century, it was the main mine of Peru and the means whereby it was acquired by a foreign company in 1901 have already been discussed. As its name indicates the Cerro de Pasco Corporation owes its existence to this mine that has always been the basis of the corporation's empire, all of whose directly owned and worked mines lie in the area under discussion--Pasco (Cerro de Pasco and the Goyllaris-quizga coal mine), Junin (Morococha, San Cristobal,

and the Mahr Tunnel concentrator and La Oroya refinery), Huancavelica (Cobriza), Lima (Yauricocha and
Casapalca). To estimate the total production of
Cerro de Pasco would merit a study in itself. As
major metals, it yields copper, silver, lead and
zinc, but, historically, it was always regarded as
a silver mine until the very end of the 19th century.
In the 19th century, it was certainly producing over
60 tons per annum of pure silver. It produces perhaps 85 tons now. An order-of-magnitude figure for
its total yield of silver since its discovery would
be 20,000 tons. The mine's proven reserves (1969)
were 35 million tons of 4.4 ounce silver, 4.6 per
cent lead, 11 per cent zinc, 0.3 per cent copper,
which even at present high production rates is enough
for 20 years. Most mines work with reserves for 4
or 5 years. The value per ton can be estimated at
over $25.

Cerro de Pasco lies among low hills that form
the northern limit to the great pampa of Junin. The
original _cerro_ (hill) has long since been removed
and the area of the mine is a vast mess of holes,
shafts, pits, tunnels, tips and ponds. Situated on
the line of a major longitudinal fault, it is bounded
to the east by the Pucara limestones of the Triassic.
To the west, are exposed the Excelsior Paleozoic
formations. The mineralization is in the debris of
a volcanic blast hole, reactivated various times,
that lifted the rocks into a dome that was subsequently eroded, thus exposing the Excelsior. The
blast hole to the east contains a massive pyrite ore,
in which lies most of the lead/zinc/silver mineralization. To the south is a copper/silver orebody.
To the northwest is a zone traversed by many small
faults, which are now worked out but which used to
contain very rich copper ores. The mineral was
enargite and the grade up to 30 per cent. Over all
was the oxidized zone where the _pacos_ (surface oxides) were worked for silver. Mining for lead and
zinc started at the end of World War II. Copper
mining, the original interest of the North American
company, lapsed for a time but was restarted in 1963.
In 1965, the development of the open pit in the
northeast part of the mine led to permission being

MAP 1

CENTRAL SIERRA

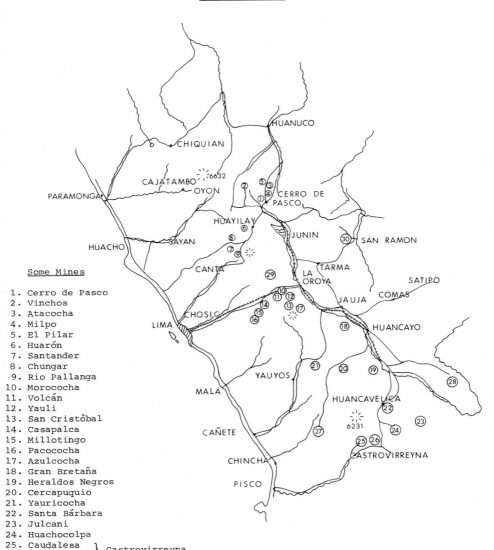

Some Mines

1. Cerro de Pasco
2. Vinchos
3. Atacocha
4. Milpo
5. El Pilar
6. Huarón
7. Santander
8. Chungar
9. Rio Pallanga
10. Morococha
11. Volcán
12. Yauli
13. San Cristôbal
14. Casapalca
15. Millotingo
16. Pacococha
17. Azulcocha
18. Gran Bretaña
19. Heraldos Negros
20. Cercapuquio
21. Yauricocha
22. Santa Bárbara
23. Julcani
24. Huachocolpa
25. Caudalesa } Castrovirreyna
26. San Genaro
27. Chavín Mines
28. Cobriza
29. Huampar
30. Chanchamina

granted to the company to pull down the old town (a living museum) and build a new one north of the mineralized area.

The mine is worked both under-ground and open-cast. The under-ground part, in the pyrite zone, yields over 60,000 tons per month. The layout of the mine is very complex, but it essentially has two shafts, one of which is very new, with 4 cages, 12 skips and goes down nearly 2,000 feet. The method of working is largely "arch-back." The lines of parallel arches work upward filling in the floor, and once the top is reached the space between them is exploited downward with "square set"--wooden framing. Some of the arches are quite a sight--a long, semi-cylindrical tunnel glittering with galena, blende and pyrite. The pyrite causes Cerro de Pasco to be one of the few potentially dangerous mines in Peru. Fire risk is carefully guarded against with doors and machinery for plugging and sealing off zones. In fact, fires are fairly frequent but are rapidly controlled. Another problem that has been with Cerro de Pasco since its discovery is that of flooding. Various major drainage tunnels have been made in the past, but now most of the water is pumped from the bottom of the mine at the rate of 9,500 liters per minute and sent to a precipitating plant. Here, a copper cement is produced yielding very approximately 40 tons per day of 70 per cent copper. The company has difficulty in procuring the scrap it needs for precipitation and uses the iron recuperated from the zinc plant at La Oroya.

The open pit to the north produces between 80,000 and 120,000 tons monthly of 9 per cent lead/ zinc ore. The pit is being developed toward the east where various mineralized bands enter. The ore is very mixed. There are copper zones of 1 to 2.5 per cent grade (if the grade is higher, the mineral goes to La Oroya directly without concentration) and surface oxide zones with 6.6 ounces silver and 15 per cent argentiferous lead. If the silicon content is over 70 per cent, the ore is sent to La Oroya as a flux. In all, over 17 distinct types of ore are classified and separately stocked.

Cerro de Pasco's concentrator is one of the more curious features of the mine. There are two lead circuits in parallel, each with a capacity of 2,400 tons daily, and a zinc circuit with a 4,800-ton-per-day capacity. There is also a small copper one. The plants are conventional in all respects, with a large amount of regrinding, except that they are built entirely on the level. Indeed, the whole Paragsha plant is above the level of the mine, while there is a perfectly good quebrada--an extensive glen--to the southwest where it could easily have been situated. Nevertheless, costs are low at $1.50 per ton. Zinc recovery is poor.

There are some 2,500 persons employed by the corporation in Cerro de Pasco. As is nearly always the case, the housing provided, even for the staff, is very uninspiring. Even the new town built to re-place the old is dreary and unimaginative--the old, though dirty and tumbled-down, is very picturesque.

Immediately beside the main mine, the Empresa Administradora S.A. (belonging to the Galjuf family), a company with an almost pathological horror of pub-licity, has a small concession owned by a subsidiary, the Compania Minerva Cerro. The company floats a bulk copper/lead/silver concentrate in its 120-ton-per-day plant.

ATACOCHA

North of Cerro de Pasco lies the important mining area of Atacocha. The two main mines are Milpo and Atacocha and are situated more or less on a major north-south fault, the Atacocha fault. To the east of this fault lie the folded Pucara lime-stones of the Triassic (at the fault, they are dip-ping vertically) and to the west is a complicated region containing a sharp syncline in the lower Cretaceous formations (Goyllarisquizga) that rises to the north until the Cretaceous is finally eroded away. To the northwest, beneath the Pucara, the Mitu appears. The part east of the Atacocha fault is raised with respect to the part west of it, which

in turn is split by a large number of small northwest striking faults. The mineralization is associated with a series of dacite intrusives that occur
approximately along the Atacocha fault.

     Atacocha mine is siutated on a steep quebrada
that runs south along the line of the fault. The
river then plunges east to join the north-flowing
Huallaga at Chicrin, on the main road from Cerro de
Pasco to Huanuco via La Quinua. As the concentrator
plant is at Chicrin, access to the mine is either
via a short but extremely precipitous road up the
quebrada or by an hour's detour around and over the
mountains. The mineralization is on the western
hillside of the quebrada, west of and underneath a
split fault. It is very irregular. Orebodies seem
to occur on the contact with the intrusive and in
the limestones there are some replacements, but all
that can really be said is that the minerals are predominantly lead, zinc and silver and that when orebodies are found they seem to plunge steeply to the
northeast. Typical ores mined are 5 per cent lead,
5 per cent zinc and 8 ounce silver. Owing to its
proximity to Cerro de Pasco, it is probable that
this mine has been known for a long time, although
first references to it are in the present century.
In 1936, Francisco Gallo Diez, a Spaniard whose family had long associations with Cerro de Pasco, formed
the Compania Minera Atacocha, and since then the
mine has developed into the principal nationally
owned mine of Peru (although in 1969, W. R. Grace &
Co. bought a 20-per-cent holding in its 120 million
soles capital). Something near 6.5 million tons of
ore have been mined containing nearly 400,000 tons
of pure lead, 300,000 tons of zinc and about 1,000
tons of silver. The company is distributed in three
areas. Atacocha, the mine itself, is where most of
the workers live and where is located a hospital,
primary school and a fine modern hotel for the staff.
Its altitude is just under 4,000 meters. Chicrin,
the concentrator and main offices, has another hospital, school and hotel and a delightful camp planted
with flowers and a woodland garden along the Huallaga
River. At Chaprin, much further north, is the hydroelectric station, with a recreation area where the

employees can go on weekends. Apart from the excellent social facilities provided, the company can always be relied upon to support mining events in
general--advertize in magazines, give scholarships
to universities, etc. Atacocha is a model company in
the mining industry. It is also profitable. In
1968, pre-tax profits were 83 million soles on sales
of 294 million or 28 per cent. This did not include
52 million soles for depletion and other provisions.

The mine is operated between 4,350 meters and
the extraction level at 3,600 meters. An internal
shaft is being sunk to a new level at 3,480 meters
to exploit two orebodies that are prolonged downward. The upper parts of the mine are largely worked
out and the main part exploited is now from below
3,900 meters. At this level, mineral was formerly
extracted and sent to the concentrator by railway
and cableway. The railway is now used for supplying
material for refilling from a gloryhole on the neighboring hillside. The galleries go more than 3 kms.
into the hill, and the main extraction one is very
long and uses powerful electric locomotives to haul
the long trains to the concentrator. The method of
exploitation is largely square set and great quantities of wood are consumed from neighboring Huanuco.
Exploitation costs, however, are low at less than
$7.00 per ton mined, while concentration costs are
relatively high ($5.00). Reserves are something
over 2.5 million tons and this is Atacocha's main
problem. At present production rates, this will
last less than five years and new reserves are not
being discovered fast enough. The nature of the
mineralization is such that finding ore depends more
on chance than anything else, although, of course,
once something is found it can be followed.

In addition to the main mine, Atacocha also exploits two small ones nearby called Vasconia and
Santa Barbara. Santa Barbara belongs to Cerro de
Pasco, and Atacocha pays that company for the concentrates extracted from that mine. They are floated
separately, the bulk (which contains 1.85 per cent
bismuth) being sent to La Oroya while the zinc concentrate is exported. The plant capacity is about

1,600 tons daily for minerals from the mine as a
whole, an interesting feature of the plant being the
bins carved out of the rock that have a 3,000-ton
capacity for the uncrushed ore. Since W. R. Grace
became a part-owner, Atacocha sells its monthly production of 2,500 tons zinc and 2,000 tons lead or
lead/copper concentrate to that firm, the Santa
Barbara bulk excepted. Atacocha has a second, older
concentrator that is not normally in use, but at
times it treats ores from the neighboring Milpo mine.

     Milpo is another Peruvian mine, very similar to
Atacocha and on the southward extension of Atacocha's
mineralization. It is similarly lead, zinc and silver, although the ore is chiefly straightforward
filling of fissures, and the mine is smaller, handling only 600 tons per day. (Milpo has suffered
from power shortages, owing to lack of water, hence
the use of Atacocha's concentrator.) The company
was formed in 1949 and has as directors much the
same people as those of Pacococha, among whom the
Baertl family figures prominently. North of Atacocha is a third mineralized area, not directly connected to the former two. The ore is frequently in
mantos (replacements of the limestone bedding of the
Pucara formation), or along the contact with the
Mitu. The mine owned here by Cipriano Proano has
closed. In the area is also the El Pilar mine, with
a 70-ton-per-day plant, owned by the Giles family
(owners of the unworked mercury deposits at Chonta,
Huanuco), while to the west in a very bleak stretch
of country lies the famous Vinchos zone. Vinchos
has been worked since at least the 18th century, and
the present exploiter is a subsidiary of the Empresa
Administradora already mentioned. There is a 320-
ton-per-day concentrator producing a lead/copper/
silver concentrate, the silver content being high
at over 3 kilos the ton.

                         HUARON

     South-southwest of Cerro de Pasco, on the road
from Canta, lies Huayllay and near it Huaron. Here,
the Compagnie des Mines de Huaron has been active

since 1912. The company is French and is connected
with the Banque de Paris at des Pays Bas and with
Penarroya. The mine covers a large area and is
worked in many different parts. In fact, there are
five major east-west lead/zinc veins distributed
over 3 or 4 kilometers, and two northeast-southwest
copper veins. The whole area is thought to owe its
mineralization to an extensive subterranean intrusive. The company produces up to 1,500 tons per day
and employs some 1,500 workers and 300 staff. This
is a large mine and it is interesting to see that,
since their ores permit it, the company has decided
to mine lead/zinc ores and copper ores separately.
The object is, of course, to avoid the problems of
separation in the concentrator, and at present ores
that contain all three metals are simply left in the
mine as reserves. This policy results in a relatively higher copper recovery of 90 per cent (this is to
be compared with a 75 per cent recovery in Casapalca
where a lead/copper separation takes place in the
concentrator) and in a low copper percentage in the
final concentrate--20 to 25 per cent, although the
mineral is largely enargite. This copper concentrate
also contains some 30 ounces of silver and 2.5 per
cent lead, some 30 to 35 tons being produced daily.
The slow response of enargite in the floatation cells
demands a relatively large quantity of frothing agent
to be added--60 grams per ton. In the much larger
lead/zinc circuit, lead is first floated in a pH
(acidity or alkalinity) of up to 11. As depressors,
sodium cyanide (40 to 60 grams per ton) and zinc
sulphate (300 to 400 grams) are used plus some 20
grams of proprietary brands, while at times sodium
sulphite (100 grams) is used as an activator for
lead oxides. The zinc is then refloated from the
tailings in a pH of 11 to 12.5, with 300 to 500
grams per ton of copper sulphate as an activator, 20
to 40 grams of xanthate collector and the same quantity of frothing agent. Concentrate production is
roughly: lead 40 to 50 tons daily, 60 to 65 per
cent lead, 1.5 to 3 kilos silver, 3.5 to 5 per cent
zinc, lead recovery 92 per cent and 80 per cent of
the silver recovered here; zinc 100 to 120 tons
daily, 53 to 55 per cent zinc, 3 to 4 ounces silver,
1 to 1.5 per cent lead, zinc recovery 85 per cent

and 14 per cent of the silver recovered in the zinc
concentrate. Huaron does careful analyses throughout the plant and is installing a spectrometer to
supplement its already large facilities. On the
social side however (housing, etc.), the company is
as 19th century as most others of central Peru.

In the neighborhood of Huaron are some other
important mines. Across the Continental Divide to
the southwest, in the department of Lima, is the
Compania Minerales de Santander, a major zinc producer. This mine is now subterranean but it used
to be worked on the open-pit basis. Some 25,000
tons of metallic zinc in concentrates are exported
yearly to feed the parent company's (St. Joseph Lead)
refinery in Pennsylvania, representing some 13 per
cent of its needs. The mine also yields lead and
silver and some copper. Back in the department of
Pasco, but not far away, is the third mine of the
Empresa Administradora, Chungar,* with a 300-ton-per-
day plant floating a bulk and a zinc concentrate.
Here, also, is the Sindicato Minero Rio Pallanga at
Alpamarca and Carhuacayan, which owns two concentrators with a joint capacity of 700 tons daily and,
similarly, floats both a bulk and a zinc concentrate.
The Sindicato counts among its shareholders a member
of the Rizo Patron family, a family that owes much
of its fame to Ingeneiro (engineer) Rizo Patron, who
worked for E. P. Fernandini at Huaraucaca and Colquijirca. He was the discoverer of the vanadium deposits near Lake Punrun, the mineral of which was
called Patronite in his honor. The vanadium mine
is no longer worked (Fernandini sold it to the
Vanadium Corporation of America in the early years
of this century), but the Fernandini family still
work the perhaps pre-colonial Colquijirca mine.
This mine, which must have one of the longest histories of all Peruvian mines, is essentially formed
from replacement mineralization of the folded Pucara
strata. Yielding some 350 tons daily, it still has

---

*In March 1971, a landslide destroyed the mine
village and 500 lives were lost.

a high silver content, the bulk concentrate containing over 2.5 kilos. A zinc concentrate is also sold.

Thus, the area south and west of Cerro de Pasco
is rich in mines--lead, zinc and silver predominat-
ing--and it is by no means certain that all that exist have already been discovered. Most of the zone
is very bleak and forbidding and does not invite the
casual prospector, but it seems probable that the
mineralization continues along the crest of the
cordillera as far north as Raura.

MOROCOCHA

The region of Morococha and Yauli must be the
best-known mining zone of Peru, lying as it does
right beside the central highway, so that every passing motorist sees it. It is also one of the least
attractive. The town of Morococha is filthy; the
altitude is 4,400 meters and above; snow, rain and
mud cover a landscape apparently composed of slag
heaps; and the presumably once-attractive glacial
lakes are now silted up with mine tailings. However,
the minerals are there even to the eye of the most
unskilled observer. Huge intrusions have split limestone hills in half, red oxide zones color the view
and many mountains have neat cuts in them where former exploiters have removed entire veins. No wonder
that Morococha and Yauli have been worked by many
miners over many years. Tschudi says that this area
was worked by the Portuguese (pre-1634), and it was
certainly being worked in his day. Morococha will
always be associated with the name of Pflucker since
C. R. Pflucker exploited the mines for copper from
the 1840's. However, the major producer today is
the Cerro de Pasco Corporation, which bought most of
the concessions in 1915. The company exploits an
extensive mineralized area of veins and occasional
orebodies for copper, lead, zinc and silver. The
mine has 7 shafts, only 3 active, and some 350 miles
of tunnels of which 50 or so are active. "Cut and
fill" techniques are the standard. The concentrator
handles 1,500 tons daily and produces some 150 tons
of bulk concentrate (16 per cent copper, 6 per cent

lead, 1 kilo silver) and 20 tons of zinc (55 per cent)
from it. Recently, the tungsten in the Morococha
area has assumed considerable importance. From the
zinc tailings some 20 tons per month of 70 per cent
tungstic oxide concentrate are recovered by gravity
methods. Tungsten is also extracted from the
Puquiococha mine immediately beside the other. This
mine is centered on an anticlyne whose rock structures, going down, are the Pucara limestones, a
brecciated area, a pyrite band, the Catalina Permian
volcanics and the Excelsior below. Mineralization
is at all levels--in faults in the limestones and
volcanics, in orebodies and the breccia and in simple filling of interstices in the pyrite. First,
the mine was worked for silver, then for high-grade
copper (no concentrator), then for low-grade copper
(with a concentrator), now it is being exploited
for zinc and mixed ores. In short, the mine has
been gone through four times and a fifth time is
about to start for tungsten, of which there are rich
regions 1,300 feet down. Puquiococha has been a
very rich mine and this has caused it problems.
There is so much ore that the mine is now largely
timber and refillings. Around the main shaft, the
loose ore still to be extracted has exerted sufficient lateral pressure to buckle the iron frame
and even reinforced concrete. The mine has another
problem. Morococha was famous for flooding and various major drainage tunnels have been dug, but with
the advent of Cerro de Pasco the final one was built
by the Empresa Desaguadora some 300 meters below the
surface. This drains out at Mahr Tunnel, where
Cerro de Pasco has another concentrator for the minerals of its San Cristobal mine (also rich in tungsten). Cerro de Pasco bought out the Empresa
Desaguadora and now Puquiococha pays them 8 per cent
of all minerals extracted from the zone drained by
it. This is the only extant example of a concession
for a socavon in Peru.

Puquiococha extracts just over 300 tons daily
and separates the ores into copper (220 tons at 2.5
per cent) or zinc (90 tons at 10 to 11 per cent).
In both cases, bulk concentrates are floated first
and the zinc afterward. The bulk contains high

quantities of zinc (11 per cent). Historically,
Morococha has always given flotation problems.
Tungsten, at present recovered from zinc tailings,
will soon be treated in its own circuit. The idea
is to float off iron and copper, which will be reground to allow recuperation of the copper, while
the tailings will be separated into three sizes by
a vibrator and passed to three different tables for
gravity concentration. The present circuit does not
separate tungsten by size and, as a result, small
particles are lost on the tables. The final concentration is magnetic and some 50 kilos daily of Hub-
nerite are extracted, but that is from current ores.
The rich tungsten ores that are yet to be treated,
as are old mine tailings, should yield much more.

    In the middle of the Morococha area is a large
disseminated copper deposit, right in the intrusive.
It falls within Cerro de Pasco's concession and it
was some time before the company took any notice of
it. However, detailed drillings now give an estimated 180 million tons of 0.8 per cent copper, while
probable total reserves have been put at 360 million
tons of 0.76 per cent copper. The ore also contains
some silver and molybdenum. There are, however, no
firm plans for exploiting this deposit, and although
it is readily accessible the amount of ore to be extracted daily (15,000 tons?) would involve a very
substantial extension of the company's transport,
concentrator and smelter facilities.

    Around Morococha are many other mines. The
Sociedad Minera Yauli, belonging to the de Osma
Gildemeister family, has a 450-ton-per-day plant
producing zinc and lead/copper/silver concentrates
and exploits a mine in Yauli and old workings to the
northeast of Morococha. To the southeast is the
important San Ignacio de Morococha with a 250-ton-
per-day plant. This company owns a zinc mine near
San Ramon in the jungle, which is soon to be brought
into operation. In Morococha, it has recently scan-
dalized its neighbors by painting its buildings
rainbow hues. Near San Ignacio is another company,
Santa Rita, and a former Banco Minero concentrator
(250 tons daily) that has been sold to the

Sacracancha Explotadora Company. Another company,
owned by Jesus Arias, also operates locally. These
smaller companies produce bulk and zinc concentrates,
but the "bulk" would be better called lead/silver
concentrate since the copper content is normally
very low at 6 per cent, while silver is even up to
7 kilos. The Yauli area was always famous for silver, and it seems clear that the copper is closely
confined to Morococha itself.

The San Cristobal mine of the Cerro de Pasco
Corporation lies to the south of Yauli. It is little visited because of its altitude. This mine,
however, has been worked by the company since 1935
and is still a very promising concession. Recently,
the Mahr Tunnel concentrator was expanded to handle
an additional million tons of copper/lead/zinc/sil-
ver ores with a 1-per-cent tungstic acid content.
There are further plans for developing San Cristobal,
which, according to geologists, is genetically related to the mines to the north and west. Indeed,
the triangle Morococha-San Cristobal-Casapalca is
seen as one vast mineralized region.

CASAPALCA

The Casapalca mine of the Cerro de Pasco Corporation is the biggest silver mine in Peru. Bought
in 1919 from Backus and Johnson (owners of the well-
known brewery), the mine consists of a few prodigious veins striking N 40° E and dipping 60° to 85°
NW. The veins are parallel to the south of the
Rimac Valley and lie in the Casapalca volcanics and
the under-lying redbeds which, so prominent from
the road, imply a recent mineralization (Miocene?).
The ore is thought to be associated with an intrusive to the southeast and another to the southwest.
The main entry to the mine is via a crosscut from
the concentrator in the Rimac Valley. The crosscut
is 1.5 kms. long at an altitude of 4,200 meters.
It crosses an old worked-out vein and hits the main
"M" vein (2.5 kms. long) in the heart of the volcanics. Above this level, the mine is exploited for
some 1,000 meters into the peaks of the Cordillera

Occidental. Below, the mine is worked for 300 meters and then there is water. This flooding occurred
when limestone was hit much further down, and the
bottom of the mine was abandoned while the Craton
Tunnel (7 miles long) was being dug to drain it.
This major project is nearly finished (1969) and,
when complete, should drain the mine some 1,000 meters below the main level. In the flooded area, the
ore is known to be worth over $30. In preparation
for the tunnel's completion, a new concrete-lined
shaft is being sunk. In the mine, in general, the
walls are very firm and the method used for extracting the ore has been "shrinkage". However, such
enormous quantities have been removed from a single
vein that the bridges left where the galleries are
have not always proved adequate for keeping the
walls apart and the company is using hydraulic refill now. At the moment, production is more or less
marking time, cleaning out odd corners, but, nevertheless, 1,500 tons daily are being extracted that,
typically, contain 6 ounces of silver, 5 per cent
zinc, 2 to 3 per cent lead and 0.4 per cent copper.
The mine's metallic silver production is over 100
tons yearly, perhaps 10 per cent of Peru's total,
and its recovery is about 85 per cent.

The concentrator is sited where the old foundry (closed in 1923) used to be. The old concentrator was up a side valley. A bulk is floated and
then separated into copper and lead. The copper
concentrate contains 27 per cent copper (chalcopyrite and tetrahedrite) and 80 per cent of the silver
produced. A zinc concentrate is also floated. The
concentrator and associated buildings are of the
usual depressing nature, but a small and select en-
campment for staff is down the Lima road toward San
Mateo. In the mine itself, some 500 people work in
two shifts: 300 by day, 200 by night. A further
300 people are employed in the concentrator, offices,
hospital, etc. It may be said fairly that in this
Morococha/Casapalca area, where the Cerro de Pasco
Corporation has operated for decades and probably
will continue to do so for many more, remarkably
little has been done to make the environment agreeable for its workers—or even to make their housing
moderately habitable.

In the mountains behind Casapalca, a Swiss miner (a former employee) is exploiting a profitable mine and sending the mineral to the Tamboraque concentrator (Hochschild) below San Mateo. Tamboraque is the site of another old foundry (there was also one at Rio Blanco) that served the mines to the south. Since 1958, Peru's most notorious mine has been producing in this area. The Millotingo mine is notorious in no pejorative sense of the word, it is simply an incredibly rich, small silver mine. Offered to Felipe Zacarias by a prospector, it was reckoned uninteresting and sold to a third party. The third party sold it back after he reckoned he had been swindled. Felipe Zacarias decided to explore this useless property a little more before abandoning it and hit what can only be described as a bonanza. The main veins (northeast-southwest) contain ore of 30 to 40 ounces of silver per ton. In 1969, this was not even being exploited, but held as a reserve, while splits with 12 ounces or so were being worked. The ore from the splits was mixed with some richer ore and the mineral arriving at the concentrator had some 18 ounces of metallic silver. Allowing for 92 per cent recovery and a price of $1.60 per ounce (it was well over $2.00 in the late 1960's), the ore is worth $26.50 per ton. The mineral also contains between 1 and 2 grams of gold.

The Millotingo mine consists of two main veins that run into the southwest side of a very steep quebrada running northwest into the Rimac gorge. The mine goes in some 400 meters and down some 250 meters. Exploration is going on under the quebrada to the northeast. The veins are nearly vertical and the walls are andesite, which has been silicified down to 5 meters depth by the high-temperature mineralization. The minerals are proustite and pyrargyrite--the famous rosicler (common silver mineral) of former days--and at times the mine yields spectacular specimens with big crystals. The origin of this mineralization may be connected with intrusives near Pacococha to the southwest. The Millotingo veins may indeed be extensions of the veins worked by that mine. They are also very similarly

placed to those of Casapalca, and it would be tempting to prospect the intervening country. In 1968,
reserves stood at 400,000 tons with a proven grade
of 26 ounces; that tonnage had been discounted 5
per cent and the grade 15.   Production was 350 tons
daily, but since then the company has bought the
Tonsuyoc plant of the Banco Minero (it used this
plant before it built its own), which would allow
production to reach 450 tons daily; so, reserves are
relatively small in quantity if not in quality.
However, the mine is exceptionally profitable.
Felipe Zacarias personally has been famous as Peru's
highest taxpayer, and in 1968 the company was the
thirteenth largest taxpayer in all Peru, only two
other non-foreign mining companies ahead of it (Corporacion Minerva Castrovirreyna and Corporacion
Minera Atacocha). Costs are low in the mine, which
needs no wood and employs 230 persons, in the concentrator, which is a straight flotation of one
product, and in transport, where a brief but hair-
raising road connects directly with the central
highway at San Mateo. No wonder that the mine, camp,
school and hospital are attractive and clean.

    Up the side valley from Millotingo are various
other concessions of the company. One is El Peru,
a lead mine, while another is Yata, a 2-per-cent
copper mine on the continuation of the old Germania
concession. The Pacococha copper/lead/zinc mine
(owned by the Milpo group) has its own 250-ton-daily
plant and also has used the Tonsuyoc one. Down the
quebrada and overhanging Tamboraque like a condor's
nest on a cliff-face is another unworked mine,
Coricancha, linked to the Tamboraque concentrator
by cable railway. In fact, the mountains around San
Mateo are full of mines. To the north lie the mines
Colqui ("silver" in Quechua) and Finlandia--owned
by a group of shareholders, of whom Loret de Mola
is the most prominent--which form the Compania Minera
Huampar, while beyond them is Venturosa, now stopped.
Huampar has a 130-ton-per-day plant and produces bulk
and zinc concentrates. In the same area is Farellon,
prospected by Northern Peru Mining Company but abandoned as not big enough.

A final important mine in the Casapalca area
is right at the top of the Ticlio pass. The Volcan
Mines Company belonged to Leon James Rosenshine,
but who its actual owners are now is not clear, except that the Beltran family is involved. However,
it is one of the few mines quoted on the Lima stock
exchange and it also publishes fairly full accounts,
and since such accounts are normally unobtainable
they are worth quoting. At the end of 1968, the
company had assets of 154 million soles, of which
62 million were fixed assets. Its subscribed share
capital was 65 million soles. During the year, it
treated 219,000 tons of ore worth 500 soles per ton.
This was turned into 36,000 tons of zinc concentrate
and 3,000 tons of lead. Mining costs were 120 soles
per ton; concentrating costs, 62 soles per ton.
General costs (offices, etc.) were 186 soles per
ton; amortizations, depreciations and royalties were
52 soles per ton; depletion, 16 soles per ton; and
reserves, 18 soles per ton. This left a profit of
44 soles per ton (9 per cent of sales), which net
of tax became 35 soles per ton. This meant a net
profit of 7.7 million soles or 5 per cent of total
assets and 12 per cent of capital employed. Volcan
Mines is a medium-sized company but its accounts
read like those of a really big one. Profits are
marginal and the sales are relatively low for the
amount of money tied up. In short, zinc mining,
except on the large scale, is a risky business, and
a dollar per ton pre-tax profit is rather tight.

SOUTH OF LA OROYA

In the southern part of the department of Junin
and neighboring Lima are various scattered mines.
Under the eastern slopes of Cerro Azulcocha, the
Compania Minera Azulcocha (Jesus Arias) has a small
copper mine producing 100 tons per day. Further
south, on the west bank of the Mantaro, is the mine
Gran Bretana. For some years, this mine was worked
for manganese but the ore ran out. The mine, however, also has very high-grade zinc (known reserves
being some quarter of a million tons of metallic

zinc) but the treatment of it is complicated by
high arsenic grades that reach 2 to 3 per cent.
The Banco Minera gave some technical help, using
the Callao laboratory to try selective flotation of
the arsenic, and finally presided over a contract
with Toho Zinc of Japan which is putting up 70 per
cent of the capital of a new company. Exploitation
should start in 1972 and, according to press reports,
the large figure of 48,000 tons of zinc concentrate
will be produced annually. Further south again, in
the district of Huasicancha, is the Heraldos Negros
mine. This mine produces zinc and lead/silver concentrates, its plant treating 130 tons of mineral
daily. The area is historically known for mines
and the valley running south toward Huancavelica was
famous. Here, Enrique Garces is thought to have
worked a mercury mine before the discovery of Huancavelica itself. If Tschudi is to be believed, the
whole Huancayo area is full of concealed veins.
Nowadays, hardly any mines worthy of the name are
worked east of the Mantaro (there is a small one
near Comas) but in the 17th century there were several above Ocopa, in particular, Suitacancha. (Even
north of La Oroya, there were mines on the river itself, e.g., Santo Domingo, which are no longer
worked.)

More into the cordillera, southwest of Huancayo,
lies Cercapuquio. The mine is situated on the east
side of a syncline with a northwest-southeast axis.
The lower beds are the Pucara limestones with Lias
sandstones on top. Between this and the Chunumayo
limestones, which contain the mineralization, is a
prominent band of dolomite that serves as a guide
over miles of country. The mineralization is finely ground lead and zinc, parallel to the stratification, in the form of replacements or small fracture
filling. There are post-mineralization transverse
faults. The very fine-grain galena is accompanied
by even more intractable zinc, which occurs as a
white amorphous chalky substance mixed in with the
panizo, or ground calcium carbonate. This zinc is
a special form of zinc sulphide known as brunckite,
and Cerapuquio is the only mine in the world to

extract it commercially. Grades are low and the
mine is only kept going by two things: First is the
cadmium content, which at 0.1 to 0.2 per cent is
high; the second is the fact that half of the mineral for the concentrator is not from the mine at all
but from old tailings dumps. These dumps are relatively rich in zinc (8 to 10 per cent) since for
many years the metal was not recognized in its
strange form. The mine is worked with a series of
very long galleries along the strike. The dip of
the strata is variable and in some places the roof
and floor are simply propped apart, whereas in others regular square sets are employed. Battery-elec-
tric trucks are used for transport. Some 500 men
are employed in the mine, a large number for a small
operation. Reserves are very low and are only expected to last for another year or two, but this is
somewhat of a joke in the industry since as long as
memory goes back Cercapuquio was always about to
close next year.

The concentrator takes some 240 tons daily and
the grade is about 5 per cent lead and 6 per cent
zinc. The amount of clay is very troublesome, but
one of the advantages of the old tailings is that
they are cleaner because of washing over the years.
Lead concentrate is first floated with a high 71-
per-cent content (recuperation is 85 to 90 per cent),
then the tailings pass to a thickener where the clay
and lead reagents are somewhat reduced. In the following zinc conditioner, dichromate of potassium is
added to depress the lead and iron, while soda ash
and sodium metasilicate are used to disperse the
clay. The soda ash controls the pH instead of lime,
but at four times the cost. Despite many experiments and the visit of many experts, Cercapuquio
has failed to improve zinc recovery above the very
low figure of 55 per cent. A concentrate with a 45-
per-cent zinc content, whose redeeming feature is a
1.2-per-cent cadmium content, is sold. The old
tailings are treated in separate circuits where zinc
only is floated with a high copper sulphate addition
of 2.5 pounds per ton. Owing to the relative clean-
liness of the mineral, recovery here is higher at

60 to 65 per cent, the concentrate containing 55 per cent zinc. In all, some 10 tons of lead concentrate and 25 tons of zinc are produced daily. The concentrates are partly dried on coal from the neighboring Goyllarisquizga formations.

Cercapuquio's mineralization is thought to be connected with the Huacravilca intrusive to the south--although others say it has no connection. This intrusive contains iron deposits at its contact with the Triassic. Studies made some 15 years ago, however, revealed the grade to be poor (below 60 per cent) and the quantity insufficient (less than 5 million tons) for commercial exploitation.

West of Cercapuquio, across the Continental Divide, the company has been prospecting for copper and silver with some success. The Yauyos region is well-known and perhaps new concessions will keep the company alive when its original mine gives out. Cercapuquio is controlled by the same group of shareholders as is Huampar.

In the same province of Yauyos is also the important Yauriocicha mine of Cerro de Pasco. Yauriocicha was the subject of litigation in the 1920's, but Cerro de Pasco has had control since 1927. For many years, the mine produced a direct-smelting ore that was sent by cable railway down to the Mantaro Valley and thence to La Oroya. In 1966, the company put in a 750-ton-per-day concentrator, subsequently increased to 900 tons and probably to 1,500 tons per day. This signified a change from handling very rich copper ores of 4.4 per cent, and 4 ounces of silver, to a larger lead and zinc production. It should be added that the zone under discussion is served by a Banco Minero office in Huancayo.

HUANCAVELICA

Like Potosi and Cerro de Pasco, Huancavelica is a town built because of the existence of a mine.

Cerro de Pasco, however, is a town that grew, whereas Huancavelica is the only town in present-day Peru
that was formally founded and constructed around a
mine.   It is, in short, a historical monument with
the added charm that it is off the normal tourist
routes.   Perhaps it is too isolated.   The decay into
which the colonial town has lapsed is sad to see,
but this, in turn, merely reflects the decay of the
mine that petered out with the 18th century.   The
famous mountain rises behind the town to the south
and is riddled with workings over a vertical extent
of more than 400 meters.   The mine is now worked by
the Fernandini family, who acquired it in 1915, but
it was not until 1954 that it started production
from an open pit at the top of the hill, facing
northwest.   The mineralization that used to be in a
well-defined vein is now disseminated through quartz-
itic sandstones, which strike east of north through
the mine dipping vertically.   The geology of the
area is confused, with overturned structures, limestones, sandstones and overlying volcanics.   In
addition to the open pit, the famous Belen adit
(entrance) is still in use.   It enters the hill from
the southwest near Santa Barbara.

     The open pit is worked six days a week on a
two-shift basis.   Between 12:30 and 7:30 a.m. there
is no work owing to the intense cold.   Some 10
benches are exploited, with 8 trucks, 2 bulldozers
and some mechanical shovels, to yield 220 tons of
ordinary coarse ore and 50 tons of fines daily.
The grade is low at 3 to 4 pounds per ton.

     The mercury is recovered by two processes.
Brought to the plant by cable railway, the ore is
separated into the coarse and the fine.   The first
passes to two parallel circuits, each of which begins with a rotary kiln.   This is operated at 600°C.,
and the mercury is vaporized and driven off.   The
kiln rotates at the rate of once every 100 seconds
and is lined with refractories that last from 1.5
to 2 years.   The vapor passes through a cyclone
where dust is precipitated and then takes one of
three routes, each of which consists of a large condensor.   The condensor is a tube that ascends and

descends, and the bends at the bottom of the "U's"
are open but submerged in water-filled buckets.
From here, the mercury is collected once every 48
hours. The residual vapors pass out at the end of
the condensor to further gas chambers and a smoke-
stack up the hillside. The buckets are emptied onto a heated rotating bed; mixed with lime and dried
mercury is then washed with benzine and put in 76-
pound flasks. Production from here is some 500
pounds daily. The fines (the other circuit) are
milled and concentrated by flotation to 700 pounds
per ton, are thickened, dried and then mixed with
the dust from the first circuit, and the mercury is
vaporized in retorts and condensed in a tube with a
water sleeve. Eighty pounds per day are collected
from the fines circuit. Mercury prices seem guaranteed for many years to come so it is to be supposed that the mine's future is secure, even though
there are problems with the reserves. The fear is
that the mineralization may be too deep to allow
economic production by open-pit methods to continue.

In addition to the main mine are one or two
small miners. These people extract ore on their
backs from old workings in the limestone. They analyze the grade by washing the ore and looking at
the color of the water. They refine the mercury in
homemade retorts over taquia (llama dung) fires and
condense it in straw-filled tubes on which they
splash water. One such mine claimed to be producing
20 to 30 kilos per week, employing 3 or 4 men plus
some old women to tend the fire.

Southeast of Huancavelica is the Julcani mine
of the Compania de Minas Buenaventura. This mine,
which is situated near Anchonga, was offered to
Cerro de Pasco but turned down by them. Alberto
Benavides, once geologist for Cerro de Pasco, took
up the offer and with 33 per cent capital from Cerro
de Pasco and the rest raised privately he formed
Buenaventura in 1953. Julcani is certainly an 18th-
century mine, so its high silver grades are perhaps
not surprising. The plant handles 400 tons daily,
floats a bulk and a zinc concentrate and has grades

of over 8 kilos of silver and 1.5 per cent bismuth in
the concentrates. Silver grades in the mine are 15
ounces per ton. The company owns another mine at
Huachocolpa that has a 240-ton-per-day plant. This
produces lead, zinc and cadmium. Formerly, it used
the Banco Minero plant nearby, still operated by the
bank for the benefit of other small miners of the
region. At Huachocolpa, there is another company,
Huanca, with a 330-ton-per-day plant for lead and
zinc minerals.

On the road from Huancavelica to the coast at
Pisco lies Castrovirreyna. Discovered in 1590, the
mines there suffered a fairly rapid eclipse owing,
according to legend, to various supernatural events.
Their resuscitation is due, in no small measure, to
the efforts of one man, Ingeneiro (engineer) Baertl
Schutz. Among the companies he helped organize,
the most important is the Corporacion Minera Castrovirreyna (principal shareholder, Luis Picasso),
which started operating in 1946. The Corporacion
is concessionaire of several mines of which the
largest is Caudalosa, at the west end of Lake Orco-
cocha. The mineralization of these mines is all in
more or less east-west veins in a predominantly an-
desite/riolite terrain. There is thought to be some
subterranean batholith. The Reliquias mine further
west is typical of the others. Three veins form a
letter Z. They bear the strange names of Perseguida,
Matacaballos and Saca si Puedes. The lowest level
is at 4,450 meters and the area is frequently covered
with snow. The mine is worked by 180 men and produces some 200 tons daily. The ore, for valuation
purposes, is reduced to its silver equivalent and
pays at 21 ounces. There are five levels in the mine
and the veins vary from 70 to 300 cms. wide. The
lead/copper/zinc/silver mineralization sometimes carries visible quantities of rosicler, and reserves in
this mine are reckoned at seven years. Other mines
are Dorito to the north, San Pablo to the west, Ma-
dona to the east, etc.

For concentration purposes, the Corporacion
divides the ore into acid and non-acid. Total plant
capacity is 480 tons daily and will probably be

increased.   The bulk concentrate produced averages
750 to 800 tons monthly, with a content of 110
ounces silver, 37 per cent lead, 11 per cent copper,
6 per cent zinc; while zinc concentrate (floated
from the combined tailings of the acid and non-acid
bulk circuits) is 56 to 60 per cent zinc and 12
ounces silver.   The plant is near Caudalosa and the
main camp.   The camp is fairly grim with poor housing, considering the very bleak location.   Wages,
too, are low, and since the mine is very profitable
this is inexcusable.   Luis Picasso has his name
written all over the front of the concentrator in
giant letters—a strange sight.

To the east near Choclococha is the other large
company.   The Castrovirreyna Metal Mines Company
belonged to Rosenshine but now has a similar status
to that of Volcan.   Its main mine is San Genaro, and
it concentrates minerals in a 250-ton-per-day plant.
In 1968, its sales were worth 80 million soles and
pre-tax profits were 18 million soles (22 per cent).
A small mine on the boundary of Huancavelica and Ica
is that of the Chavin Mines Corporation.   The mine
is reached from Huancayo and the concentrator from
the coast, the connection between them being a
cableway.   A 120-ton-per-day concentrator gives a
bulk product.

The Banco Minero has recently sold its La
Virreyna concentrator plant to a former user, Jesus
Arias.

COBRIZA

Peru's newest mine to be put into production
is Cobriza, at the other side of the department of
Huancavelica.   Reached by a long but good road from
Huancayo and Pampas, Cobriza is in the bottom of
the huge gorge beyond the first bend in the Mantaro.
Following the north-northwest course of the river
are the rock structures.   To the east are the Copacabana slates, with an undated intrusion at the
bottom of the gorge.   West, a large-scale anticlyne
causes the Mitu to feature some 10 kms. away, but

the region of the mine is all the Copacabana late
Carboniferous formation. Because of the anticlyne,
the dip on the west bank of the river is from 45°
above to 70° below. In this region are the three
mineralized mantos, two bands of limestone facies
and one of quartzite, the result being 30-meter-
wide "veins" with grades of 2 to 2.5 per cent copper. In fact, the mineralization tends to concentrate on the lower side of the manto, where a thin
arsenopyrite band is followed by a rich copper one
(4 to 20 meters), while the remainder is pyrrhotite
or magnetite. Reserves are put at more than 25
million tons with more than 2 per cent copper, but
it is generally believed that they are at least
double that.

The mine is exploited using cut-and-fill techniques. There are some six levels spaced vertically
at 30 to 50 meters going into the hill that forms
the west slope of the gorge. The top level at 2,510
meters, in fact, goes right through a spur to get
water from the other side, but even the shorter lower levels penetrate 1.5 kms. Because of the width
of the mantos, large mechanized equipment is used.
A much-vaunted machine for loading from the face
into a large carrier behind, which was then emptied
out the bottom down specially prepared ore chutes,
has proved a failure. The machine did not work on
the gradients required, and the necessity of refit-
ting the chutes with special doors every time the
level was raised was a great inconvenience. The
mine is now exploited with mechanical shovels and
small trucks. A production of 1,300 tons daily is
achieved with 150 men in the mine, three of the 6-
ton machines (when they work), five 3-ton loaders
and 7 trucks. Three _tajeos_ (working zones) were in
operation in 1969 and preparations were being made
for an ore pass from the top to the bottom of the
mine, where the main extraction level is for the
concentrator.

Cobriza is an exceptionally rich mine and has
already been the source of some controversy. The
area has been a mining one at least since the 18th

century, and Cerro de Pasco has owned Cobriza itself
for many years. In 1968, the mine was inaugurated
by the then President Belaunde. Cerro claimed an
$18-million investment. With the degree of mechan-
ization employed, the economical cutoff has been
put at 0.9 per cent copper, but, in fact, the company was not working grades below 2.5. On a conservative reckoning, the company should pay off its
investment in less than three years' production.
The controversy lies in the fact that the mine has
been unnecessarily high-graded and was rushed into
production before it was fully prepared. The high
degree of mechanization has not given a high production, which the mine's reserves amply justify, but
rather low employment and high profits. Production
has been limited by a woefully inadequate concentrator. Moreover, the mine itself has not been fully
prepared and extraction has taken place from the
front and not at the back as it should. All the indications are that the Cerro de Pasco management
took fright (on political grounds?) and has been
trying to get its money back as fast as it can by
ransacking the mine. A more careful preparation
and investment already could have made Cobriza a
really large long-term producer, not in a few years'
time.

   The straightforward concentrator yields a cop-
per/silver product of 23 per cent copper, 8 ounces
silver. Recovery is 91 per cent. Some difficulty
is experienced in depressing arsenopyrite and
pyrrhotite. Production is 120 tons of concentrate
daily, and this is sent by road to Huancayo and by
train to La Oroya. In all, the mine employs 550
workers and 80 staff. Housing is good for Cerro de
Pasco and wages, with bonuses, reach 150 to 180
soles daily. Nevertheless, Cobriza has suffered
various strikes already. The workers claim that
the mine's extreme isolation inflates all costs.
Another explanation would be that there is nothing
else to do at the bottom of the Mantaro gorge except organize strikes. It will be some time before
Cobriza achieves anything like the status of a town.
It is to be hoped that this will be attained and
that the camp will assume a more permanent air since

it appears that there is much more mineralization
in the area than was at first thought. To the south,
an equally large copper deposit is said to have been
located.

   On the hill above Cobriza, there is a small
mine, Santa Rosa, that uses a concentrator plant
rented to it by Cerro de Pasco. Otherwise, none of
the mines formerly worked in this area are active.
In the early 19th century, there was gold here.

CONCLUSION

   The central sierra yields 90 per cent of the
zinc mined in Peru, over 80 per cent of the lead,
some 80 per cent of the silver and perhaps a quarter of the copper. This predominance is, however,
no indication that the area is exploited to its full
potential--it is merely a demonstration that other
areas have been badly neglected until very recently.

5

THE MINES
OF
THE SOUTHERN
COAST

The second most important mining area in Peru
extends from coastal Lima, through the department
of Ica, coastal Arequipa and Moquegua, to Tacna.
This very extensive zone is characterized by three
metals--copper, iron and gold--and has certain other
features tolerably uniform throughout it that justify this crude grouping. A glance at the geological map will show that the coastal batholith extends
more or less to Ocona and that from there south a
series of Tertiary volcanics and continental formations (the Moquegua) cover the area between the
coastal cordillera and the slopes of the Andes. As
intrusives similar to the batholith are found near
Arequipa and Toquepala, it is not unreasonable to
suppose that, in general, the mineralization is associated with the batholith that is probably more
extensive than it appears, owing to later covering
by the Tertiary formations. The whole area is
desert, except where it is artificially irrigated
or in the immediate neighborhood of the rivers.
Communications are good, with the Panamerican Highway running the complete length of the zone and a
railway serving Matarani and Arequipa--the natural
capital of the south.

COPPER

Throughout the area, copper is common and no geological knowledge is required to locate one's own mine. Frequent mineral-staining of the hills is to be seen even from the road, and many small outcrops of oxides are not even disturbed by small miners, such is their abundance. The problem is the economic viability of these small low-grade deposits. The boom, which started in Ica in the 1860's and 1870's, was short-lived and was caused by a sudden rise in copper prices to over £100 per ton (gold at the time was 84 shillings per troy ounce, much the same copper/gold ratio as today), and as the mines were easily accessible they could be brought rapidly into production until the larger producers eventually forced them to close. Nevertheless, a few of these mines are still worked, the ores being leached and the copper precipitated. However, in recent years, a renewed interest has been shown in some of the more sizable of these deposits and two mines are working near Mala, 100 kms. south of Lima, each with a production of over 300 tons per day from the mine.

The first of these mines is called Raul and belongs to the Compania Minera Pativilca (in 1969, owned 45 per cent by Hochschild, 45 per cent by the de Osma family and 10 per cent by Alberto Brazini). It started production in 1961 but had long been known as Mina Perdida (the lost mine) because of its former exploitation in viceregal times for the gold among the copper oxides. The geology is complex. Basically, the deposit lies in a band of sediments of the lower Cretaceous which strike N 20°—30° W and dip 35° to the southwest. At the base, the sediments are quartzite, but above they are a mixture of limestones, shales and sandstones with innumerable bands of submarine volcanics—typical of all this part of the coast. There are also areas of breccia. The sediments have then been intruded (twice) by dacite porphyry dikes and sills and later faulted, both at right angles to the strike and in an east-west direction. The chalcopyrite mineralization penetrated via these faults to form veins

MAP 2
THE SOUTHERN COAST

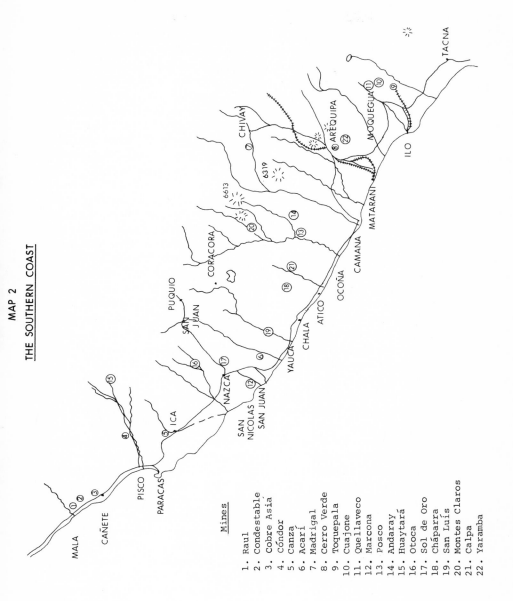

Mines

1. Raul
2. Condestable
3. Cobre Asia
4. Cóndor
5. Canza
6. Acarí
7. Madrigal
8. Cerro Verde
9. Toquepala
10. Cuajone
11. Quellaveco
12. Marcona
13. Posco
14. Andaray
15. Huaytará
16. Otoca
17. Sol de Oro
18. Cháparra
19. San Luís
20. Montes Claros
21. Calpa
22. Yaramba

and also replaced some of the limestones. The richest ore is formed by the filling-in of interstices
in the breccias and pipes (4 to 5 per cent), while
there is also a large body of disseminated copper
in the tuffs and lava flows (1.7 per cent). The
overall grade now worked is about 2.7 per cent and
the reserves (1969) stand at some 1 million tons
averaging 2 per cent copper. The mineralization has
caused metamorphism and there is much actinolite.
There was more faulting subsequent to the copper
deposition and some later lead/zinc mineralization.
There is also some molybdenite in the mine.

The mine is worked in three main areas--the
fourth, near the mine entrance, being exhausted--and
extends over some 3 kms., with extensive and complex
subterranean interconnections. The deepest level is
100 meters below the zero level (723 meters above
sea level), and the method of exploitation varies
according to the very local type of ore. Most commonly, orebodies are extracted leaving pillars as
supports and little wood is used. The mine is dry.
About 320 men work in the mine and a frequent system
of employment is that a group of eight men (four per
each of two 8-hour shifts) contract to extract a
given quantity per day, with bonuses or penalties
for excess or otherwise. A typical effective wage
is 100 soles daily.

The concentrator plant is very straightforward.
Handling some 340 tons daily, the crushers are preceded by a 300-ton bin and followed by two 200-ton
bins for the ore that goes to two ball mills and
spiral classifiers. (One ball mill and associated
classifier are of Peruvian manufacture, the other
is coupled with a rod mill. Apart from this ball
mill, all the equipment is imported.) The flotation
circuit has under-gone various alterations and has
a long row of scavengers coupled to a remilling
circuit and a final automatic sampler on the tailings.
Recovery is 91 to 98 per cent, and some 30 tons per
day of 27-per-cent copper concentrates are produced.
They are exported by the parent company, Hochschild.

Raul is a successful mine in a very convenient
situation, one hour from Lima on the coast. The

company has nearly 3,000 hectares of claims and may
be expected to expand.

Next door to Raul is Condestable owned by
Nippon Mining. Essentially, it has the same mineralization, but the mine is much simpler. The copper
is all in replacements and conformal with the metamorphosed sediments (dipping 45° W) that have their
strike along the hill with surface exits at each
side. There is no need for a shaft like the one at
Raul. The lowest level is 120 meters below the top
of the hill and gives access to an easterly part of
the mine, which also has some veins and is being
developed. The grade worked is 2.8 per cent, and
the method is simple extraction of the mineralized
strata, very few pillars being necessary owing to
the hardness of the rock. Reserves are about
800,000 tons, and it is planned to raise production
from its actual 320 to 500 tons per day. There is
some magnetite in the western part of the mine.

The exploitation is done with 100 miners (50
per shift)--i.e., much fewer than Raul--and the
mine has a more organized appearance with interior
fluorescent lighting, polythene ventilation tubes,
etc.; but it is a much simpler deposit to work.
The plant has a recovery of some 92 per cent and
produces copper concentrates at 24 to 26 per cent,
which are exported to Japan.

Raul and Condestable are typical of the medium-
sized coastal copper mines, and they are followed
to the south by Cobre Asia at Canete (a small national producer belonging to the Milpo group--230
tons of concentrate yearly), Condor, inland from
Pisco (a more important national mine with nearly
9,000 tons of copper concentrate a year), the mines
near Ica, of which the most important is Canza, and
Cobre Acari in northern Arequipa, owned again by
Hochschild and Alberto Brazini but rented to Carlos
Cochrane. It produces some 2,000 tons of concentrate annually. In the late 1960's, a Canadian
company was planning the exploitation of another
mine near Acari.

The next commercial copper deposit to the south
is way inland near Chivay, north of the city of
Arequipa, and it is known as Madrigal. It has considerable lead and zinc as well and is on the edge
of the area considered here. The 1,600-hectare
prospect is owned by the Homestake Mining Co. of the
United States and is said to have some million tons
of proven reserves before exploitation. Its exploitation represents a $10-million investment, largely
financed by Japanese loans. The mines at Chapi
(south of Arequipa) are also Japanese, owned by the
same company that owns Condestable. For some years,
they were worked on a small scale, but in 1969 a
new plant was opened to handle 800 tons of mineral
per day. In the same area is Yarabamba, owned by
the Milpo group, a small copper/lead mine with an
annual production of some 800 tons of concentrates.

South from Arequipa to Chile are the biggest
copper deposits in Peru: Cerro Verde, Cerro Negro,
Toquepala, Cuajone and Quellaveco. Until the end
of 1970, they were all U.S.-owned and only Toquepala
was in production.

Cerro Verde earns its name from its visible
copper oxides (brochantite), which for a long time
were worked by small miners. The concession was
owned until 1970 by the Andean Exploration Company,
a subsidiary of Anaconda. The deposit lies on and
under the east side of the hill. It is bounded to
the east by granodiorite and diorite intrusives
followed by some metamorphosed rocks containing up
to 13 million tons of 0.67 per cent copper pitch,
which as yet cannot be treated economically and will
have to be removed. On the eastern flank are also
some areas of quartz-porphyry. The most recent
formations are the various breccias that crown the
hill and contain much of the prominent oxides (25
million tons, 0.9 per cent copper). The oxides
overlie the sulphides at depths of 60 to 200 meters
under the summit. There are an estimated 118 million tons of sulphides at 1.05 per cent copper, the
primary mineral being chalcopyrite and the secondary,
chalcocite. The molybdenum grade is 0.002 per cent.
The deposit certainly presents some problems, of

which the need to write off the leaching plant for
the oxides completely in ten years at the initial
production of 10,000 tons daily and the amount of
sterile rock to be moved to get at the sulphides are
the two major ones. There is also a formidable need
for water in an area that lacks it and has many agricultural demands. The mine would require perhaps
5 million cubic meters per year. Electricity is
another problem, an installed capacity of 30 megawatts being estimated for the sulphide plant, power
that would have to be generated by oil burning and
waste heat from the blister copper smelter--although,
where this smelter could be sited so as not to damage the surrounding agricultural lands lying to lee-
ward is unknown. The total investment for all this
over the first ten years is estimated at $110 million,
but at 1 per cent grades and a copper price of $1,000
per ton (discounted 40 per cent for refining costs,
etc.), the value of production can be roughly estimated at $200 to $250 million over the same period.
This leaves a healthy profit margin--the cutoff is,
in fact, 0.7 per cent--and it may well be wondered
why the project did not enter the exploitation
phase, particularly when $5 million are said to have
been spent on exploration.

Anaconda, in fact, has now suffered the annul-
ment of its concession rights on Cerro Verde for not
exploiting it, and the same has happened to other
major copper prospects in similar situations. It is
hard not to blame Anaconda itself for having caused
this. The company owned the concession from 1917,
over 50 years, and had still not entered into production. It is not as though the mine could not be
exploited by anyone else. A medium-sized producer
could probably make a successful business cut of
the oxides alone. The re-introduction into Peruvian
mining law of clauses against non-exploitation of
concessions was largely inspired by this particular
case. It now appears (1971) that the state-owned
company, Minero Peru, will exploit it--probably
with Belgian finance.

Cerro Negro lies slightly to the east of Cerro
Verde and here the Cerro de Pasco Corporation owns
a 1,600-hectare concession for copper, with also

some lead and silver. The Corporation has other
copper properties in Ica, but its plans for these
coastal deposits are unknown.

Further south in Tacna lies Peru's richest mine.
The Toquepala deposit is said to have been visited
by Raimondi in the 19th century but it is first
specifically referred to by Velarde in 1908. Its
low grade was, of course, uninteresting at the time
and it was not until World War II that its importance
was realized (but Cuajone had definitely been worked
in the 19th century). A Peruvian engineer who had
denounced the mine offered it to the Cerro de Pasco
Corporation, which in turn seemed unenthused, so it
was then proposed to the Northern Peru Mining Company. The result was that both companies then
claimed the mine and a famous lawsuit was engaged.
The verdict was in favor of Northern Peru although
the Cerro de Pasco Corporation still maintained a
stake, and after some financial wrangling the
Southern Peru Copper Corporation was formed with
22.5 per cent Cerro ownership (they also contributed
their Cuajone concession), 51.5 per cent American
Smelting and Refining (Northern Peru's owners), 16
per cent Phelps Dodge and 10.25 per cent Newmont
Mining Corporation. Southern Peru, consequently,
had the concessions on Toquepala (400 million tons),
Cuajone (500 million) and Quellaveco (200 million),
all in the Moquegua/Tacna area. Certainly, the
total concessions are in excess of 10 million tons
of pure copper. The economic and political implications of such a concentration of wealth are discussed elsewhere (see Chapter 12).

The deposit consists of an elliptical orebody,
mushroom-shaped, based on a breccia pipe. This ex-
plosive hole is thought to have been blown through
and refilled with collapsed debris various times.
The surrounding rocks are late Cretaceous and early
Tertiary volcanics intruded by diorite. In the
mine itself, the breccia follows a north-south axis
with dacite porphyries and diorites to the west and
some riolite to the east. The breccia is irregular,
containing dikes, pebble breccia and tourmaline in
parts and the main mineralization is in it, although

there are disseminations in the neighboring rocks.
The primary copper (chalcopyrite) has been almost
completely leached at the surface, leaving a mush-
room-top of secondary chalcocite up to 250 meters
under-ground to the west of the mine, an area where
there are also extensive later volcanic flows.
Thus, the deposit is covered with an enormous quantity of waste material that is being progressively
removed.

The mine is exploited using the dry glen that
follows, roughly, the breccia axis. The mouth of
the glen is the entrance to the open pit, and the
sides are being removed and extended outward as the
mine goes down. Benches of 15 meters are used.
Some 150,000 tons of rock are moved daily with perhaps 43,000 going to the concentrator plant as ore.
Ammonium nitrate explosives are employed and the
biggest blasts are up to 180,000 tons. The ore is
taken to the plant by trucks and trains, the trucks
loading the trains at the pit mouth where there is
some congestion. The grade now handled, according
to the company (1969), is approximately 0.96 per
cent,* although initially it was 1.8 per cent--the
primary orebody now being more fully exploited.

A 60-inch primary crusher precedes the concentrator plant and secondary crushers that supply
—.75-inch ore to the three-and-one-half sections of
the mill. Each section comprises two rod mills and
four ball mills. Then follow twelve 14-cell roughers, a separator and regrind circuit with cyclones,
four 6-cell cleaners and four 4-cell recleaners.
Water is reclaimed from the tailings that are carried to the sea by a special channel. Since the
initial circuit was designed, it has been altered
and expanded with some extra mills, and cyclones
replacing classifiers--a tendency common in Peru.
Apart from these somewhat ad hoc additions, the
plant is very impressively laid out--an enormous
building with all the sections in parallel. The

---

*Nevertheless, according to Cerro de Pasco's an-
nual report, the 1968 grade averaged 1.21 per cent.

concentrate from the recleaners passes to the molybdenum circuit, again an addition to the original
plan.   Here, the heads are some 30 per cent copper
and 0.3 per cent molybdenum, and the copper is depressed by lowering the pH from 11.9 to 8 or 9 with
sulphuric acid.   Sodium hypochloride (produced from
salt imported from the Bahamas) is also added to
kill the copper activators together with sodium
ferrocyanide, while the molybdenum is floated with
fuel oil.   Two banks of roughers and two of cleaners
are followed by another bank of cleaners and a re-
grind/cyclone circuit.   Then come eight cells whose
tailings are thickened and returned to the regrind
mill.   A long series of cells follows, the copper
tailings being continually returned backward through
the circuit until the molybdenum concentrate is
judged pure enough (less than 1 or 1.5 per cent copper), when sodium cyanide is added to dissolve and
lose whatever copper is left.   The molybdenum concentrate is about 90 per cent MoS_2 and between 500
and 1,000 tons are produced annually, very much depending on what part of the mine is being exploited
at the time.   The copper concentrates themselves
are 26 to 30 per cent copper (i.e., some 91 per cent
copper sulphides) and recovery is 88 per cent.   The
reagents in the copper circuit are Z11 and Aero-
promotor 3302 (collectors--0.03 kilos per ton),
Aerofloat 73 and pine oil (frothers--0.04 kilos per
ton) and lime made from local sea shells (to depress the pyrite).

      The concentrates are freighted by train to the
smelter at Ilo.   If production is raised, as it is
hoped, to some 50,000 tons of ore through the mill
per day, this will imply some 1,500 tons of 30 per
cent concentrate daily.

      The mine has a very pleasant campsite in a
hilly but desert area and is, of course, equipped
with schools, hospital, recreation facilities, etc.
Perhaps 2,800 workers are employed plus 420 on the
staff, so the shole campment counts between 12,000
to 13,000 people, allowance being made for families.
The complete site is guarded and entry restricted

to visitors (e.g., small traders)--the only mine so
organized in Peru. The Toquepala concession is for
some 33,000 hectares, grossly in excess of the mineralized area.

The impact on the local economy is obviously
great, the mine being a major source of work. However, it must be remembered that the work is unproductive in the sense that the copper has no use in
Peru and that the pay is not "earned" by the com-
pany--the soles are bought with dollars and are
released on the local market with the inflationary
effect that could be predicted, the only real gainer
in Peru being the central bank foreign exchange reserves. The workers, of course, have excellent
living conditions, but this is also so in Raul and
Condestable. In those mines, one man is employed
for every 2 or 3 kilos of pure copper extracted
daily. In Toquepala, the figure is one man for
every 130 or 140 kilos. Thus, as an employer of
labor, the big mine is noticeably less useful (50
times) than the smaller mines, so it is again emphasized that from the Peruvian point of view the
prime function of the mine is as a dollar earner.

As a dollar earner, it is shown elsewhere that
a foreign company is considerably less efficient
than a national one (export of profits, depreciation, amortization and larger foreign purchases).
In the case of Southern Peru, this is particularly
so. The company operated until 1968 under special
tax concessions* authorized in the Mining Code,
Article 56, to operators of marginal deposits. It
is difficult to understand how these concessions
were granted to a mine whose grade in nine years of
operation has averaged well over 1 per cent, when
many mines (Chuquicamata in Chile, for example)
work open pits with grades of 0.8 per cent or less.
A commission formed to inquire into the finances of
the mine found that only 20 per cent of its earnings

---

*The concession consisted of granting guaran-
teed tax stability at the then rate of 30.4 per
cent (1954) until the investment should be recovered.

were spent locally or paid in taxes, and, indeed,
it is obvious to the visitor that the amount of imported products of every sort and kind are in much
higher proportion than in the Cerro de Pasco mines,
which follow a deliberate buy—Peruvian policy. The
company's detractors have also claimed that it is
guilty of tax evasion and cite the figures supplied
to the U.S. Securities and Exchange Commission as
compared with those given to the Peruvian tax authorities, which are said to have inflated figures for
depreciation, etc.; but such charges are hard to
establish and unlikely to prove true except within
the margin of error. However, it is true that, for
some incomprehensible reason, the company, which
only operates in Peru, chose to keep its books in
dollars and not in soles. This has now been changed
by law. Southern Peru then complained that they
were being asked to write off for depreciation purposes dollar items valued in soles at the then rate
of exchange, the sol having been since devalued 40
per cent, or they would be taxed for revaluation of
assets.

Two things are clear from all this. First,
that the public image of Southern Peru is very tar-
nished and that it has not enjoyed the relatively
tolerant acceptance that the Cerro de Pasco Corporation has. Second, that the company has been
making money handsomely, as none of these public
outcries and changes in tax status, etc., have affected its productivity or incurred any desperate
defense on the part of the company.

Toquepala is said to have been a $216—million
investment, and Cuajone, whose contract was signed
at the end of 1969, will be even bigger at $355
million, of which 49 per cent will be for the
"infrastructure"--everything not directly concerned
with the mine, i.e., roads, electricity, housing,
etc. It was quite clear that even American Smelting
and Refining would not have the financial resources
to launch Cuajone and Quellaveco together, let alone
their former Michiquillay property in Cajamarca.
If Peru deemed it desirable to exploit all these

deposits at once, then it was necessary that some
of them should be relinquished by the company immediately. If it was not desirable, but some national
copper reserves should be maintained, it was equally
important that the country's copper should not be
monopolized in this way. It was rediculous that
one company (American Smelting) should control what
must amount to nearer 2,000 million rather than
1,000 million tons of copper ore reserves. Accordingly, in 1970 first Michiquillay and then Quellaveco
reverted to the State, since adequate development
plans were not forthcoming from the concessionaires,
who indeed refused offers of State participation.
The financing of Cuajone is still in doubt (1971).

IRON

There are three iron regions on the southern
coast, of which one is in exploitation--Marcona/
Acari. Of the other two, one is in the gneissified
rocks north of Mollendo, a sedimentary metamorphosed
deposit thought to be of great antiquity, and the
other is a hematite magma deposit at Morritos in
Tacna.

The Marcona deposit consists of replacements
in both Paleozoic and Jurassic rocks, which are
flanked to the west by intrusives. Its origins are
uncertain but one explanation is that the intrusives
are late Cretaceous, which served to fracture the
surrounding rocks that were then penetrated by the
magnetite. The deposit is on an arid plateau some
800 meters above sea level, covered by alluvium and
sand varying from 0 to 25 meters deep. It is cut
by much block-faulting. The primary ore has been
leached and there are now three types--30 meters of
hematite, 15 meters of intermediate and an unknown
depth of primary magnetite. The area mineralized
is some 20 by 5 kms., and proven reserves are put
at over 250 million tons with an equal quantity of
probable ore.

The mine was located in 1905 by a Peruvian
geologist, Federico Fuchs, on the basis of observed

compass deviations (and, so the story goes, an analysis of wrecks along the coast thereby occasioned).
After some preliminary studies, the state claimed
the mine in 1929, employed more consultants to survey it in the 1930's and finally made it over to
the Corporacion del Santa in 1945. The Corporacion
already had been authorized to proceed with the creation of a steelworks at Chimbote, based on the iron
from Marcona. The Corporacion set about developing
the site with a campment and the port at San Juan,
and established a proven orebody of 70 million tons.

     At the end of 1951, a law was passed authoriz-
ing the Corporacion to lease the exploitation to
outsiders for a period of not more than 30 years,
and within three months the Utah Construction Company had signed a contract to operate the mine.
The bases of this contract were:

     1. that the Corporacion del Santa receive a
royalty on mineral exported;

     2. that mineral sold to the Corporacion for
Chimbote should be at a price cheaper than actual
world prices;

     3. that the exploitation should always main-
tain proven reserves in proportion to the mineral
exported. In fact, the proportion was two tons of
reserves for every one ton (up to 10 million tons)
exported, and one for one thereafter.

     The contract was for 21 years, until 1973. In
fact, it has been modified several times since, but
it is worth remarking that, if it had still held,
the Corporacion, even in 1969, would have been the
owner of a reserve of some 80 million tons corresponding to some 70 million exported up to the end of 1968.
When the contract lapsed, this would be over 100 million tons at present production rates. In 1953, the
Marcona Mining Company was formed with the principal
shareholders the Utah Construction Company and the
Cyprus Mines Corporation (and also the Prado family),
and the contract was transferred to this company
and extended to 1982. In 1960, a new contract was

signed to enable Marcona to develop a concentrating
and pelletizing plant and port at San Nicolas (with
clauses referring to the possession of this plant
when the contract lapsed), and the restrictions on
the Corporacion's reserves were relaxed in favor of
Marcona. (At this time Manuel Prado was President
of Peru and Max Pena Prado president of the Corporation). Finally, in 1965 a further contract was
made whereby the concession would be extended beyond
1982 on a 50-50 basis, and the total national reserve for that date was fixed at 70 million tons.

It is clear that the separate contracts have
been progressively to the benefit of the Marcona
Mining Company rather than to that of Peru, as embodied in the Corporacion. Why is this? It is
natural to assume that the American company had access to capital that the Peruvian State had not,
but a glance at the figures will show that this is
not so. By 1958, five years after the formation of
Marcona, the accumulated investment was $20 million
and the accumulated profits (net of royalties), $29.5
million. Debts on borrowing stood at $3.5 (origi-
nally $7.5) million, some $5 million had been written
off as depreciation or paid as interest and $9 mil-
lion had been paid on royalties. This is to be compared with the Southern Peru Copper Corporation,
which signed its contract with the State in early
1955 and five years later was only just starting
production after investing some $200 million. Even
now, the ratio of gross earnings for the two companies is only 2:1. There can seldom have been a
more attractive opportunity for Peru to have had a
direct stake in its own mining industry at so little
capital cost. It is all the more the pity that the
opportunity was handed away as the mine could have
produced badly needed foreign exchange to finance
the steelworks at Chimbote.

The mine consists of a series of open pits,
with 12-meter benches. Blasts are up to 1 million
tons of rock and nearly 40 million tons are moved
yearly, of which nearly 12 are ore for the crushers.
Huge 100-ton diesel electric trucks are employed,

and the ore is carried to No. 1 crushing plant
(36,000 tons daily, primary jaw crusher, secondary
cone) and No. 2 (48,000 tons daily, primary gyratory,
two secondary cones). From there, the ore passes
via a conveyor belt 9 or 10 kms. to San Nicolas.
The descent is used to generate 60 kilowatts from
the belt brakes.

At the plant various products are produced:
direct sinter ore from the hematite and transition,
fines concentrate (—.25-inch), coarse-ground concentrate and pellets. The chalcopyrite in the magnetite
(up to 0.4 per cent) is lost in the magnetic separation and dumped in the sea. The pellets account for
some 3.2 million tons annually (the two machines have
a joint capacity of 3.5 million tons) against a total
production (1968) of 8.7 million tons (i.e., 37 per
cent). The pellets are .25-inch, 65.5 per cent iron
and 4 per cent silica (ground sand being used). The
concentrates are blended to meet customer require-
ments, typically 65 per cent iron and less than 1
per cent sulphur. Size (for blast furnaces) is of
course important and is controlled. A small computer
is used for stock control, payroll, etc., and it is
proposed to extend its use to blending. The mineral
is then shipped from San Nicolas Port, the Marcona
Corporation (the holding company) also owning and
chartering a fleet of nearly 1.5 million tons dead-
weight. The main customer is Japan (Nippon Steel).
The company is experimenting with a method of pumping
iron ore as a slurry, which, it is claimed, could reduce their transport costs by as much as a third--
perhaps $1.70 per ton.

The company has a clean if not very inspiring
camp (less attractive than Toquepala's), all modern
comforts, schools, etc., and employs, in all, nearly
3,000 people--a population of 13,000. It has been
beset by labor problems despite paying very high
wages for the industry, the average workman taking
home nearly 250 soles daily.

The value of production f.o.b. San Nicolas
(1968) was some $67 million, just over half of which

was from pellets. Costs that year, according to the
company, were $2.8 million monthly so earnings net
of costs were some $33 million or $3.80 per ton.
(The figures given earlier show earnings net of costs
equal investment--largely auto financed--plus profits plus royalties plus depreciation less debts
equal $60 million made by 1958, against exports of
15.2 million tons, or just under $4.00 per ton).
Thus, the company's cost of production would seem to
be now about half its total f.o.b. earnings and in
the earlier years even less. From the earnings net
of costs, apart from tax, depreciation etc., the
Corporacion's royalties are paid at the rate of 25
per cent, which would produce in 1968 something
over $8 million. Unfortunately, it is written into
the contract of 1965 that costs are $6.50 per ton
pellets, and $3.75 per ton iron ore or concentrate,
so that on this reckoning costs for 1968 were roughly $42 million, the royalty being $2 million less.

A new contract was signed with Marcona in 1970
authorizing a $24-million investment to raise pro-
duction of pellets to 4 million tons per year. The
concession is to run until 1985 when it will revert
to the State either in whole or in part. Meanwhile,
Marcona has guaranteed tax stability. The company
has, however, been forced to register 50 per cent
of its shipping under the Peruvian flag.

It will be appreciated from the above that Marcona is a very lucrative business, launched with
very little capital considering the scale of the
operation. It is astonishing that the State ever
relinquished the exploitation of its nearly 70,000-
hectare concession to a foreign company, let alone
confirmed it and strengthened it in its position
with further contracts.

If Marcona is a profitable business for its
exploiters, the same, unfortunately, cannot be said
of the neighboring iron field of Acari. The deposit
apparently had reserves of some 10 million tons when
the Panamerican Commodities Company was formed to
exploit it in 1957. The company, essentially

Peruvian, originally counted with some U.S. person-
nel and finance. It started exporting in 1959 and
reached figures of 800,000 tons yearly. Production
never was high enough to be profitable (and probably
never could have been, given the size of the reserves), and soon Panamerican Commodities was borrowing more money ($5 million from the Chase Manhat-
tan Bank, guaranteed by the Peruvian government) to
pay off the initial debts. By 1967, the company
was virtually bankrupt and a brief respite provided
by the devaluation only prolonged its life into mid-
1968. By then, it had exported something under 7
million tons valuing perhaps $45 million. Apart
from the $5 million debt to be met by the state, the
company owed over 70 million soles to the Banco
Minero. Leaving aside the company's books, said to
be chaotic, it is clear that there was gross technical mismanagement. Expensive and lavish port and
transport facilities were built to handle a production far in excess of the capacity of the mine.
The project was conceived on the grand scale when
the reserves were hardly significant.

GOLD

All the coastal copper deposits from Lima to
Arequipa have traces of gold and yield a few grams
per ton in the concentrates, but the gold area proper can be said to extend only from about the latitude of Pisco to that of Camana. In fact, only one
mine was working in 1969, owing to the artificially
maintained low price of gold. This mine is Posco
(owned by the Zacarias family with a 20-per-cent
interest by Minerco), which produces gold and silver concentrates, the gold being some 300 to 400
grams per ton. In 1965, the total metallic gold
content was 93 kilos. Posco lies inland from Ocona
and beyond it is Andaray, which closed down recently.
Andaray Gold Mines (owned by Rosenshine) produced
over 300 kilos of refined gold yearly, the fines
being treated by the cyanide process and the rest
by the traditional mercury amalgamation. The mine
is very inaccessible, the final descent to it being
by mule.

Other gold mines and concessions from north to south are in Huaytara (Huancavelica), Rosario del Yauca (Ica), the Otoca/Concepcion area (famous from colonial times and now largely owned by the San Juan de Lucanas consortium) and Sol de Oro near Nazca. This mine is exhausted, but it was worked recently for a six-year period producing some 15 kilos monthly from grades in excess of 6 grams per ton of mineral. Further south are San Luis and Saramarca (inland from Yauca), the area of Huano Huano, the Chaparra region near Chala (also famous in colonial times) and Calpa near Caraveli, which was closed down on account of insufficient water for an economic level of production. Nothing has been heard of the Montesclaros gold mine on the Cotahuasi River since Babinski examined it in 1882 and recommended its re-exploitation. Near Arequipa, the small copper mine of Yarabamba produces 15 grams of gold per ton of concentrate and may be reckoned a producer. The exporting companies pay for gold grades greater than 3 grams per ton.

The silver zone that borders the area to the east also carries commercial gold grades, notably in the mines of San Juan de Lucanas, Arcata and Caylloma. When the price of gold rises again, all these mines may be expected to attract interest as they did after the 1931 increase.

6

THE MINES
OF
NORTHERN PERU

Northern Peru is taken to comprise the departments of La Libertad, Cajamarca, Piura, Lambayeque, Tumbes, Amazonas and San Martin--the area north of Trujillo, roughly speaking. The division is somewhat arbitrary but has for geological basis the fact that the area is north of the main outcrops of the coastal batholith, and also of the batholith of the Cordillera Blanca, which undoubtedly has its own associated mineralization. West of the Maranon, the principal metals are still copper, silver, lead and zinc, as in so much of Peru, but the country is noticeably lower than the mountains further south. Isolated remnants of the puna surface (high, cold, arid plateau) reach 4,200 meters, but as one goes north even these tops drop to below 4,000 meters, and there are no high peaks anywhere. The area is dominated by the Cretaceous sandstone and limestone formations, overlaid by Tertiary volcanics, which have been eroded into wide and pleasant upland valleys, such as those of Cajamarca and Bambamarca. The consequent agricultural activity has had a profound effect on the mining in the area. In the first place, mines are not easily discovered as the topsoil, not to say heavy vegetation, conceal the rocks, and, second, the incentive is less because most of the population make an adequate if not

comfortable living off the land. Cajamarca, while
boasting no large cities, contains many pleasant
country towns and after Lima has the largest departmental population in Peru. As a quiet rural area,
it has never attracted attention as has the much
less hospitable zone of, say, Puno. In short, this
part of the sierra is relatively virgin mining territory.

The other two topographical units that make up
the northern area are at present of little mining
importance, although this is likely to change. The
coastal zone, which in the north is, of course, the
main oil-producing region, still has deposits of
iron, gold and copper--suggesting the influence of
the batholith, although its appearance is intermit-
tent. The area east of the Maranon is, above all,
famous for gold, but it is likely that there are
copper/lead/zinc/silver deposits in the Chachapoyas
region, which has been prospected very little since
early colonial times. As for the Huallaga Valley, it
is still so inaccessible as to be hardly worthy of
mention. However, it is thought that the gold of the
Paleozoic extends to the east of the Cordillera Central, and when the new roads eventually open up that
area it can be expected to develop.

From north to south, the mines of the western
sierra follow. The first is Turmalina, a molybdenum
and copper mine spectacularly situated at 2,500 meters on the road from the coast to Huancabamba. The
mineralization is around the perimeter of a vertical
granodiorite chimney of 150 to 200 meters diameter.
The mineralized band is some 6 to 8 meters thick
with molybdenum at 1.5 per cent above, dropping to
less than 1 per cent lower down where copper grades
are 2 to 3 per cent. The mine is owned by Hochschild
and is worked on four levels with a shaft, two further lower levels being in preparation (1969). As
the location is a virtual cliff face, access to the
mine other than by the shaft is by scrambling down
the hill, and extraction is impossible from the lower levels because the shaft has not yet reached
them. Production is very small at some 60 tons per
day, although it is hoped this will be raised to
200. If the whole chimney is considered, the average

MAP 3
NORTHERN PERU

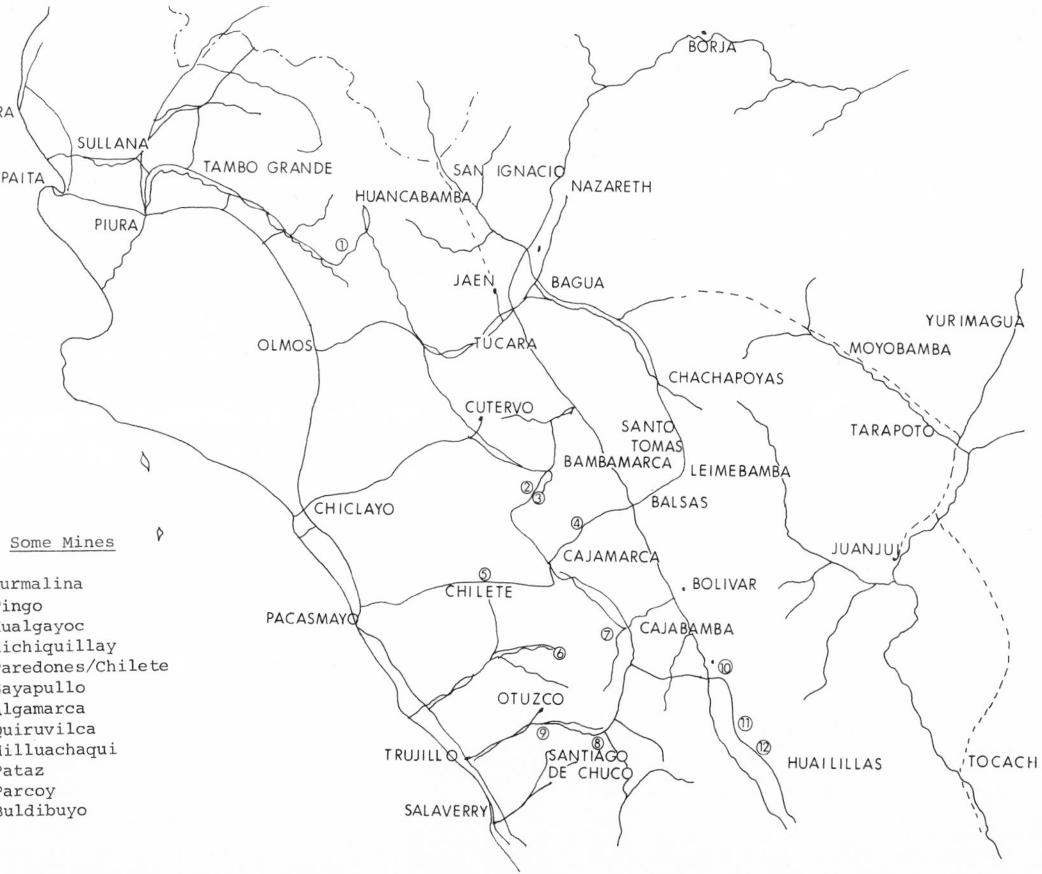

Some Mines

1. Turmalina
2. Tingo
3. Hualgayoc
4. Michiquillay
5. Paredones/Chilete
6. Sayapullo
7. Algamarca
8. Quiruvilca
9. Milluachaqui
10. Pataz
11. Parcoy
12. Buldibuyo

molybdenum grade is 0.3 per cent, and with the copper (and also zinc lower down) it is not unreasonable to suppose that the whole could be mined on the
grand scale, extracting ore worth some 10 soles per
ton. On this reckoning, total reserves might extend
to 10 million tons, justifying a large production
level. As it is, considering only the perimeter of
the chimney, reserves are some 300,000 tons of minus
1 per cent MoS_2 and some 2 per cent copper, while
costs are some $15 per ton. Apart from the diffi-
culties of the terrain, a major reason why the option
has been made for small-scale operation serves well
to illustrate the difficulties of mining in Northern
Peru. Quite simply, the local agriculturists object
to the mine. Tailings that fall or blow down the
cliff onto their farms, the already serious water
shortage in the area and the farmers' lack of ac-
quaintance with mines makes them hostile. Indeed,
Turmalina had to import miners from Puno initially,
as no Piura miners could be found. The farmers'
case is a good one--land is a permanent asset, whereas a mine is a very temporary affair in comparison.

The mine has a small concentrator that first
floats the molybdenum (40 per cent being recovered
from two initial unit cell/conditioners) and then
floats the copper. MoS_2 recovery is 65 to 70 per
cent and the concentrate is over 90 per cent. The
copper concentrate is 25 per cent (chalcopyrite)
and recovery is 93 per cent. The concentrates are
exported by the parent company via Salaverry, the
port of Trujillo.

Turmalina is a new mine in a non-mining area
but, nevertheless, there is evidence that it was
worked in the past, probably mistakenly for silver.
There are other traces of mining activity as far
north, e.g., on the lower Huancabamba River and near
Jaen. It is not improbable that there may be some
big deposits in this zone.

Further south lies the most northerly major
colonial center, Hualgayoc. This area has been discussed in the historical chapters but it is worth

repeating that it was rediscovered in 1771, shortly
before the Nuevas Ordenanzas de Mexico came into
force authorizing a big increase in the maximum concession size.   Thus, the mine was discovered just
too early and has since been plagued by innumerable
small unworkable concessions.   At the moment, there
are nearly 200 concessions, many of which are of 1
or 2 hectares (1969).   The law that imposes the
sobre-canon (supplementary tax) on unworked concessions should also have a salutary effect here.   The
picturesque town of Hualgayoc is situated in the
bottom of a steep glen that runs northeast out into
a more open area.   To the north of the town is the
famous hill, a spiky intrusive outcrop riddled with
workings that are uneconomically too small to be
active.   It was, of course, worked for silver, but
there are those who think that the whole hill may be
a suitable target for opencast copper mining, and
concessions have been made out on top of the old
ones--waiting for them to lapse.   To the east, where
the glen emerges through the dip slope of an anticline in the aptian shales and sandstones, are the
larger mines--Compania Explotadora de Minas San
Agustin (CEMSA), El Dorado, Imperial, etc., while on
the other side of the glen lies Los Negros.   However, perhaps the most important zone lies a few
kilometers northwest at Tingo.   Here, another intrusive cuts some later limestones, and there is a
whole series of further concessions.

The mineralization is in typical east-west
veins in the intrusive, but there are many replacements and parallel deposits in the sedimentary
strata.   Proven reserves for the area are nearly 1
million tons at the grades currently mined--typical-
ly, 10 per cent zinc, 2 to 3 per cent copper, 5 per
cent lead and varying quantities of silver.   Some
of the mines are exploiting colonial refillings
yielding up to 8 kilos of silver per ton.   Many of
the veins are badly oxidized, but it is universally
agreed that Hualgayoc is a rich deposit still relatively unworked, the copper (enargite) being particularly attractive.

In view of this richness, several studies,
sponsored by the State, have been made of the area

and the Banco Minero has a concentrating plant for
treating the mineral of the small miners. Hochschild
has also installed a 250-ton-per-day plant at Sinchao
near Tingo, and CEMSA treats minerals other than
from its own mines as well. The area is well-suited
to become a showpiece of the pequena mineria (small
mining), but so far this has not happened. Three
reasons may be advanced to explain this failure.
First, there are an excessive number of small concessions whose owners sit on them rather than work
them, as both they and their miners can live com-
fortably off the good agricultural land just northeast of the area. Second, the State's aid is financially insufficient. The Banco Minero plant has a
capacity of 50 tons per day. It is on a very steep
hillside with no room for expansion, let alone for
tailing dumps, is so short of water that it has to
pump it up from the glen below, is short of electricity and, in brief, has costs of up to $8.00 per
ton treated while it charges $4.20 for floating one
mineral, $4.80 for two. The reason is that the
plant was bought from a mine that was closed down,
rather than built for the purpose. Studies for a
new plant upstream of the town of Hualgayoc have
been in existence for years, but it has never been
built. The third reason for the lack of progress is
the absence of active direction. If it is desired
to develop the small and medium mining industry
(and this is much more desirable than developing the
big mines), then it is not enough to give passive
aid. It is necessary to teach, actively advise if
not direct and generally impel the small miners into
working their concessions continually and rationally,
instead of doing sporadic digging whenever the harvest is bad.

    Of the larger Hualgayoc mines, CEMSA is the
most important. It employs some 150 people and has
a plant of 130-tons-per-day capacity, 70 tons of
which are from its own mines either near Hualgayoc
or at Tingo. The company now has, and formerly had,
various Italian mining engineers who generally end
up by opening their own independent mines in the
area. This has also happened with ex-managers of

the Banco Minero plant. CEMSA is owned by the
Lercari and Lanatta families. Other mine owners of
the area are the Srs. Montoya, Carassai, Vidalon,
dalla Porta, Santolalla and the Cerro de Pasco Cor-
poration--as yet without exploitation.

THE NORTHERN PERU
MINING COMPANY

The area of southern Cajamarca--La Libertad of
the sierra--is dominated by the Northern Peru Mining
Company, an offshoot of American Smelting and Refining and the Guggenheim empire, all of which operate
locally. Surprisingly for such a big concern, active
here since the 1920's, it has never yet developed a
really large mine. The only mine in active exploitation (1969) is Quiruvilca, which is handling some
1,000 tons per day. Quiruvilca* has a long but obscure history dating from colonial times, and, even
in the 20th century, has known several owners and
periods of shutdown--very surprising, considering
that it is a rich mine. Under Northern Peru, all
has not gone smoothly either, the mine being closed
in the 1930's and an abortive smelter being built
and abandoned at Shori some years later. At the
start of 1967, a big modernization plan was completed, which has resulted in an impressive concentrator at Shori and a new shaft in the mine, together
with a production increase from the former low level
of 500 to 600 tons daily. The mine is just below
4,000 meters and is based on a major 2-km. vein
known as Napoleon, running east-west in andesinite
rock. The offices and two shafts are in the west
end, the new shaft, Almiranta, and the major development being toward the east complex (3 per cent
copper, 2 per cent lead, 5 per cent zinc, 5 ounces
silver). Ores are being brought into production in
contrast to the prominently copper (enargite, tetrahedrite) ores of the west that were worked formerly.

---

*Quiruvilca is clearly the Navilca of Ciro
Alegria's <u>El Mundo Es Ancho y Ajeno</u> (Buenos Aires:
Ediciones del Nuevo Mundo).

Some seven levels exist in the mine, one main level,
100, connecting all the different parts, while a
lower level, 220, is used for extraction by trains
to the bottom of the valley to the southwest, where
the ore is crushed and transported by a long 360-
meter belt up the opposite side to the plant. In
the mine, cut-and-fill methods are used with a variety of techniques for supporting the workings--rock
bolts, shot grit, meshing and wood (from Huamachuco).
Two shifts operate with over 300 men each, most of
them on a contract system. The "contract" includes
four men, two per shift, with a guaranteed minimum
wage of, say, 70 soles daily. Exceeding the agreed
tasks earns a bonus, which might typically be 2,000
soles monthly. These wages are somewhat less than
what might be earned in a comparable mine in central
Peru but are not bad for the area.

A feature of the mine is the quantity of acid
waters percolating through it. These waters, varying, of course, with the seasons, are used in a
precipitating plant to recuperate copper "cement."
The precipitation is by scrap iron, costing 1,100
soles ($25) per ton on site, 2.8 tons being used
for every ton of copper produced. The process lasts
a week, then the water and copper are drained off
from the bottom of the precipitating tank and left
a further week in a settler for the copper to deposit itself at the bottom, and then be dried. From
40 to 200 tons per month of 70-per-cent copper
cement is produced, which probably give the company
a profit of $600 per ton on this simple operation.
The conventional concentrator plant is divided into
two circuits for the copper and complex ores, capac-
ities being some 700 and 300 tons, respectively.
The plant is full of new equipment and has some
modern controls (e.g., density controls). From the
plant, the concentrate is sent a prodigious distance
down to Samne by a cableway, installed in 1923 and
which used to extend to the mine (to supply the
plant with ore) and beyond to some coal fields (to
supply the unsuccessful smelter?). The existence
of this cableway has meant that the mine had not
felt the need to improve, or press the authorities

to improve, the shocking road from the coast to
Quiruvilca. From Samne, the concentrate all goes
by road to Salaverry and thence is exported to the
parent company's refineries in the United States,
copper to Tacoma, Washington, zinc to Corpus Christi,
Texas--it requires special treatment because of its
0.04 per cent mercury content--and lead to Selby,
California. This is a good example of the fact that
the American companies' objectives in having mines
overseas is not only to make money, but also to
guarantee supplies for their domestic factories.

Quiruvilca's costs have been brought down by
modernization from over $20 per ton to some $16 or
$17 per ton. These costs are not all incurred in
the mine. Apart from the non-productive camp at
Samne, Northern Peru must have large overheads.
There is the Lima office, a mine in exploration in
Lima, Chilete and, until recently, Michiquillay.
These two latter merit some comment.

Chilete, it may be remembered, was one of those
old silver veins reputed to have been worked by the
Portuguese in the early 17th century. Re-exploited
in the 19th and 20th centuries, it was worked from
1951 by Northern Peru. Ten years' life was planned,
but, in fact, it gave 17 before shutting down permanently, exhausted. The closure of the mine was
associated with the closure of the Chilete railway
and perhaps 450 people were put out of work in the
mine alone. A large and attractive campsite, still
guarded and maintained over a year after the mine
shut, has virtually no inhabitants. The miners and
their families have dispersed. It is hard not to
conclude that this mine would have been better
worked at 100 tons daily for two generations by a
small company, giving stable employment in the zone,
rather than at over 350 tons by a large company.
If the small company were Peruvian, the annual net
dollar earnings for the national reserves could
easily have remained unchanged.

Michiquillay is a huge disseminated deposit
one hour's drive from Cajamarca on the road to

Celendin. It is variously estimated at 500 to 600
million tons of ore, but one official figure puts it
at 592 tons of 0.75 per cent copper. It was discovered in 1955 by a local prospector, who, noticing
some copper oxides, mistakenly took it for a vein
deposit, and then sold it to Northern Peru. The
deposit is associated with a prominent intrusive, and
it is very strange that no geologists of the company
passing along the road in the previous 30 years had
gone to inspect the region. Why has it not been exploited yet? The reason is that American Smelting
and Refining wanted a special contract with taxation
concessions, in accordance with Article 56 of the
Mining Code, as they claimed that it is a marginal
deposit. Examination of the diamond-drilling results
suggests that the first 100 million tons should be
well over 1 per cent. The company (according to
World Mining News, April, 1969) planned to initiate
production at 145,000 tons per year of pure copper,
which implies 1 per cent ores if a maximum of 40,000
tons per day are treated--a smaller figure is likely.
In short, it appears that a "marginal" deposit of
nearly 600 million tons of 0.75 per cent copper could
also be viewed as a "rich" deposit of, say, over 100
million at over 1 per cent. It is worth remarking
that a copper mine in Sweden is working, from the
beginning, 0.5 per cent ores, from reserves of 150
million tons, at a production level of 6,000 tons
daily. Either the Swedes are much more efficient
than American Smelting, or the latter were claiming
that a deposit is "marginal" when it is not. The
company would probably reply that the political risks
in Peru must be covered, to which the answer is that
the political risks have largely been caused by past
cases of this sort of thing (e.g., Toquepala).*

     The deposit is under a steep hill, centered on
a sharp glen running west. The smelter would be
built to the north to carry fumes away from the

----

     *The result has been that, failing to produce
plans for its immediate exploitation, Michiquillay's
concessionaires have seen it revert to the State
(1970).

neighboring agricultural land. A beautiful site
has been selected for the campment. Michiquillay
must have weighed heavily on Northern Peru's overheads because at one stage three airplanes were
based there--the place is eminently accessible by
road--and everything about this unproductive mine
was maintained in style, not to say luxury.

Apart from the deposits already mentioned,
Northern Peru has worked gold in Milluachaqui (where
a small Peruvian company is active--Compania Minera
Acre) and Pataz, both closed, and has many other
concessions in the area, e.g., in Huamachuco.

OTHER MINES IN THE AREA

In southern Cajamarca exist two other mining
companies, both Peruvian. Sayapullo has a 200-ton-
per-day concentrator, handles copper/lead/zinc/sil-
ver ores and is associated with the Rio Pallanga
syndicate. Algamarca, further east, is an old silver and gold mine, where copper is now also mined.
It belongs to the Orbegoso family and works some
120 tons per day. With good silver prices, Algamarca
has been an important producer in the north. There
is also a mining company at Huamachuco and various
small miners in Santiago de Chuco and toward the
south--a region considered to belong to the Ancash
area.

Of considerable interest in the zone of northern Peru are the gold deposits. In Chimu times, it
is clear that a great quantity of gold must have
been produced in this area, but exactly where is unknown. The gold mines of Pataz, Parcoy and Buldibuyo are very remote from Chan-chan or Batan Grande.
They are, however, rich deposits, none worked at
the moment, but will certainly be re-exploited when
gold prices rise. At the moment, this area east of
the Maranon--a formidable barrier to communications--
is being developed for copper. Gold washing goes
on in the Maranon and its tributaries. Some years
ago, a Spaniard made a handsome fortune near Balsas
in this way, and many locals further south pave the

river, peg down "golden fleeces" or divert streams
onto friable veins when they feel the need.   In
such a wild and remote part of the world, production statistics are not available--it may be safely
presumed that the gold mined is not declared and
pays no taxes of any form.   However, it is probable
that there is workable gold much nearer the coast.
The Salpo area has long been famous and there are
many denuncios (claims, concessions) for gold in the
province of Otuzco--including one of 3,000 hectares
by the Instituto Nacional de Investigacion y Fomento
Minero.   Right behind Trujillo is a gold concession,
and mines have also been worked in Santiago de Chuco.
Again, when prices rise, interest will certainly return to the area.

Apart from the metals already discussed, there
is a mercury concession in Cascas, which may or may
not be significant, and further north in Piura the
famous unworked iron fields of Tambo Grande.   This
is a big hematite deposit covered by a 300-hectare
concession and, after Marcona, is the most interesting in Peru on account of its accessability.   It is
not properly studied and the reserves are unknown.

As will be appreciated, northern Peru is a very
heterogeneous zone from the mining point of view.
Some studies on the mineralization have been made
and it is generally concluded that veins are less
profound and long than those of central Peru.   However, it is safer to state that the reserves of the
area are not even qualitatively known, still less
the metalogenesis.   Japanese companies have been
actively prospecting, particularly for copper, but
further finds like Michiquillay are not unlikely.
The north of Peru has a promising mining future.

The area supervised by the Jefatura Regional de
Mineria of Huaraz is a stronghold of the small miners. The mines are scattered along two fairly well-
defined mineralized belts, east of the Cordillera
Blanca and the crest of the Cordillera Negra, and are
essentially owned by small national companies. The
Cordillera Blanca area has its own peculiar mineralization. Apart from the typical lead/silver ores of
Peru (which characterize the veins of the Cordillera
Negra), it contains tungsten, molybdenum, copper and,
most surprisingly, a small tin mine. The mineralization is thought to be closely allied to the batholith of the Cordillera Blanca, and, indeed, it is
frequently on the contact between it and the Chicama
shale formation, which appears to have trapped the
solutions near their source.

The most interesting mines in the whole area
are, undoubtedly, the tungsten mines of Pasto Bueno.
Discovered by the famous don Fermin Malaga Santolalla,
the family still owns most of them and they are actively managed by a grandson. They have been in
production since about 1910 and had a tremendous boom
during World War I. The town of Pasto Bueno was, in
fact, obliterated by a landslide some 20 years ago,
and the mines are now centered on the concentrator
plant of Consuzo, slightly further down the very

175

steep glen to the west. To the north lies the main
bulk of the granitic stock of Consuzo, intruding the
Chicama formation, while southeast and south there
is a complicated series of overthrusts and faults
(toward the east) and the later Cretaceous formations.
It is thought that these tectonic movements correspond to the end of the Cretaceous era, while the intrusion of the batholiths (the Consuzo stock is seen
as an extension of the batholith of the Cordillera
Blanca) and the associated mineralization and volcanic
activity were the next stage at the start of the
Cenozoic.

The north-south veins that cross the quebrada
near the town are largely worked out. Some 600 meters higher, however (at 4,100 meters), almost vertically above to the north, is the Consuelo region,
which is still actively exploited. A north-south
vein dipping steeply to the west splits, and the "Y"
so formed is closed to the north by a third vein dipping 40° to the north-northwest. In this small triangle, perhaps 300 by 300 by 200 meters, the tungsten
is mined on some six levels. The veins are solid
quartz with spectacular strips and sheets of wolframite running through them, and there is also some
enargite. The cajas are granitic or, occasionally,
slate. A fourth vein extends northeast in the direction of Huayapon where the company owns another mine,
whose ores are tipped by chute from above into this
extension and carried through the mine, the whole
production being finally extracted from the lowest
level and sent to the concentrator via an ore pass.
The ore pass is nothing more or less than a gully on
the mountain face down which everything is tipped.

To the northwest at Tamboras, no distance as the
crow flies but two hours by road on account of the
ferocious quebradas, the company owns a third mine
called Mundo Nuevo. In this region, besides wolfram,
there is also some chalcopyrite and molybdenum, and
the veins, as in Huayapon, are in the Chicama shales
and not the granite. Mundo Nuevo sends a pre-concentrate to Consuzo and has some jigs installed for that
purpose. Between the three mines of the company,
less than 100 under-ground workers are employed and

MAP 4
ANCASH & HUANUCO

Some Mines

1. Tamboras
2. Pasto Bueno
3. Macate
4. Colquipocro
5. Santo Torribio
6. Pompey
7. Huancapetí
8. Antamina
9. Huallanca
10. Queropalca
11. Raura

the total production is some 250 tons per day, averaging: tungstic oxide, 0.5 per cent; copper, 1 per
cent; lead, 1 per cent.

The concentrator plant separates out the fines
after initial grinding for thickening, although it
is now proposed to separate them before grinding
since the ore is fairly well-pulverized on arrival
at the plant. The rest passes via a rod mill to the
jigs, from which a 30-per-cent tungstic oxide concentrate is directly recovered; while the overflow is
reground and split by a cyclone into two streams,
each of which goes to separate sets of tables where
a further 14-per-cent tungstic oxide concentrate is
separated. The middlings from the tables are united
and passed to other tables, where more tungstic oxide
is collected; final tailings are thrown out and the
middlings unite with the original tailings to pass
to a ball mill. From there, they are floated and a
15-per-cent copper, 10- to 20-per-cent lead bulk concentrate produced. The thickened fines from the
original crushers are also floated for copper, the
tailings being passed to a table to extract the wolfram. The company is not particularly satisfied with
the circuit and is planning improvements.

All the tungsten concentrates are united, dried
(a rotary kiln is planned), graded by size (together
with the pre-concentrate from Mundo Nuevo) and passed
to the magnetic separators. These give a final 73-
per-cent tungstic oxide product together with a
lead/copper concentrate by-product. Total production
is perhaps 1.5 tons per day of tungsten concentrate
and the same for the 15-per-cent copper concentrate.
The price of tungsten rose sharply in the late 1960's,
and a ton of concentrate is probably worth nearer
$4,000 than $3,000.

There is another tungsten mine, disused, belonging to Wolfram Fortuna immediately to the east of
Consuelo; a small company at Tamboras also extracts
tungsten with its copper; there is a concession near
Tarico to the south; and in 1969, the Japanese Mitsui
company denounced a large area just north of Huari
for the same mineral. This may indicate that the

tungsten zone extends the whole length of the region
of influence of the batholith of the Cordillera
Blanca, and considering the frequent association of
tin and tungsten, perhaps the small tin mines near
Chavin de Huantar are not as anomalous as they appear.

In the region of Pasto Bueno are also some gold
concessions--gold is panned in many of the streams
that flow into the Santa from the northeast--and a
well-known copper deposit named Magistral, now the
property of Cerro de Pasco and unworked. Magistral
is not far from Conchucos, which was one of the
famed mining areas of viceregal days and was associated with the Portuguese, but there are no active
mines there now. Further south is the region of
Tarica, once worked by various Germans at the turn
of the century, with lead and zinc and silver mineralization associated with a granodiorite stock. To
the north and east of Tarica are further old mines,
abandoned, but this time without any visible associated intrusive. More mines, this time associated
with Italian owners, exist west of Chacas where
Giovanni Rosson owns two very small concentrator
plants for treating lead/silver minerals from the
Pompey and Vesubio mines. The mines are intimately
connected with the contact of the batholith, contain
some copper and mark the start of a zone that lies
to the south and contains various, all unworked,
molybdenum prospects.

One of these molybdenum deposits is Antamina--
Raimondi found it there--but this large mine southeast of Huari is better-known for copper, as its
name would suggest. Explored and denounced over 50
years ago, Antamina was then acquired by the Cerro
de Pasco Corporation, which, in fact, did diamond
drilling there in 1924. The mine is a disseminated
copper orebody that contains some 100 million tons
of 1 per cent plus copper. There are higher grade
zones and the proposal has been to exploit the mine
beginning with them, producing perhaps 8,000 tons
of copper yearly, say 2,400 tons of ore daily; but
although the investment is put at the relatively
modest figure of $20 million Antamina is, as yet,
nothing more than a project. Once again, the failure

to exploit a concession has resulted in its reversion
to the State (1970). It is to be hoped that Antamina
becomes a reality--the area would benefit greatly
both from the stimulus to other small mines and from
the impact on the local infrastructure.

THE CORDILLERA NEGRA

If the east side of the Cordillera Blanca contains many unworked mines, the Cordillera Negra is
almost a continual succession of them. From Macate
in the north to Recuay in the south, Raimondi lists
innumerable mines, particular areas of concentration
being the two forenamed and the regions around Colquipocro (Well of Silver) and Santo Torribio. However, it is the Recuay and Ticapampa area that is
the one of major importance today.

The mines of Collaracra and Huancapeti (on the
crest of the Cordillera due west of Ticapampa) certainly have been known since 1621. A re-organization
of an existing company in 1904 led to the formation
of the Anglo-French Ticapampa Silver Mines Co.,
which only sold out in the late 1960's. Two aged
directors in Paris felt unable to administer the mine
properly, were unwilling to invest and finally got
into debt. They offered the concession to W. R. Grace
& Co. Grace very wisely declined to buy it in its
entirety and, instead, formed the consortium called
Alianza in which they have a controlling minority
interest of 40 per cent, 35 per cent being owned by
the Corporacion Minera Castrovirreyna and 25 per
cent by the Compania Minera Condor. Thus, Grace can
control the operation, earn its profit and yet avoid
the political stigma of being a foreign mining company. One can only wish that other foreign miners
were as enlightened.

Geologically, the veins are formed from fractures in the volcanics of the early Tertiary and
have associated intrusive stocks, which may have
been the original vents. The mineralization has
sometimes replaced some of the andesite walls of the
veins, and in the main productive vein west of the

watershed (Hercules), it falls off sharply when the
vein passes into some subterranean metamorphosed
shales. Hercules is some 350 meters long, strikes
N 20° W and dips 40° to the east. It is up to 5 meters wide. There are five levels in the mine and a
sixth is to be made 100 meters further down. Access
is via a crosscut from the west. Above level 5,
there are some 500,000 tons of reserves at 12 to 15
ounces silver, 5 to 7 per cent lead, 8 to 10 per
cent zinc and less than 0.8 per cent copper. No
prospecting has been done below this level, but it
is hoped that level 6 will increase reserves by at
least 50 per cent. To the east on the watershed, in
a very obviously mineralized area, lies Huancapeti,
where the company owns a northeast-striking, north-
west-dipping vein. This part of the mine is badly
ventilated and, again, a new crosscut is being dug
(1970) from the west 80 meters below the bottom of
the old mine, which was reached by an internal winch
in the days of the former owners. The present policy
is to extract ore on the level with battery locomotives.

Toward Ticapampa is a third vein, this time
some 2 to 3 kms. long, striking east-northeast. Collaracra is largely exhausted on the known levels but
it is being explored lower down. Silver grades are
lower, but the length of the vein in an area where
most veins are short makes one wonder whether it is
not genetically more related to the very characteristic trans-Andean (east northeast-west southwest)
veins of central Peru than to its immediate neighbors.

Alianza's existing concentrator plant is a very
antique affair in the ruins of the old company's
leaching and smelter plant. Existing capacity of
170 tons daily is, with a new ball mill, being raised
to 250 tons, and a lead/silver concentrate is first
floated (55 per cent and 230 ounces, respectively)
followed by a zinc concentrate. A 500-ton-per-day
new plant is being built up the hill to the west.
The contractors for the machinery are Magensa, a
Peruvian firm that will supply predominantly locally
made equipment. This new plant is situated very
strangely, neither at the mine nor on the road, but

the company believes that it is the economic mean for
minimizing both water-pumping costs from below and
ore-transport costs from above. The old company used
a small funicular railway for ore transport. Viewed
as a whole, the operations of Alianza seem a bit of
a gamble since the total capacity for concentration
(the new plant was in operation by early 1971) should
deal with known reserves in less than three years.
However, the gamble will probably pay since the area
is a proven mineralized zone and, moreover, the company has other concessions not too far away.

At Huancapeti, the Compania Minera Aija also has
a 180-ton-per-day concentrator, which is fed from its
mine to the south consisting of vertical north-south
veins in an intrusive outcrop. The mineral is predominantly lead (5 per cent), with 6 or 7 ounces silver and perhaps 4 per cent or less zinc. The company
is named after the village of Aija to the west (where
there is a further mining company), from which a road
is being constructed to the coast at Huarmey. It
belongs to the concessionaires of the Santo Torribio
mine near Huaraz. Whereas Alianza generates its
electricity from the Santa River right beside its
plant, Aija has a hydroelectric station to the north
on a side stream. As always in Peru, water is a
problem and the Santa Valley is very much an agricultural zone.

Southeast from Huancapeti lies Florida, where
various small miners and Alianza have concessions.
Florida has more copper minerals than the zones discussed. The number of small miners in the area encouraged the Banco Minero to build a concentrator
plant that is being bought out progressively by its
users. The plant is situated at Catac, is of modern
design, Peruvian-built (essentially Comesa, although
Fundicion Callao has supplied the primary crusher)
and, with the associated offices, is impressive. It
is quite small, handling 100 tons daily, and has
some 40 users, of which four are major. One of these
users has a mine to the south near Conococha but the
others are more local. The plant cost some 14 million to 15 million soles and came into operation at
the start of 1969. The users pay $6.50 per ton

treated and, since the Banco Minero buys the concentrates, this money is simply deducted from the price
they receive. The nominal cost of treatment is
$4.00--$1.50 is for depreciation and $1.00 pays for
the share they are given in the ownership. When depreciation and the subscribed capital cover the cost
of the plant, it will be handed over to a cooperative
of the shareholders--some of whom will probably sell
their shares to the larger owners. This should occur
in 1973 when the plant will have been written off 60
per cent. For the Banco, this is a novel system.
In the past, they have built and run concentrators
on their own and later sold them to private owners,
but a planned hand-over such as that of Catac has
not yet been tried. To all appearances, the small
miners are maintaining supplies and the plant is
working very satisfactorily. It is capable of floating a bulk concentrate and a zinc one at the same
time, but not of producing lead, zinc and copper concentrates independently and simultaneously. The
Banco Minero has an office in Huaraz and has been
involved in rehabilitating another plant just north
of Huaraz. There are, in fact, in Ancash a large
number of small unused concentrators. Santo Torribio
owns a 250-ton-per-day plant just outside Huaraz that
is fed from its lead/silver/zinc mine in the Cordillera Negra. The group of companies is predominantly owned by Dr. Aguilar Cornejo and Ingeniero
Caro Ramirez.

While none of the Cordillera Negra mines are
large, many of them have had a long existence. A
multitude of small veins with sufficient silver to
make the lead and zinc pay is an ideal background for
a successful development of small mining. It is to
be hoped that the Banco Minero will try to operate
another plant like the Catac one, but this time
situated in the Macate/Colquipocro region. One could
also ask if a small smelter would not be justified.
Lead/silver minerals are very easily treated and,
in former days, were always smelted on site. At
present, all concentrates are exported since La Oroya
is very remote, but no studies have been done to see
if this is really economical or not. From the point
of view of dollar earnings, the advantages of local

refining are clear, and one can go so far as to
imagine the silver being used by local artisans in
this well-populated region of high tourist potential.*

HUANUCO

From the copper deposit of Antamina running
south-southeast on the Atlantic side of the Continental Divide are a series of mineral deposits lying in
the department of Huanuco. Despite the attempt in
the 19th century to establish a school of mines in
Huanuco itself (see Chapters 2 and 3), this department
(with Apurimac) must be the most neglected of those
that have any mining potential at all. Its mines are
closely associated with the famous Durand family of
the late 19th-early 20th century.

In 1968, the Mitsui corporation started re-
exploiting the famous Huallanca silver zone (discovered in 1721), this time for lead, zinc and copper.
An $8-million investment was made, one positive as-
pect of which was the improvement of the road leading
from Huanuco via Huallanca and Conococha to the
coast. The company, which is called Huanzala, however, does not make visitors welcome--perhaps on account of the fatal accidents they have had in the
mine. A small Peruvian company is also active in
the area. South of Huallanca is the silver zone of
Queropalca, near Banos, and in the same region the
famous mercury mines of Chonta (discovered in 1756).
These mines were very active in the early 19th century but are not worked now, although they are
denounced.

Further south again, beyond the 6,632-meter peak
of Yerupaja, lies Huanuco's most important mine,

---

*The foregoing paragraphs were written before the
terrible earthquake of May, 1970, that resulted in
the loss of 50,000 lives, largely in this region,
partly owing to the collapse of buildings, etc., and
partly to the devastating rockfalls and landslides
from the Cordillera Blanca. It will be many years
before this area recovers from the catastrophe.

Raura. Situated spectacularly at the source of the
Amazon, surrounded with glaciers, Raura is one of
the more important copper, lead, zinc and silver
mines of Peru. Genetically, it probably belongs to
the mines of the Cordillera Occidental of central
Peru. The known mineralization extends over some 7
square kms., is in typical east-west veins with occasional orebodies and is associated with a diorite
porphyry intrusive to the southwest that has apparently spilt over in dacite flows to the northeast.
There are other small stocks in the limestone country rock, which itself has a marked anticline and
syncline running north-south through the zone. The
northern part of the mineralized zone can loosely be
described as copper/silver, while the southern part
is lead/zinc, but, in fact, this only indicates the
predominance--the four minerals are everywhere. Two
major faults are thought to run east-west through
the area, but glaciers and their morranic remains
obscure the underlying rock structures. To make this
typical picture of a Peruvian mine complete, it is
only necessary to add that it was certainly worked
in the last century and probably (according to Llano
Zapata) in the 17th and 18th centuries. Indeed, the
stains of mineralization are so obvious that it is
unthinkable that any Peruvian passing that way (it
is on a pass across the Andes) could fail to see
them. What is more surprising is that in view of
the general retreat of the glaciers in Peru, which
almost certainly is also taking place at Raura, anyone should have supported the climate there when it
was worse than it is now. There are old workings at
over 5,000 meters and dizzy llama paths along vertical rock faces.

The mine is centered on the offices on the south
side of the small glacial lake Santa Ana. Immediately
to the west is the Nino Perdido vein crossed north-
south by a very irregular orebody known as Catuvo.
This orebody is right along the contact of an intrusive stock and the Machay limestones and is predominantly lead/zinc. At the southwest end are large
oxidized zones near Lake Ninacocha--the official
source of the Amazon. The ore is wet and loose and
some fine-grained galena contains considerable quantities of silver. There are some 45 active drills

in Catuvo, 8 mechanical shovels, 19 winches, and as
the ore is extracted the mine is refilled from above
by lorries. The timber for supports comes from
Huaraz. The internal layout of Catuvo is that of a
rabbit warren. It produces some 250 tons per day of
10 per cent zinc and 3 per cent lead, and costs are
put by the company at $13 per ton delivered at the
plant. Northwest of Lake Santa Ana are the Esperanza
and Flor de Loto veins. In former times, these were
the ones worked particularly for silver--freibergite.
The lake has recently been drained and Esperanza is
being explored at lower levels where it ran into the
lake, the hope being that there is a zone of secondary enrichment since Esperanza has a 1.5-per-cent
copper content. Its cost of exploitation is, however, $21 per ton. Two other big veins, Balilla and
Lead Hill, south of the mine offices are not at the
moment worked, but Hada, more to the southeast, has
been exploited on the surface and is now being worked
under-ground. It yields 10 per cent lead, 6 per cent
zinc, costs $18 per ton and is exploited at 200 tons
per day.

The mine's known reserves are about 1.2 million,
which at actual production rates will last about six
years. In addition, there are some 750,000 tons of
oxides and also some low-grade ore. However, there
are large areas as yet unexplored (e.g., Toramina to
the northeast in limestone, which has some nice gar-
nets) and it is very probable that Raura has a long
future ahead of it. It has all the appearances of
another Morococha.

Wages in the mine are 81 to 117 soles per day
(1969) and a system of colectivos is used: A group
of men work as a team and have a given norm, which
if they exceed earns them a bonus. There are over
300 men in the mine.

The concentrator plant is preceded by two 150-
ton bins, one for Hada minerals and one for the
rest. A 3-inch primary crusher is followed by a .50-
inch secondary and two more 150-ton bins, as before,
for fines. The main circuit is being amplified to
start with a rod mill and cyclone followed by unit

cells from which a lead/copper bulk concentrate is
floated, the tailings passing to a ball mill and cyclone for further reduction. Two cleaner, five
rougher and five scavenger cells follow where more
bulk is floated, the zinc tailings passing to another
row of cells via a conditioner. The zinc previously
depressed with zinc sulphate is reactivated with copper sulphate in the conditioner and floated at a pH
of 11. The concentrate produced averaged (before
the amplification) 25 tons daily of 54 per cent zinc,
1.3 per cent lead, 1.8 per cent copper and 4 per cent
iron. The bulk concentrate is also conditioned with
bichromate of sodium or potassium (0.8 to 1.2 pounds
per ton) to depress lead, more zinc sulphate and
some cyanide to depress zinc, and a copper concentrate is floated from five roughers, one pre-cleaner
and one cleaner. The feed is 48 per cent lead, 7
per cent copper, 5 per cent zinc, 4 per cent iron;
the copper concentrate is 32 per cent copper (tetrahedrite), 10 per cent lead, 10 per cent zinc, which
is castigated in the price paid for the concentrate,
and some 180 ounces of silver; and the tailings that
form the lead concentrate are 60 per cent lead, 9
per cent zinc, 3.5 per cent copper and 30 ounces of
silver. Production, before amplification, was 5 and
15 tons per day of copper and lead concentrate, respectively. As will be appreciated, Raura has difficulty in separating the copper and lead and is
also losing perhaps one quarter of its zinc to those
concentrates. This lead/zinc/copper separation problem exists in most mines of central Peru. One solution, which Raura practices with the Hada ores, is
to keep the minerals separate. In this case, a
straight lead/zinc separation is made and a 75-per-
cent lead concentrate floated followed by a 59-per-
cent zinc one. The concentrates are sometimes sold
to Hochschild but largely go to Cerro Commercial,
and the copper goes to La Oroya. The company is, in
fact, owned 60 per cent by Cerro de Pasco, while 40
per cent belongs to the Puquiococha company. The
latter is in charge of the day-to-day management.

Although Raura is in Huanuco, the road to it is
from the coast via the Sayan and Churin Valley. At
the head of this valley, northwest of Quichas (where

Simon Dunstan once worked), lies the silver zone of
Chancas, which the company is planning to re-exploit.
The hydroelectric plant is also on the river. Newly
installed, it produces some 1.1 megawatts, but water
shortage does not permit it to meet all the needs of
the mine and the compressors are worked off diesel
engines. Given a solution to the water problem,
which also affects the concentrator, Raura's operations should develop much further. It is the only
mine in a rich zone. The triangle Cajatambo-Oyon-
Raura has been well-known for its minerals for some
300 years.

8

THE MINES
OF
THE SOUTHERN
SIERRA

The vast area of mountainous country that is included in the departments of Ayacucho, Apurimac,
Cuzco, Puno and that part of Arequipa bordering on
Cuzco is scattered with an almost countless number of
abandoned mines. Abandoned for various reasons, political, technical or personal, the fundamental cause
of their lack of exploitation is geographical--their
isolation. The area may be conveniently divided into
two, the northern part being the departments of Ayacucho and Apurimac. Essentially, there are only two
roads in these departments, one coming from Huancayo
through Ayacucho and Abancay and leading to Cuzco,
the other from Nazca on the coast through Puquio and
Challhuanca, joining the first in Abancay. Across
the puna above Puquio are various tracks, one of
which goes to Andahuaylas, and, recently, Ayacucho
got a new access to the coast via Castrovirreyna;
but, nevertheless, it can be said that the area is
almost roadless in comparison with its size. Abancay is some 18 hours from Nazca, Ayacucho some 12
hours from Pisco by the new road (for trucks, these
times are considerably longer); Ayacucho has an air-
port, Abancay has not; neither town has a buying
agency for minerals; in Ayacucho, there are two mining companies worthy of the name, in Apurimac, none.

AYACUCHO AND APURIMAC

The most important company in the department of
Ayacucho is that of San Juan de Lucanas. This mine
lies in the extreme west of the department and borders on the gold zone, previously discussed, which
is inland from Nazca and near Parinacochas. Indeed,
the mine contains gold in variable quantities--per-
haps 2 to 8 grams per ton--but its principal product
is silver, for which it has been famous since the
early 18th century. The operations are now controlled by the Banco Minero, following the bankruptcy
of the former owners and debtors, and the Banco, in
turn, employs a contractor to operate the mine. The
contract is for not less than 13 ounces of silver
per ton and production is some 7,000 tons monthly.
In the mine are also small quantities of zinc (just
over 1 per cent) and a little lead.

The mine lies on the northeast side of a beautiful but profound valley--made famous in the short
stories of Jose Maria Arguedas ("Agua")--and three
main veins run from the south curving eastward into
the hills above. Some more north-south veins lie to
the east. The mineralization is very irregular and
the mine very difficult to work, due to the loose
nature of the andesite rock and the tendency of the
veins to appear and disappear. Moreover, all sorts
of rare silver minerals are present--querargite,
hessite--and studies done in the Callao laboratory
of the Banco Minero have implied grinding to mesh
number 600 for their flotation. (Normally, ores are
ground to, say, 50 per cent less than 200, without
worrying about finer grinding.) In fact, the mine
does not rely entirely on flotation and the tailings
are treated by the MacArthur and Forrest cyanidation
process. Before the Banco took over, these tailings
were up to 7 ounces per ton in silver grade, but the
flowsheet has since been altered to shorten the circuit and remove immediately a silver concentrate before it has time to sink. The result has been to
reduce the feed grade to the cyanide plant to 1
ounce silver, and the justification for the plant's
existence is now in question. The silver concentrate

MAP 5

SOUTHERN SIERRA

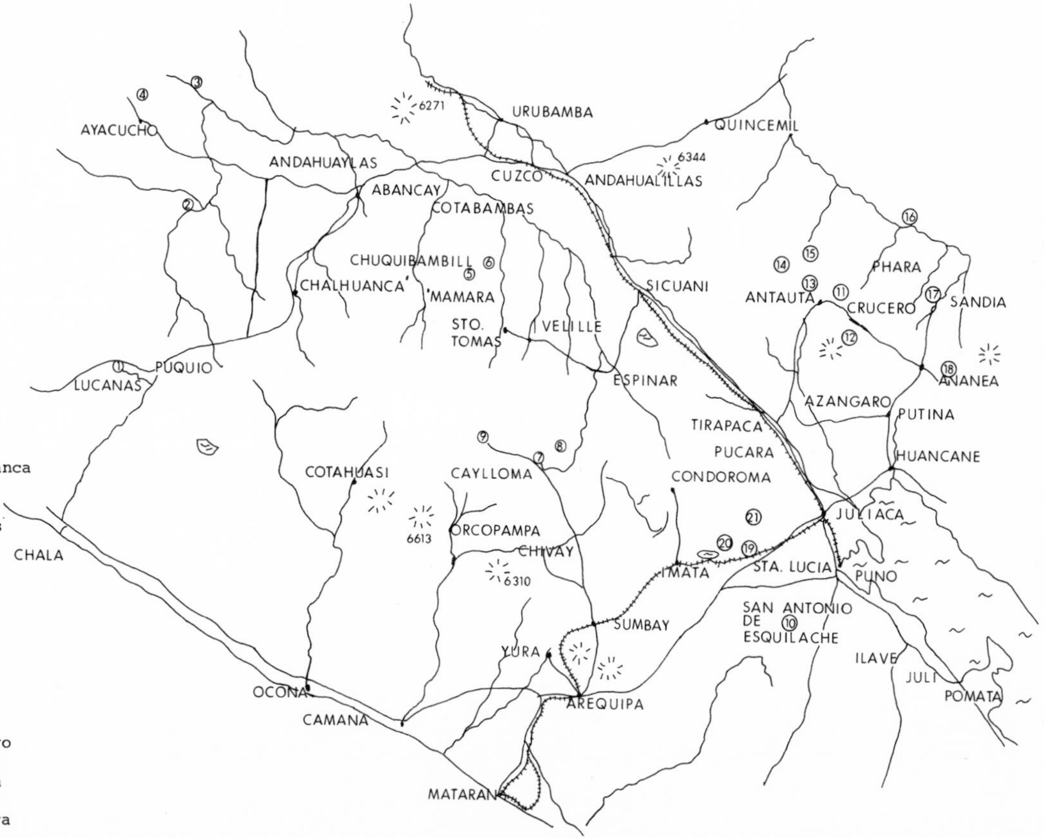

Some Mine

1. San Juan
2. Catalina Huanca
3. Rapi
4. Huanca
5. Cochasayhuas
6. Ferrobamba
7. Caylloma
8. Sucuitambo
9. Arcata
10. San Antonio
11. Crucero
12. Potoni
13. San Rafael
14. Quena Mari
15. Korani
16. Santo Domingo
17. Sandia
18. Pampa Blanca
19. Berenguela
20. Santa Bárbara
21. Palca

produced in 1968 was averaging 150 tons per month at
12.4 kilos per ton.

The tailings from the concentrator pass to three
thickeners, the water from which is returned to the
rod and ball mills; they then pass to 14 agitators,
in the first three of which some 0.2 per cent of
calcium cyanide is added. This large number of vessels is to permit a period of 72 hours for the cyanide to dissolve the silver. After the last agitator
is a separator whose tailings are filtered and re-
washed and filtered twice, the water returning to
the separator, and whose overflow is treated with
lead acetate and zinc dust (90 grams per ton of
solids) to precipitate the silver. The precipitate
is collected in bags, and the "barren" water is used
for washing the separator tailings. Precipitate in
1968 averaged 450 kilos monthly at 8.2 per cent silver. Recovery was low. The Banco Minero was founding the precipitate in silver bars. In the 1960's,
three cyanide plants for gold have been closed
(Buldibuyo, Calpa and Andaray) and this last leaching
plant for silver in San Juan de Lucanas is likely to
follow. So closes a chapter that was opened in 1892
with the introduction of the Patera process to Peru.

Some 160 kms. to the north-northeast of San Juan
de Lucanas, by a bad road, lies the mine of Catalina
Huanca, owned by the Compania Minera Canaria--a new
company heavily financed by the Banco Minero, which
made a loan of 12 million soles to it. This is a
lead/zinc/silver mine producing some 150 tons daily.
It lies at the northern extremity of a zone once
well-known for its mines but now virtually inactive.
This zone, centered on Chipao and the Pampamarca
River, is referred to by Cieza de Leon in the 16th
century and by Demetrio O'Higgins in the early 19th
century and there is no reason to think that it would
not be of interest today. It is, however, extremely
inaccessible. Similar remarks might be made about
the nickel/cobalt mines of Rapi, San Miguel, northeast
of the city of Ayacucho. A quotation from Raimondi's
catalogue of Peruvian minerals for the 1878 Paris
Exhibition will serve: "Les minéraux de nickel sont
assez peu répandus au Pérou mais ils sont en assez

grande abondance dans le district où ils existent et pourraient, à la faveur des prix qu'atteint le nickel aujourd'hui, donner lieu à une exploitation très-avantageuse." Nickel prices have, in fact, been very high in more recent years--namely, in 1969.

Two other mining zones in Ayacucho are worthy of mention. One is the province of Huanta, long famous for silver, where some dozen small miners have concessions; the other is the western part of the province of Cangallo, due south of Huachocolpa in Huancavelica. The Compania de Minas Buenaventura is very active in this part of Huancavelica and has concessions of over 3,000 hectares in Cangallo.

The department of Apurimac, which all falls within the Jefatura Regional de Mineria of Cuzco, is devoid of active mines worthy of the name. The famous gold mine of Cochasayhuas was worked early in this century but is now abandoned. In the region east of Chuquibambilla, there are, however, various concessions for gold and silver, and Cerro de Pasco had some for copper in the provinces of Cotabambas and Grau, the most important of which were Ferrobamba and Chalcobamba. These concessions have now reverted to the State. It is thought that there may be other important porphyry copper deposits here (there are promising intrusives), and, recently, both the Banco Minero and the Servicio Nacional de Geologia have been making studies of this very isolated area. A Swiss consortium has also been prospecting for molybdenum in Apurimac. There are concessions for it in Abancay and Aymaraes. Historically, there are plenty of reasons to think that Apurimac has mining potential, and Helms (1790) cites, albeit imprecisely, several important mines here. In 1786, a certain Garcia de Avila of Cotabambas even wrote a textbook on metallurgy and mining.

CUZCO AND AREQUIPA

The second part of the area considered, the southern sierra, is comprised of Cuzco, Puno and the neighboring part of Arequipa. About most of Cuzco,

there is little more to say than that it is as abandoned as Apurimac. In the city, there is a Jefatura
Regional de Mineria and Hochschild has an unimportant
buying office, but the Banco Minero is absent. It
is to be hoped that they will establish at least a
deposit for buying minerals here. Cuzco used to
have a mint, but much of the silver must have come
from Puno or Caylloma as there are few mines near
it. There are gold and silver concessions in Vilcabamba (also known for molybdenum), there is active
gold washing near Quincemil and there are tungsten
and antimony prospects in Quispicanchis. Elsewhere,
there are the usual scattered lead/silver concessions.
However, the provinces of Espinar and Chumbivilcas
and neighboring Arequipa are centers of importance.

The most famous mine here is Caylloma, dating
from the 1620's. A long colonial history was revived at the end of the 19th century (see Part I),
and, today, the mine is still in production, albeit
with low grades. Its owner is the Compania Minera
Caylloma S.A., which was formed in 1932 and has as
shareholders various prominent citizens of Arequipa--
including descendants of the English community, once
much involved in the railway, and the former Caylloma
Silver Mining Company.

The mine covers a large area, comprised essentially of a hill between two streams running south
that unite and turn east. These streams, in fact,
are the source of the Apurimac. The terrain is andesitic varying to diorite, and the east northeast-
west southwest veins are thought to be cooling
fractures in a large batholith that appears locally
through the Jurassic formations. The main vein is
San Cristobal, 3.5 kms. long and, at present, essentially worked on three levels. Level 10 (altitude,
4,590 meters) is being exploited from the southwest
with small compressed-air-operated mechanical shovels, which have raised production considerably. The
vein, at times, is up to 8 or 10 meters wide and although the grade is very low, at 200 grams per ton,
high production rates make the mine pay. The gangue
is 70 per cent calcite and 10 to 20 per cent quartz,
while there is also some rodonite and gold to the

northeast--it is from this direction that the mineralization is thought to have originated. A problem
in the mine is that of refilling with waste, and a
sort of gloryhole is planned--blasting down the rock
via a conical funnel from the surface, which is some
100 meters above. Further into the hill there is a
higher level 8 that is also in exploitation, this
time using ore-shrinkage techniques. A third level
4 at 4,770 meters enters from the northeast and is
only starting. From this side of the hill, the old
colonial workings are clearly visible above, the vein
being neatly removed like a trench across the crest.
Below level 10, no exploration has been done, but
assuming the grade does not fall even a further 10
meters down it should give 750,000 tons--and there
are still large reserves above this level. Thus,
production is being stepped up from 350 to 700 tons
per day, and productivity should reach 45 to 50 tons
of ore per month per man employed (both under-ground
and elsewhere). In the case of Caylloma, high productivity is a necessity if the mine is to continue
in existence.

The plant floats the silver via eight banks of
roughers (in parallel), two banks of pre-cleaners
and one bank of cleaners. There is also a bank of
scavengers. It is worth recalling that Caylloma was
probably the first mine in Peru to use flotation
techniques for silver ores. Concentrates have a 6-
to 8-kilo-per-ton silver content. Recovery is not
good. The concentrates are sent by truck to Sumbay
and thence by rail to the coast. The mine generates
its electricity from a hydroelectric plant. The
plant takes 3 cubic meters per second, which is
enough to empty the 25-million-cubic-meter lake in
9 to 10 months. This illustrates nicely the problem
common to so many mines. The rains, which last perhaps 2 months, have to fill the reservoirs for the
rest of the year, and their arrival is anxiously
awaited. Snow is even more welcome.

Immediately next to Caylloma is another company
called Cuchilladas, working a small vein to the north.
The Compania Minera Caylloma itself owns several
other veins, for example El Toro and Eureka (near

Cuchilladas, and once worked by the English company),
San Pedro and some antimony veins to the south of
San Cristobal. Not far away to the northeast lies
Sucuitambo, once owned by Hochschild but abandoned,
now worked by a Swiss, Sr. Juilland, with an Arequipa
partner. Production is 35 tons daily and the grade
is high at 6 grams gold and 30 ounces silver. The
problem with the mine is flooding, much of which is
caused by water coming in via old colonial workings
on the surface. The owners are installing large
pumps. Hochschild is much involved in the neighborhood. Its famous mine of Arcata (very isolated) is
a rich gold/silver deposit--another old colonial
site. Less successful was Condoroma in neighboring
Cuzco, where Hochschild closed down after working
old tips for some years, and San Antonio de Esquilache
(in Puno), which belonged to the Compania de Minas
del Peru, the same Hochschild subsidiary that owned
Sucuitambo. When Hochschild was driven out of Bolivia
in 1952, the company, in a not unworthy attempt to
keep its staff, bought up any mine it could in neighboring Peru--hence this selection of old viceregal
mines in Cuzco, Puno and Arequipa. San Antonio de
Esquilache was bought from the well-known Arequipa
miner, Arthur Williams, and rapidly ruined. Hochschild stepped up production to a level quite out of
proportion with known reserves, sacked many of the
old Indian workers and then suffered a collapse.
The mine closed down some years ago, but small miners
are back at it again today.

     Arcata lies at the head of the river Andahua.
Downstream to the south is Orcopampa, where the Compania de Minas Buenaventura is also opening a new
silver/gold/copper mine, and nearby there are gold
concessions at Tintaymarca. North of Arcata, across
the Continental Divide, is Santo Tomas in Cuzco,
another colonial zone (there is a town called Colque-
marca, which means the place of silver) that is being
re-explored by a Japanese company. Gold was discovered near here (Chalhuani) in 1775. Cerro de Pasco
had a copper concession at Tintaya that it had been
sitting on for 50 years before it reverted to the
State in 1970. Thus, this whole zone, which may
loosely be described by its Inca name of Condesuyos,

is rich in mines but woefully inaccessible. An excellent way of opening it up would be to link Cuzco
and Arequipa by a direct road via Velille and Caylloma, improving the shocking existing roads and
building new stretches where needed.

PUNO

     In the whole of the southern sierra, undoubtedly
the region with most immediate prospects of mining
development is that of Puno. The department of Puno
is even more than Ancash the stronghold of small
mining. Historically, this is partly because of the
revolt of Tupac Amaru, which scattered the big mine
owners in the late 18th century; partly because of
the remoteness and inhospitality of the altiplano,
which did not invite the foreigners in the 19th century (as did central Peru); partly because of the
superior mineral attractions of neighboring Bolivia;
and a great deal because of the widespread belief
that while there are mines in Puno there are none of
a size worthy of a large investment. This belief has
been questioned, but meanwhile the small miner has
established a firm footing, thanks largely to the
office of the Banco Minero in Juliaca. In 1967, the
bank's direct short-term loan stood at 115 million
soles, of which 79 million were in southern Peru and
the remainder in northern and central Peru. Their
Juliaca office buys some 3,000 tons yearly from up
to 50 small miners without concentrators, and Hochschild, who has a similar office in the town, is also
an important buyer. The competition between them
undoubtedly helps to maintain prices.

     The Puno mines, although widely scattered, have,
of course, certain preferential zones. The first is
that of Crucero where there are about 20 small
lead/silver mines. To the south, near the Nudo de
Sunipani, are some bigger prospects owned by the
Dammert family due to come into operation in the
early 1970's. West, near Antauta, is the San Rafael
mine of Minsur (Grace, 67 per cent) once owned by the

Lampa Mining Company.* San Rafael has a 300-ton-per-
day concentrator and floats copper from a 4.6-per-
cent ore. The ore also contains some 1 per cent tin,
which is recuperated on tables from the tailings, but
owing to its fineness the percentage recuperation is
very low--perhaps 20 per cent. This mine is by no
means the only indication that the Bolivian tin
fields may extend northward into Peru. The deposit
is associated with an intrusive and is composed of
various veins in an anticline in the Paleozoic slates.
West again lies Quenamari, where Mitsui is prospecting for copper, and to the north is the Korani mine
belonging to Ingeniero Mario Samame Boggio, a small
lead/zinc producer.

The Carabaya and Sandia regions are the most
famous for gold in all Peru. The Sangaban River is
known from colonial times, there are small gold
washers in Ituata and Coaza, and recently the Canadian Early Bird Mines bought the Santo Domingo concession of Inca Mining, which had such a spectacular
spell at the start of this century. There are gold
washings near Sandia itself, at Apuroma east of the
Inambari and near Ananea. The Ananea mines are the
biggest producers, or rather the single gold mine of
size now operating in Peru is the Natomas Company of
Peru situated at some 5,300 meters east of Ananea.
The operation is by means of a small drag that handles some 10,000 cubic yards daily. The drag is
floating in a pond in an extensive glacial morrain
in which the gold lies. Although there is no bedrock
as far down as 120 feet, the drag works only to 30
feet below water level with a 10-foot bank above.
The gold is not found lower down, and it is conjectured that the deposit is owing to a single recent
glaciation. Working on a 320-foot front, the drag
maintains three faces, advancing several feet in one,
then moving to the next, etc. When working, it pivots
about a vertical plug sunk into the bottom of the
pond, which is lifted and resunk whenever it moves
forward or sideways to a new face. The 9-cubic-foot

----

*Minsur was bought by Luis Banchero in 1971 for
$1.8 million.

buckets scoop up the gravel at the rate of 23 per
minute, the gravel passing to a circular inclined
drum through which the coarse material passes to be
dumped out behind. The fines fall through holes in
the drum to 12 channels on each side. Each channel
consists of two layers that begin with riffles, inclined 40° away from the water flow, into which the
heavy gold falls. Further down are rubber traps
with mercury in them to catch the gold, and then more
riffles. The dredge maintains an 85-per-cent utility,
including the halt, every ten days, when the riffles
and traps are cleaned and the gold recovered. The
gold is washed in a box, excess mercury is squeezed
out and an amalgam of 50 per cent gold is recovered.
The quantity is 15 to 26 kilos every ten days. The
amalgam is taken to the laboratory where the mercury
is driven off over a furnace and recovered in a small
still. The gold is then founded in a crucible with
silicon and broken glass. After some 4 hours it
melts, the silicon crust is removed, the gold poured
into a mold lined with coal dust (to prevent sticking) and the bar left to cool. The silicon crust is
ground down and specks of gold recovered by panning
with a silvered pan. The gold is 23.5 carats, the
rest being silver. Cerro de Pasco acts as agent for
Natomas in selling it.

Natomas is a very marginal operation. The deposit pays if it is worth $0.25 per cubic yard (per-
haps 0.1 gram per ton) and production is maintained.
Everything depends on the availability of the dredge,
and if daily earnings fall below $1,500 the opera-
tion runs at a loss. The company is a U.S. subsidiary of a California firm, and the deposit is rented
from the San Antonio de Poto company belonging to
the Pena Prado family. The contract was signed in
1961, when Manuel Prado was president, and it created
a scandal. The reason was that the deposit lies
within 50 kms. of the frontier with Bolivia, and
Peruvian law forbids foreign mining companies to
operate within that limit for security reasons (a
precaution well-justified if the Chaco War between
Bolivia and Paraguay is remembered). Pleading exceptional circumstances, the contract was allowed
and approved by the chamber of deputies on the grounds

that it would bring substantial social benefits and
large-scale employment to a very poor area of Puno.
In fact, this was nonsense. The company employs
less than 100 people (even small under-ground mines
employ more) and, in fact, it is occupying a site
where the local population happily used to pan for
gold on their own. To the company's credit, it turns
a blind eye to these clandestine operations that
still continue. Nevertheless, the fact remains that
the law was broken for the benefit of the President's
nephew and hardly anyone else at all--Natomas is of
the belief that they have been swindled too, since
the actual gold encountered does not measure up to
the samples they had when they signed the contract
for the concession.

All around Ananea, the morrain is panned for
gold, channels are prepared with paved floors for
when the rains come, streams are diverted onto sand
cliffs to wash them down (large-scale "booming" was
once practiced here) and further east, at La Rin-
conada, there are actual gold mines. The ore is
hacked out of tiny quartz veins--deep in the Paleozoic slates--by hand, is carried to the small village
(5,400 meters high) where the women crush it by hand,
is then ground by a water mill in the valley beneath
and finally recovered by amalgamation with mercury.
The gold is sold by the adarme (an ancient Spanish
weight equalling 1,797 grams) to a buyer from Juliaca
who also supplies the mercury.

The mines of Puno are not confined to the Cordillera Oriental. Along the axis of the department
are several small mines (lead/zinc/copper), and there
is an important antimony mine between Putina and
Azangaro. The Banco Minero buys some 20 tons monthly
of 65-per-cent antimony concentrate. There is also
an old mercury prospect on the shores of Lake Titicaca
near Huancan. However, the other major concentration
of mines is in the crescent that goes through Puno,
Santa Lucia and Pomasi. East of Puno lie some dozen
small lead/silver mines not far from the notorious
Laicacota. At Santa Lucia, the old Lampa Mining
Company was centered, with a foundry for producing
copper matte at Limon Verde. The company's two major

mines are since disposed of. One, Santa Barbara,
has been sold to Minsur, which is planning to restart
production; the other, Berenguela, is rented to Char-
ter Consolidated, who hopes by improved metallurgy to
make its intractable copper ores pay. Lampa used to
mix them with ore from the San Rafael mine. Near
Pomasi is the other mine of Samame Boggio, Palca.
Palca is a lead/silver producer and the plant also
floats a zinc concentrate. Capacity is 240 tons per
day. The mine has a relatively large number of employees.

The Banco Minero operates no concentrator in
the Puno region so the small miner is faced with
high transport costs, unless he handpicks his minerals carefully. Legislation (1969) for small miners
stated that the government would issue certificates
of 10 per cent of the f.o.b. value of exported minerals (minimum value, 200 soles; maximum, 600) to
producers in isolated zones, the certificates of
which could be used to pay taxes. It is hoped that
this legislation will be applicable to much of eastern Puno, but it is essentially only transferring
the cost of isolation onto the government. In the
long term, a more satisfactory solution would be the
extension of the Banco Minero's facilities, including
a concentrator plant, to these remoter areas and the
opening of an office in Cuzco. At the moment, the
few existing Cuzco miners are exporting their minerals to Bolivia to be concentrated at the Matilde mine.

9

SMELTING
AND
REFINING

There are three major metallurgical plants in
Peru. The first is at La Oroya, owned by the Cerro
de Pasco Corporation, and produces a wide variety of
non-ferrous metals. The second is at Ilo, owned by
the Southern Peru Copper Corporation, and only produces blister copper. The third is the SOGESA plant
at Chimbote, producing steel.

LA OROYA

The smelter at La Oroya started operation in
1922 and since that date has had a virtual monopoly
in Peru. Built in a narrow gorge, presumably to be
centrally placed for Cerro de Pasco's mines and on
the railway, the space available for it is woefully
inadequate. The poisonous fumes scarcely escape from
the glen, the limestone hills around are dirty, depressing and devoid of vegetation, and the filthy
town of mean houses would provide a good illustration
for any polemical work on the Industrial Revolution.
It is hard to believe that this place was built less
than 50 years ago--it has all the appearances of an
early 19th-century town. Laborers live and work
there because there is endemic unemployment in Peru.
Staff, however, has a very high rate of turnover,
few foreigners endure it for more than two years, and

the result is that there is a tendency for few young
people to reach any decision-making posts--these being held by company veterans waiting to claim their
pensions. The nature of the plant, the climate, the
surrounding dead landscape and the altitude all combine to make La Oroya a horrible place.

However, La Oroya is very interesting, as the
smelter itself must be one of the most complex in
the world. Three main circuits produce copper, lead
and zinc, while a series of elaborate smaller processes yield bismuth, silver, gold, selenium, tellurium, cadmium, antimony and indium. Considering
first the copper circuit, it is fed with concentrates
typically of 25- to 30-per-cent copper content,
which also contain some silver and gold. These concentrates are mixed to produce fairly constant percentages and are then roasted on a series of beds,
being raked down from one to another. The roasting
takes place at about 700°C., and its primary objective is to reduce the sulphur from around 30 to some
17 per cent. From the beds, the copper passes to
two reverberatory furnaces, where a 40-per-cent matte
is produced, while some iron is removed in a silicate
slag. The copper matte passes to four convertors
that are operated on a two-blow system. The first
blow is designed to produce an $FeO-SiO_2$ slag, which
is removed, while the second copper blow causes the
reactions $2Cu_2S + 3O_2 = 2Cu_2O + 2SO_2$ and $2Cu_2O +
Cu_2S = 6Cu + SO_2$. The sulphur dioxide, of course,
escapes as gas. The conversion runs at some 1,300°C.
and a 98-per-cent blister copper is produced that is
cast into anodes. These anodes are of very poor
quality, the "blisters" being so large as to require
specially large spacing between anodes and cathodes
in the subsequent electrolysis. Apparently, the
quality could be improved by over blowing, but the
loss in silver and gold prevent this. Poling with
coke-oven gas to release sulphur dioxide is being
planned, and, indeed, various schemes are being put
forward to improve the running of the convertors.
A computer model is being developed, and experiments
have been made that show that present production
needs only three, not four, convertors. Production
is only maintained by buying in concentrates, and in

the late 1960's Cerro de Pasco had to buy from the
Philippines as its Peruvian prices were not competitive. (It bought perhaps half of the copper concentrates for sale in 1968 in Peru.)

The blister copper passes to the nearby electrolytic refinery. Here, over 10,000 anodes are processed at a time. Each anode lasts some 24 days and
yields three cathodes of 99.95 purity, after seven,
eight and nine days. The cathodes are made from
stripping other cathodes after 24 hours' immersion.
The solution is copper sulphate and sulphuric acid,
made at La Oroya. The copper sulphate is extracted
for sale by means of a centrifuge and is much used
throughout the mining industry as an activator in
zinc flotation. The refined copper is sometimes sold
as cathodes but is also founded and cast into wire
bars, and thence rods (there is a rolling mill owned
by a Cerro de Pasco subsidiary in addition to the
refinery). The anode slimes from the refinery contain some 30 per cent silver and 20 per cent lead
and are further treated. In 1968, La Oroya produced
some 53,000 tons of copper, mostly refined although
some was sold as blister (owing to the temporary in-
capacity of the refinery), 40 per cent of which came
from mines not belonging to the company.

The lead circuit at La Oroya begins with a rudimentary pelletization of concentrates, which are then
treated on several parallel sintering belts, the purpose being the conversion of galena to lead oxides.
The sinter with coke added passes to some small blast
furnaces that are continually tapped to various set-
tling vessels. Here, a copper dross slag is formed
with the aid of sulphur powder, which is removed,
solidified with water, treated in a furnace to separate lead from copper matte and the lead returned to
the settler while the copper matte goes to the copper
circuit. The lead is cast into anodes, a new machine
being now used for casting under pressure. The 97-
per-cent pure anodes go to a huge electrolytic refinery of 320 cells, 40 anodes to the cell. In a
fluosilicate solution, they last four days, and after
a further four days' washing the scrap returns to
the foundry. The cathodes, made from pouring pure

lead, initially are also washed, founded and cast
into ingots. The anode slimes, united with the anode
slimes from the copper refinery, pass to the bismuth
plant.

The lead produced is largely antimonial. Should
pure lead be required, the antimony can be removed by
adding caustic soda to the molten refined lead (or to
the settlers), whereby a slag is formed. In 1968,
87,000 tons were produced, a third of which was from
purchased ores and concentrates.

The third major circuit, the zinc circuit, is
quite inadequate for the company's own concentrate
production. In 1968, it produced some 66,000 tons
of refined zinc while Cerro de Pasco exported about
80,000 tons in concentrates, and these two together
still only represented 45 per cent of Peru's production. The reason for this small capacity is, of
course, the large consumption of electrical energy
that the electrolytic refining process requires. If
this is put at 2.2 kilowatt hours per pound of refined zinc, Cerro de Pasco must have used about 20
per cent of its 190-megawatt installed capacity for
this purpose alone. The investment required to provide merely the electric power for refining the
other 80,000 tons may be put at $10 million to $15
million. Considering the nature of the ores that the
company extracts, it is strange that a more active
interest has not been shown in the Imperial Smelting
combined lead/zinc refining process. As it is, the
current process consists of turning zinc sulphides
into oxides. This is done by pelletizing the concentrates, treating it on two fluid beds at some 800°C.
(half the zinc oxide is recovered from the beds, the
rest from the dust) and then milling it. A German-
made turbulent-layer process acts in parallel with
the fluid beds with a designed capacity of 220 tons
per day, the sulphur dioxide produced from it being
used to supply (partially) a new 200-tons-per-day
sulphuric acid plant. The zinc oxides are then
leached with sulphuric acid (and the spent solution
from the electrolytic cells) and zinc, copper and
cadmium go into sulphate solutions, while iron, arsenic and antimony form a sludge, the two streams

being separated by a filter. The dirty stream (the
sludge) goes to the new "pilot plant," while the zinc
solution is purified of copper and cadmium by adding
powdered zinc. This precipitates them and they are
recovered from further filters. The pure zinc solution is the electrolyte of the cells that have lead
anodes and aluminum cathodes from which the refined
zinc is stripped. Founded in an electric furnace,
the zinc is then cast on a continuous machine into
slabs, while some liquid zinc is sublimed in graphite
retorts and then distilled to supply the zinc powder
used earlier, also used in the bismuth circuit.

The "pilot plant" mentioned above is used to
recuperate the zinc-leach filterings. Various products are obtained, but perhaps the most important one
is, strangely enough, iron. This iron is used for
precipitating copper solutions in the mines, particularly in Cerro do Pasco itself, the price of ordinary scrap being reckoned high at 1,200 soles per
ton. The process consists first of a pelletization
with coke and bentonite and then treatment for two
to three hours in a rotating kiln. The kiln handles
50 tons daily--a 200-ton one is under study. The
output from the kiln is an iron sponge with some silver content, the silver being recovered in the copper
precipitate in the mine, while the gases are condensed
and leached to give first, zinc and cadmium, and
second, indium. A lead cake is left. In 1968, some
240 tons of cadmium and 220 kilos of indium were produced at La Oroya, worth about $3.60 and $60 per kilo,
respectively.

The three main circuits described--copper, lead
and zinc--account for two thirds of the sales of La
Oroya. The remaining third comes from some insignif-
icant-looking buildings facing the Mantaro River,
where one would hardly imagine that over $50 million
were produced yearly were it not for the barbed wire
and the armed guards. La Oroya is the largest bismuth producer and, more importantly, the second producer of refined silver in the world. Bismuth,
silver and gold all come from the anode slimes of the
copper and lead electrolytic refineries. The slimes
are dried and then smelted in a small reverberatory

furnace whose dust goes to the antimony plant. They
then pass to a convertor from which an antimony slag
is removed after eight hours. This slag is sent to
the copper circuit. After a further time, a second
slag is taken off, which contains most of the bismuth and which also has a large (50 per cent) silver
content. The bismuth is in oxide form produced from
the reaction $2Bi_2S_3 + 9O_2 = 2Bi_2O_3 + 6SO_2$, although
some Peruvian mines actually yield native bismuth.
What remains in the convertor is 50 per cent silver
together with gold, selenium and tellurium, all of
which pass to the cupel. There are four such convertors for separating bismuth from the precious
metals.

Following the bismuth process further, the convertor's second slag is founded in a reverberatory
furnace with carbon to give the reaction $Bi_2O_3 + 3C =
2Bi + 3CO$. A first silver slag is removed and re-
turned to the convertor and a second copper matte
slag goes to the copper convertors. The bismuth itself passes on through an incredibly complex procedure of refining in six kettles. In the first kettle,
a copper slag is returned to the reverberatory furnace and after agitation with air and caustic soda
an arsenic/antimony/selenium/tellurium slag is taken
to the selenium and tellurium plant. In the second
and third kettles, the bismuth is desilverized by
the Parkes process--scattering a little zinc dust and
stirring. In the fourth kettle, lead is removed as
a chloride, chloride being pumped through it for 12
hours. In the fifth, residual chlorine is itself
removed by oxidation; and in the final sixth kettle,
remaining impurities are skimmed off after stirring
in caustic soda. The bismuth is then cast in bars
and small pins, for the pharmaceutical industry.
Cerro de Pasco is very proud of its bismuth plant,
which besides being the world's largest producer also
yields the metal at 99.999 per cent purity. The
operations that achieve this result somewhat resemble
those of a witch's cauldron. The bismuth produced is
approximately 50 per cent from purchased ores and in
1968 totaled 792,000 kilos. There has been a very
considerable increase in La Oroya's bismuth production since the 1950's when the level was about 40 per

cent of that achieved now. Perhaps 15 per cent of
this bismuth comes from the Julcani mine of the Compania de Minas Buenaventura, 34 per cent owned by
Cerro de Pasco.

The silver that passes to cupellation is blown
with air on the surface until a bismuth slag is
formed, which is returned to the bismuth reverberatory. Selenium dust is also given off. When the
silver is 90 per cent pure, sodium nitrate is added
and a selenium/tellurium slag removed. The metal,
now nearly 99 per cent pure silver plus 0.2 per cent
gold, is cast into anodes, placed in bags and laid
in shallow nitric acid baths, whence it is deposited
on graphite cathodes as pure silver (with 0.05 per
cent copper, 0.03 per cent lead, 0.05 per cent bismuth). The cathodes are scraped down and the silver
crystals smelted with some soda nitrate in an induction furnace, the slag going to the bismuth circuit.
Silver bars of 41 kilos weight and 99.99 per cent
purity are cast, and sterling (925) silver is also
made for sale, via the banks, to Peruvian jewelers.

The anode sludge from the silver electrolysis
remains in the bags. It is washed, dried, smelted
in retorts and yields an 18-per-cent gold, 70-per-
cent silver metal. This is treated with sulphuric
acid ("partition"), which dissolves the silver to be
precipitated with iron. The gold sands that remain
are washed and founded in 280-ounce bars of 99.98 per
cent purity. Attempts are being made to improve the
gold production.

In 1968, La Oroya produced some 550 tons of refined silver and about a ton of refined gold. Some
silver and gold were exported in blister copper, approximately 15 per cent more.

The selenium and tellurium by-products are recovered by leaching with caustic soda. The residual
solids return to the initial anode sludge of the bis-
muth/precious metals circuit, and the tellurium is
then separated out as a cake by adding sulphuric
acid. Selenium of 99.9 per cent purity is precipitated from the remaining liquid with bisulphate of

sodium, while the tellurium cake is washed, again
dissolved with caustic soda and collected by electrolysis using stainless steel anodes and aluminum cathodes.   The tellurium purity is also 99.9 per cent.
Selenium and tellurium production in 1968 was approximately 5,500 kilos and 16,600 kilos, with prices of
$10 and $13 per kilo, respectively.

A final companion metal produced at La Oroya is
antimony.   Essentially, the raw material is dust from
flue precipitators all over the plant, which is then
roasted to remove arsenic.   From there, the mineral
goes to two convertors.   In the first, the antimony
is removed as a slag leaving lead behind, and in the
second, the antimony is purged of chromium by adding
soda ash.   The process has never worked very satisfactorily and pure antimony is seldom produced.   In
general, bars of 70 per cent antimony with the remainder lead are sold, although 95-per-cent antimony
bars are also produced.   Production is variable and
may be put at some 400 tons per year, worth slightly
less than $1.00 per kilo.

Besides the sulphuric acid and copper sulphate
already mentioned, the plant produces another chemical by-product--zinc sulphate, used as a depressor
for zinc in flotation cells.   La Oroya also manufac-
tures metallurgical coke from the coal from the company's mine at Goyllarisquizga.   For a long time,
this mine's existence has been threatened (it has
known some dreadful accidents) as the coal is of
poor quality, but imported coke is so expensive--it
has recently reached nearly $50 per ton--that the
decision to close the mine has not yet been taken.
La Oroya does not produce tungsten.   Peru's tungstic
oxide production in 1968 was some 650 tons in concentrates, a quarter of which came from Cerro de Pasco's
own mines at San Cristobal and Morococha.

La Oroya is certainly interesting, but in the
way that a museum is interesting.   The smelter and
the associated town are sadly in need of modernization.   The mildly chaotic and inefficient copper circuit (copper, after all, is a well-understood metal)
is sufficient evidence of this.   One could also add

that the zinc plant is much too small and is apparently grossly wasteful since official statistics, albeit of 1965, show that nearly 30 per cent of the
zinc content of the concentrates was lost in refining.
The antimony plant does not work properly and the
gold is of substandard purity.

ILO

The smelter at Ilo handles Toquepala's concentrates, which are basically chalcopyrite although
there is some chalcocite. Consequently, copper content is about 30 per cent and sulphur may be taken
as slightly more, although the 40-per-cent figure
given by the company may be doubted. The concentrate
passes straight to two 115-by-34-foot reverberatory
furnaces without any previous roasting, as in La
Oroya. (The concentrate is already sufficiently dry
and is prevented from blowing away on its train trip
from the mine by a surface-fixing spray.) The reverberatories have suspended roofs and handle some 650
tons per day each. They are charged from the side,
and each is equipped with two waste head boilers that
can produce up to 60,000 pounds of steam per hour per
boiler, which, in turn, is used in generating electricity. The 40-per-cent copper matte from the furnaces passes to four Pierce-Smith convertors, the
slag being dumped on the beach.

According to the company, matte analysis gives
a 25-per-cent sulphur content, which would indicate
a largish quantity of iron sulphide. The slags
formed in the removal of this are returned to the
reverberatories, and it may be suspected that the
convertors are considerably "over-blown" with consequent loss of other metals, namely gold and silver.
Silver in the final blister copper is 5 ounces per
ton while gold is nil, which is a bit surprising
considering the location of the mine. The blister
copper is cast in 700-pound bars of much better
quality than La Oroya's anodes. They are exported
from the company's own port.

The smelter employs nearly 1,000 people. It is
situated almost on the shore and, indeed, one of its

subsidiary plants is a kiln for making lime from
shells collected by a drag. Despite the large quantity of sulphur passing through the plant, 400 tons
per day, no attempt is made to produce sulphuric
acid. Anaconda's Cerro Verde mine in the neighboring
department is in need of sulphuric acid for leaching
the oxide ores that are to be mined in the first ten
years.

In addition to the waste-heat boilers, the plant
has two other oil-fired boilers (215,000 pounds per
hour each) and two more larger ones on order. The
associated generating turbines produce up to 110 MVA,
which, at the moment, is much in excess of the smelter's and mine's needs. The low-pressure steam from
the turbines is used in a four-stage desalinating
plant for sea water, which treats some 500 gallons
per minute.

Socially, Ilo has given rise to two long-standing
complaints. The first is that the pier built by the
company has been reserved for their exclusive use,
so that a second pier has had to be constructed for
everyone else. Certainly, this seems an unnecessary
waste of effort, but the tonnage shipped by the company averages 400 tons per day and the pier is only
200 meters long. The second complaint is about the
fumes from the smelter, which are said to damage the
crops in the Moquegua and even the Tambo Valleys.
Here, one must sympathize with the company, since the
prevailing winds and the distances involved show
these complaints to be nonsense. If Ilo pollutes the
Tambo Valley, then the whole of Western Europe must
be judged to be poisoned. It would be more reasonable to complain about the company's exclusive nature.
Ilo handles only Toquepala's ores and then converts
them only to blister copper--the reason for the latter, of course, being that the shareholders largely
own refineries in the United States. Nor has it
shown any interest in refining the silver (as a by-
product of copper refining), which amounts to over
20 tons per year, or the molybdenum from Toquepala,
whose quantity, although small at 700 to 800 tons
per year, is worth about $2 million. In the future,
both the tungsten produced by Cerro de Pasco and the

molybdenum from Southern Peru's copper concessions could be of use in the steelworks of SOGESA at Chimbote.

SOGESA

La Sociedad Siderurgica de Chimbote S.A.--SOGESA--has been one of the most controversial State under-takings in Peru. Owned originally by the Corporacion Peruana del Santa (now a dependency of the Ministerio de Energia y Minas), it has since issued shares to the government as the company has run into problems in meeting its foreign currency commitments. Indeed, the present financial situation of SOGESA is extremely complex, and the government has taken responsibility for all its overseas debt, which is very large. To consider only one item: The contract for the plate and sheet mill completed in 1970 was for $45 million, and with financing, nearly $70 million. It is not surprising that a foreign-built steelworks producing for national consumption should have problems in paying foreign-currency debts. The dollars for repayment presumably are to be bought with the company's profits. If the company makes sufficient profits to do this, the impact on the foreign exchange reserves is obviously large, perhaps sufficient to provoke a devaluation. Devaluations do occur (one in 1967), and these in turn reduce the dollar equivalent of the company's profits--unless they raise its prices. One might summarize this very briefly by asking, can Peru afford such an expensive importation?

The political controversy has not, however, centered on this important question. The problem has been as to whether the company should be State or private owned, a question largely irrelevant to the fundamental one of how to repay the foreign-currency debt. Needless to say, in the often virulent campaign waged by the private sector against SOGESA, demands have been made to turn the company over to private ownership, but those same persons showed no willingness to under-take the risks of the initial investment. What has, in fact, happened is that to

avoid a State monopoly licenses have been given to
construct two rolling mills for angled sections (one
in Lima and one in Arequipa) in addition to the capacity that SOGESA itself has for these products.
National capacity is now so in excess of demand that
SOGESA's own mill is permanently inactive (a political decision), the Arequipa mill is in continual
difficulties and the Lima mill is working far below
capacity. Three mills instead of one have to be
paid for, and none of them can make sufficient profit
to buy the dollars--even if they were readily available. The total steel market in Peru (it is extremely unstable) is perhaps worth $70 million or
$80 million yearly, and there is no reason to suppose
that a State-owned company should not be able to pay
for itself through savings on imports as far as foreign currency is concerned. What, however, must be
supposed for this to happen is that the company gets
full political support, that the dollars it has "indirectly earned" are reserved for its exclusive use
and that its domestic expenses are at least temporarily subsidized. This has not happened in the case of
SOGESA and, indeed, some of its difficulties have
been because of deliberate sabotage.

The original plant, which dates from 1956, was
largely French-built. Designed to use the mineral
from the Corporacion's iron fields at Marcona, it
consisted essentially of two electric reduction furnaces with a combined pig-iron capacity of 60,000
tons per year, two electric arc furnaces with a
66,000-ingot steel capacity (later 80,000) and a
rolling mill for producing steel for reinforced concrete, wire-making and small angles. Power came
from the Canon del Pato hydroelectric plant on the
Santa River, which had an initial capacity of 50,000
kilowatts. In 1962, an ambitious plan for expansion
was initiated, the objectives of which were: (1) a
pier for bulk-handling of iron ore, (2) a blast furnace, (3) a Linz Donawitz (LD) steel-making plant, (4)
a continuous casting plant for billets, (5) an amplification of the existing rolling mills and (6) a new
rolling-mill plant for plate and sheet steel. A
description will be given of these items.

The pier is designed to handle two 20,000-ton boats at a time, has two cranes and is connected by a conveyor belt to the dumping area near the blast furnace. This furnace has a 5-meter hearth and a nominal capacity of 600 tons of pig iron yearly. The coke for the blast furnace is imported and, although anthracite from the Santa coal fields has occasionally been mixed with it, this is an expensive item. The coke rate is some 624 kilos per ton, so at capacity coke imports could cost some $6 million or $7 million yearly. It has been suggested that coal be imported and coke made locally; it would enable a larger use of local coal, produce gas and save foreign currency.* The iron now used is almost entirely Marcona's pellets (1.4 tons per ton of iron), and the pig iron produced has been exported to Japan, but when the new sheet mill is fully running it is likely that blast furnace capacity will prove inadequate for the steel plant's needs.

The LD plant consists of two convertors of 25-tons capacity each (they are usually charged to 30) and their associated mixer. The plant has been working since its initial trials in December 1966. Early problems with lining wear, owing largely to thermal shocks from cooling and heating on account of the low production rate, seem to have been overcome and lining life has risen from 100 casts to over 200. Capacity is to be 240,000 tons per year, and there is confidence that 30 casts per day can easily be achieved. The electric arc furnaces are also in use and handle scrap at the rate of 1 ton per 5 tons of pig iron. The continuous casting plant is fed usually by the LD's, which are alternated to maintain a supply of liquid steel. Four billets are produced at a time and annual capacity is some 90,000 tons. Steel otherwise is cast into small ingot molds of only 3/4 ton and the cold ingots pass to a stockpile. The ingot molds are manufactured locally.

The existing rolling mill starts with a reheating furnace and then a mill for producing 60 or 80

*See note on p. 217.

millimeter square billets and two sizes of round
ones. The extension to this mill has been in existence since 1968 but, as has been said, owing to excess national capacity so far no angled pieces,
sections, etc., have been produced. Instead, billets,
including those from the continuous casting plant,
are sold to the two private companies--SOGESA only
produces wire rods. Ten sizes (3/8 to 1.5 inch) are
produced both in corrugated and ordinary rods for
reinforcing. Rods for drawing into wire are produced in three sizes, and they are largely bought by
the neighboring PROLANSA factory.

The new rolling mills for sheet steel were the
subject of bitter argument that led to the board of
SOGESA resigning en masse. The subject was the contractor for it, the board favoring an Italian company
and government officials, other ones. The dispute
lasted throughout 1966 and only in April, 1967, after
a new series of quotations, was the contract awarded
to an Italian-French consortium. Over one year's
delay was occasioned so that the mill, which should
have been available in 1968, was not ready until
1970. The effect of this delay on the rest of the
plant has been serious. Admittedly, the economy has
been fairly stagnant since the 1967 devaluation, but
then this would have been an ideal time to run in the
new mill--it is planned to start at 50,000 tons per
year and to reach 150,000. Instead, the mill will
probably still be in its teething stages when demand
for its products is highest; meanwhile, an expensive
iron and steel-making plant has been waiting semi-
idle, still not paid for. The new mill will consist
of soaking pits for 5- and 7-ton ingots, followed by
a combined blooming/slabbing mill that supplies large
billets for steel sections, finished plates for ship
building (40,000 tons yearly) and feed for the Steckel
mill. The Steckel mill produces rolled sheet to be
sold directly or to pass to the pickling, cold-rolling
and annealing line. The cold sheet has a width of
1.27 meters, is 0.16 to 1.5 millimeters thick and is
to be sold as rolls or already cut up. A plant for
galvanizing and corrugating sheets is also being constructed.

Surprisingly, there exists no plan for making railway lines, which surely must be an easy addition and which are imported to the quantity of over 10,000 tons per year. Tinplate, too, is not envisaged. This is, of course, much more ambitious--Peru imports over 20,000 tons yearly worth some $5 million.* In the past, there has been excess billet capacity and it probably was a mistake not to produce large ingots earlier rather than small ones that had to be used for these billets. Large ingots could probably have been exported to more sophisticated steel makers, the exporting of steel by relatively under-developed countries being certainly possible as illustrated by the Chilean Compania de Acero del Pacifico (also State owned and very successful).

SOGESA has had its share of difficulties and it is to be hoped that in the 1970's they will end. One problem, of course, has been labor. Apart from too-frequent strikes, etc., there has been the need to train relatively unskilled people in the use of sophisticated equipment. SOGESA employs over 1,500 people, many of whom are from the sierra. One or two foreign technical advisers say that the serranos are, in fact, the easiest trained because they are willing to learn. This is not always the case with those who already have some technical education, and if they have a professional title the situation is still worse. In fact, the problem of an industry such as SOGESA is not that of finding capable labor but rather that of finding competent technical management.

---

*At the end of 1970, ambitious new investment plans for SOGESA were announced totaling $248 million. These include a 150,000-ton-per-year coke plant ($15 million for 1973), a 100,000-ton-per-year tinplate line (for 1972), extensions to the steel-making plant to raise production to 1.2 million tons per year ($105 million for 1974) and an increase of the sheet-steel capacity to 1 million tons per year, 50 per cent for export ($115 million for 1974).

10

SELLING
THE PRODUCTS
OF
THE MINES

The products of the mines are either concentrates or high-grade minerals. These latter are essentially produced by the small miners who have not the capital to build concentrating plants and whose costs of production per ton are so high as to make low-grade mining impossible. Frequently, the minerals are hand picked to separate rich ore from obvious gangue. In general, perhaps 4 per cent of the production of Peru's mines is in the form of minerals rather than concentrates--zinc and gold being exceptions. No zinc minerals are produced as they have no sale unless separated from lead and copper, which nearly always accompany them. Gold, on the other hand, is sometimes sold from the mine directly in the refund state--that is to say, 22- or 23-carat gold can be recovered in grains by washing, without any further metallurgical treatment. Small-scale mercury amalgamation is also used in remote mines. Such gold is marketed locally, the miner coming to pay off small traders who have let him have boots, food, shovels, lanterns, etc., on credit. The negotiating of the sale takes place after dark in the back of the shop, the outside door being locked.

The concentrates and minerals are sold either for export or to a local foundry. The first task, clearly, is to transport them to the buyer's office,

which, in general, is on the coast, although between
them the Banco Minero and Hochschild have deposits in
Huaraz, Huancayo, Arequipa, Juliaca and Cuzco, while
Cerro de Pasco, of course, buys at La Oroya. Transport costs vary enormously depending on the situation
of the mine, and it is not very meaningful to talk of
average figures, although the Anuario de la Industria
Minera shows that, in general, between 3 and 4 per
cent of the price received for products is spent on
transport (not only of those products, of course).
As an example, Raura has transport costs per metric
ton of 240 soles to the port of Huacho, 300 to Callao
(some $6.00 to $7.50). However, the value of the ton
transported could be anything from $60, in the case
of zinc concentrates, to $500 or even $600, for cop-
per/silver concentrates. In the case of transport
from the mine to concentrator, a typical cost might
be 8 soles ($0.20), the ore being worth from $15 to
$25 per ton, but these figures only apply to medium-
sized mines. Large-scale producers (Toquepala,
Cobriza) will handle lower-valued ores at, say, $10
per ton with lower transport costs: Toquepala having
a private railway from the mine to the concentrator
and on to the smelter; Cobriza, a highly mechanized
system of extraction from the mine. At the other end
of the scale, a small miner who carries his minerals
by mule to a roadhead, and thence by a specially
hired truck to a concentrator plant belonging to a
larger mine, is paying some 120 soles ($3.00) per
ton in Huaraz. The incentive for hand picking is
obviously great, and small miners must be producing
$30 per ton of ores to pay their way.

It is to be expected in a country with a terrain
like Peru's that transport costs are often decisive.
At times, transport is not only costly but impossible.
Roads are obliterated annually by huaycos (mud slides)
and the area centered on Apurimac, for example, owes
its low mining activity not to lack of minerals but
to an almost total absence of roads. Such are the
difficulties of transport that few mines assume the
responsibility, preferring to leave the repair and
maintenance of trucks to contractors, although frequently they maintain the roads themselves. Where
it is possible, the railways are used, Cerro de Pasco,

for example, freighting copper concentrates by road
to Huancayo from Cobriza and thence by rail to La
Oroya (although the road is excellent). Cercapuquio,
however, freights by road to Huancayo and on by road
to Callao in different trucks. The economics of a
railway are not easily analyzed but it is almost
certain that if some of Peru's railways had been
built on a more ambitious scale, or even if the
original plans had been completed, rail transport
would be much more used by the mines. The line
(closed) to Chilete, which could have been extended
to Cajamarca and so to Michiquillay; the Chimbote-
Huallanca line (threatened), which was intended to
go to Pasto Bueno or thereabouts; and the railway
to Huancavelica, which was meant to reach Castrovirreyna are three examples. That a railway is not
necessarily uneconomic and out of date is shown by
the one specially built by Southern Peru between
Toquepala and Ilo.

EXPORTING CONCENTRATES
AND MINERALS*

Considering first the sales of concentrates and
minerals for export, these represent very approximately 15 per cent (copper), 45 per cent (lead), 45
per cent (silver), 70 to 80 per cent (zinc) and perhaps 50 per cent (gold) of the total production figures. The silver and gold normally occur in the
copper, lead or zinc concentrates as bonuses. The
Banco Minero and four major commercial houses, Hochschild, Grace, Minerco and Tennant, handle this business almost exclusively, all operating on the same
basic principles. The buying is done in three ways--
at risk, as an agent or "normally."

---

*The Ministero de Energia y Mines has, since its
creation in 1969, indicated on several occasions that
it intends to make the commercialization of mineral
products a State monopoly. However, at the start of
1971, no clear indications had been given as to how
this would be done.

Buying at risk means that the buyer pays cash
for the concentrate at his depot and sells it as best
he can overseas. In fact, this is only done by Hochschild and the Banco Minero to any extent, both of whom
are interested in the small miners who want instant
cash and cannot wait for final liquidations two or
three months later. Buying at risk is only done from
small and irregular producers--people who appear with
a truck-load of mineral at random intervals and are
not seen between times.

When the exporting house acts as an agent,
essentially it takes care of all the paperwork involved, accepts responsibility for the concentrates,
fixes the shipping, etc. The mine will probably have
a contract with a refinery overseas, agreeing on a
price based on the London or New York market price
averaged over the month after the day of delivery of
the concentrate at the door of the refinery. The
price might be the mean of the two market prices
applied to the metallic content of the concentrate,
less refining costs, treatment losses and discounts
for undesirable elements (arsenic, antimony). Bonuses
are paid for certain additional metals (e.g., gold,
silver and copper). This is the price paid by the
refinery. The mine gets this price less handling in-
surance and freight charges, less an explicit commission for the agent, which will typically be 1 or 2
per cent of the liquidation price. The agent will
probably have helped in finding the client and drawing up the contract. Such a system is used by Malaga
Santolalla, which sells its tungsten concentrates
to General Electric of the United States and to Japan
--Hochschild acting as agent.

The difference between acting as an agent and
the normal contract, which controls most of the sales,
is that the latter contains no explicit fee for the
exporting house. The mine (the seller) brings the
concentrate to the exporter and asks for a quotation.
He may insist, say, that the concentrate be sold in
Japan if he thinks he will get better prices. The
exporter analyzes the concentrate in his own or a
third party's laboratory and the metallic content is
agreed on, the seller, of course, having made his own

previous analysis. The gross weight of concentrate
is then reduced to dry weight, less--typically--2
per cent handling losses and the total metal weight
then determined from the percentage analyses. Refining costs, etc., for Japan are subtracted, and
the price likely to be paid at the refinery is determined. Then, the exporter subtracts a lump sum
known as the _maquila_, which implicity covers all the
shipping charges and also his profit. The maquila
might be $45 per gross wet ton of concentrates. If
the seller does not like the quotation, he may try
another exporter, the original one having to meet his
own analysis costs with nothing to show for it. If
the contract is accepted, a further 4 per cent on the
net price to the seller is subtracted in accordance
with Article 50 of the Mining Code--this 4 per cent
is an advance on profit taxes for the mine, i.e., a
tax credit. The seller will hand over the concentrate and, typically, receive a 90-per-cent cash
payment. The final liquidation is made once the
concentrates have reached the refinery, and the
balance settled in accordance with what the refinery
in Japan actually paid. Thus, the exporter earns his
profit in the maquila, and by skilful exploitation of
the world markets he may be able to place the concentrate where there are high prices and low freights,
if the seller gives him complete freedom. The quotation may be worded in such a way that the agent benefits directly from high prices, but more likely he
only benefits indirectly by gaining the confidence
of the seller.

This system is essentially fair. The exporter
may make a small percentage on the value the refinery
pays, but he cannot make exorbitant profits at the
expense of the mine. The competition is sufficiently
strong to ensure this, and, above all, there is the
Banco Minero whose express policy is to offer better
prices to those most in need. Nevertheless, very
roughly speaking, copper in concentrates earns 65 to
70 per cent; lead, 60 to 65 per cent; zinc, as low as
50 per cent; silver and gold, 85 per cent of world
prices when sold in Peru. The balances go to the refineries (zinc is very costly), to the shippers or,
in a reasonable profit, to the exporters. It is

patently obvious what a benefit it would be to Peru
if all the metal production was refined in Peru, but
until that time is reached it is worth looking briefly
at the other two "middlemen."

The exporters pursue a perfectly legitimate business and, indeed, render a considerable service as
their world-wide connections and offices enable them
to place the concentrates advantageously. They also
give credit, make loans and sometimes own mines themselves. However, the Banco Minero excepted, they are
all foreign companies. Hochschild is a trust whose
head office is hard to locate, but it operates from
the Bahamas, Panama, New York and seems to have predominantly German members controlling it. Minerco
is a subsidiary of Engelhardt of the United States.
Grace and Tennant are two well-known New York firms.
Once again, the failure of the wealthy Peruvians to
enter a business involving initiative and enterprise
is made clear. It is very surprising that no Lima
capitalist has tried his hand at it with an office
in New York and one in Europe--it involves only
buying and selling and needs little technical knowledge. The Banco Minero operates very successfully,
although handling only some 10 per cent of the market (those concentrates that are up for sale as
opposed to being shipped to the parent company's refineries or going to La Oroya), and it is obvious
that the business does not require facilities un-
available to Peruvians. The market is worth some
$60 million annually (f.o.b. Peru prices), and in
1969 the Banco Minero made a gross 8-per-cent profit
on its buying and selling of concentrates and minerals. This profit did not include its expenses, but
a pre-tax figure of 3 per cent on f.o.b. prices may
be reasonable for the business as a whole, or roughly
$2 million annually. Allowing for taxation and the
Banco Minero's stake, perhaps $750,000 is exported
annually as net profits by the foreign operators.

SHIPPING

On the other hand, shipping, as is commonly ac-
knowledged, is not fair. Freights are expensive and

since they are, of course, per gross wet ton (not per ton of dry mineral content), their incidence is particularly felt in the export of concentrates. Freight charges for concentrates can be made in three ways. The normal way is from shipside in the port of embarkation to shipside in the port of disembarkation. To Europe, Japan or the United States charges are about $23 to $25 per ton, although silver concentrates might cost over $40. A second method of charging freights is "free-in," or "free in and out," when the exporter pays for loading and unloading. This brings the price down to around $10 per ton. Finally, regular shippers can establish long-term contracts and get cheaper rates, which are about $18 or $19 per ton. These freight charges are agreed on by the conferences that monopolize the world shipping routes, and in which the richer countries of the world predominate. It is not at all clear how the prices are arrived at, and it is puzzling why U.S. freights are not noticeably cheaper than European ones. In view of the superior prices paid for metals (lead excepted) in Europe and Japan, and the absence of lower freights in favor of the United States, it is to be expected that concentrate sales to the two former buyers should be large.

When the destination of the concentrates is looked into, this supposition is confirmed. Japan takes about 50 per cent of zinc concentrates and 80 per cent of iron; Europe, 10 to 30 per cent of zinc, copper, iron and lead; the United States, 45 per cent of lead concentrates and about 30 per cent of copper and zinc. Argentina buys some iron, the only significant Latin American buyer of concentrates. One reason that restricts the sale of concentrates to Japan and Europe, whose higher prices seem to reflect lower smelting costs, is that some mines are tied to the smelters of their parent U.S. companies. Two such mines are Quiruvilca and Santander, whose joint f.o.b. exports are worth some $13 million. Cerro de Pasco, however, although exporting zinc concentrates on its own account, has no parent smelter in the United States and so seeks the best market available.

A special case of shipping is that of Marcona. The company owns and charters its own fleet of bulk

carriers to ship its iron ore, pellets and concentrates (largely to Japan). This fleet is not registered in Peru but in Liberia. It is not known what
the freight charges are but if $5.00 per ton is
assumed, Marcona's earnings from freight alone reach
the enormous figure of $45 million. With such sums
of money, the temptation to adjust the freight to
minimize taxation between Peru and Liberia must
obviously be great. Until 1970, no pressure had been
exerted on Marcona to register its fleet in Peru--
although it was acquired with the profits of the mine
and exists for it. In that year, however, a new contract stipulated that 50 per cent of the fleet be
registered under the Peruvian flag.

How could Peru recuperate some of this loss of
earnings in freight? One method would be to tax
freight, as indeed is done already with certain
stamps and harbor dues, but this really only gains
money for the State at the expense of the miners--who
in any case all pay tax locally. A much more satisfactory method would be to enforce all exporters of
concentrates (and, indeed, of other commodities) to
consign a certain percentage of their business to
shipping lines registered in Peru. This method is
being tried, 20 per cent being the proportion fixed
for Peruvian boats. A figure of 40 per cent should
be aimed at, leaving another 40 per cent for the
fleets of the country of destination (to avoid re-
taliations) and 20 per cent for third parties. Such
a law would be quite fair and, since freights are
arranged monopolistically and are standard, the exporters would not lose out. Peru has a State shipping
line, the Corporacion Peruana de Vapores, and also one
large private one.

At the moment, foreign shipping lines dominate
the business. These are all represented by agents in
Peru, whose income (out of which they have to pay
their costs) is typically 2 per cent on freight in
and 5 per cent on freight out. If exports of concentrates are taken as 400,000 gross tons and average
freight costs are put at $20 per ton, the shipping
business is worth, certainly, $8 million yearly.
(This excludes Marcona's nearly 9 million tons a

year--a case apart.) At the moment, if the agents do
not repatriate their profits or make none, perhaps
$2 million remains in Peru. If the national shipping
line were used for 40 per cent of the exports of concentrates, an additional $2 million would be earned
for the foreign exchange reserves.

From the above reasoning, although only approximately, it is clear that it is highly desirable, from
the national point of view, that Peru should have a
larger stake in the business of exporting her own
mineral products.

SELLING TO SMELTERS AND
REFINERIES IN PERU

There are three metallurgical plants in Peru:
Chimbote, Ilo and La Oroya, whose technical aspects
have been discussed in Chapter 9. Chimbote buys only
iron from Marcona, the price being 63 per cent of the
f.o.b. price for pellets during the preceding year,
while minerals and concentrates have the same price
less $3.00 per ton. Since, for example, in 1968 pel-
lets averaged $10.80, the prices paid by Chimbote in
1969 would have been $6.80 and $3.80 per ton of pellets and concentrate/minerals, respectively. This
is a very fair price to Chimbote, and Marcona will
still be making a profit on the operation. These
sales, however, are only a small part of a contract
that has been criticized earlier as contrary to the
interests of Peru, as embodied in the Corporacion
Peruana del Santa.

The smelter at Ilo takes only copper concentrates
from Toquepala, its design and capacity being matched
to the mine's. It is not known if it was ever considered to buy in concentrates for smelting, but the
two most likely local vendors would be Chapi and now
Madrigal. Both these companies are foreign-owned and
are probably tied to smelters in Japan or the United
States. Since Toquepala and Ilo are all part of the
Southern Peru Copper Corporation, the sale price of
concentrates to the smelter is only a matter of internal bookkeeping, Peruvian taxation being levied on
the profits made from the exports of blister copper.

La Oroya is, thus, the sole smelter in Peru
buying from the mining industry in general. As has
been mentioned in Part I, this situation has not always existed. Before La Oroya was built, Cerro de
Pasco had another smelter at Tinyahuaroo; Fernandini
owned one at Huaraucaca; Huaron, one at San Jose;
Backus and Johnson, one at Casapalca; and there were
two large foundries in Yauli and one in Rio Blanco,
not to mention many small lead/silver smelters in
other parts of the country. When La Oroya came into
operation in the 1920's, all these foundries closed
down, the last to survive being San Jose. Although
Cerro de Pasco had bought one and closed it itself,
and some others never worked satisfactorily from the
start, the implication is that La Oroya, being that
much larger and more modern, could operate at lower
costs and so offer higher prices to sellers of concentrates. In particular, it was designed to recover
as much as possible the rarer metals present in the
ores, from bismuth to selenium. If La Oroya could
then kill all domestic competition, it should surely
now be able to oust foreign competition and work
perpetually at capacity. Freight charges for blister
or electrolytic copper are roughly equivalent to
those for concentrates (or slightly cheaper), but
since the copper content is perhaps four times as
great in the former, the saving attained by exporting
it instead of concentrates is around $70 per ton of
metallic copper. Added to this are savings in handling charges and in agents, plus the advantage of
being on the spot, so that one might think that La
Oroya could offer liquidation prices for concentrates
up to 10 per cent higher than the exporters. The
same figure should apply to lead concentrates, the
higher metallic content of which is compensated by a
lower specific value. Unfortunately, this is not the
case. Lead production is near capacity, but in 1968
La Oroya had sufficient spare copper capacity to absorb concentrates from Northern Peru, whose Tacoma
(U.S.) smelter was inaccessible owing to a dock
strike, as well as nearly 35,000 tons of concentrates
imported from the Philippines--although they also had
to absorb a similar quantity from their new mine at
Cobriza. All this would suggest that, as a buyer, La
Oroya is not competitive with the exporters, for
unknown reasons.

The terms of sale to La Oroya are similar to those to overseas refineries, the deductions for refinery costs, freight, etc., being, of course, different. The refinery does not refine as a service, as a concentrator plant might, but buys in direct. Various mines of the center send some or all of their concentrates to La Oroya, but its influence does not extend much further. As examples, Huaron, Raura, Puquiococha, Millotingo, Julcani (an important source of bismuth) and Atacocha may be mentioned as well as all the company's own mines. La Oroya does not buy zinc concentrates, as its capacity is less than 50 per cent of the production of the Cerro de Pasco Corporation by itself.

SELLING REFINED PRODUCTS FOR
EXPORT AND DOMESTIC CONSUMPTION

The problems of Sogesa have been discussed in Chapter 9. It is sufficient to say here that its steel products are placed entirely on the domestic market and average prices are $200 per ton. The quantity sold varies, but under 100,000 tons yearly was the figure for the late 1960's. Chimbote's production will not become normal until the new rolling mills are fully operating in the 1970's; meanwhile, it has been exporting some of its excess pig iron to Japan.

Ilo's blister copper production is exported in its entirety, some 140,000 tons a year. Of this production, 60 per cent is sent to the company's four U.S. owners, because, although the Cerro Corporation does not own an electrolytic refinery in the United States, there are industrial uses for blister copper. The other three owners, American Smelting and Refining, Phelps Dodge and Newmont, either refine the blister copper or use it directly. The remaining 40 per cent of production is exported to the best buyer, often in Europe (Belgium, Germany). The company owns and operates its own (exclusive) port at Ilo so the freight charges it pays are free-in, e.g., $17.75 to Antwerp. The difference between this and the free-in freights to the United States or Japan is not

significant in comparison with the enormous fluctuations in world copper prices.

It is in the interests of Peru that the company
should earn as much for its copper as possible, as
its increased profits will be reflected in increased
taxation earnings for the country. Criticisms that
state the copper should be sold at the London Metal
Exchange prices rather than the New York ones or,
indeed, that the copper should just be sent to Europe,
are met by the objection that the London prices are
not representative and are unstable. This objection
is valid. The Chileans pegged their copper prices
to the three-months' forward price of London, which
remained for several years lower than the spot price.
When, in 1968, they changed to the spot price, the
market responded by reducing it to below the three-
months' forward price. The London prices are sufficiently unrepresentative to enable an unscrupulous
operator to manipulate them to his advantage in his
outside dealings. Even outside London, copper prices
fluctuate wildly between $1,000 and $1,400 per ton,
and if Peru is to gain the benefit of higher prices
more forceful action would have to be taken than just
chancing the copper on another market. Two courses
would seem open. One, which is likely to be studied
if not taken up, is that the poorer-producing coun-
tries--Chile, the Congo, Zambia and Peru--set up some
sort of body for regulating the market, with a buying
fund and a stockpile. They already have regular meet-
ings to discuss policy within the Consejo Interguber-
mental de Paises Exportadores de Cobre (CIPEC). The
second course is that Peru should form a stockpile
of her own. Peru would not, of course, be in a position to control world prices but could certainly take
advantage of them. Producing companies could be obliged to sell to the stockpile, when required, at
the world prices of the day. It will be objected
that the country does not have the money to do this,
but the case will be argued in Chapters 12 and 13
that it does--namely, some part of the foreign exchange reserves, say $30 million, which would cover
perhaps 20 per cent of the refined or blister copper
production. There is no reason why both methods
should not be applied simultaneously, or combined in

some way. The refined products from La Oroya are
either exported or sold locally. The exported products are sold via a sales corporation and registered
in the United States, which places them on the world
markets. The sales corporation is intended to be a
non-profit organization that charges perhaps 2 per
cent to cover its costs. For the purposes of Peruvian
taxation, final liquidations of all sales are sent
to Lima so that the f.o.b. prices are seen to be
just. Essentially, the prices are world prices less
freight, etc., and sales expenses--lead and zinc being fairly stable at $240 and $260 per ton, respectively; copper, the usual gamble; and silver, from
$37 to even $65 per kilo. Gold is freely exported
by the company and sold wherever it chooses, presumably
in Europe at some $40 the ounce. Rarer metals are sold
similarly. In some cases, Cerro is in a position to
unilaterally dictate prices, and in 1969 the price of
bismuth was raised from $4.00 to $5.25 per pound.

It is not easy to find out what the value of
Cerro's refined products for export is, particularly
when copper and, to a lesser extent, silver predominate, both having unstable prices, but a figure of
some $140 million annually will approximate it. This
figure is slightly less than the value of Southern
Peru's blister copper exports. In addition, La Oroya
probably sells some $9-million worth of refined prod-
ucts locally, comprised of some 5,000 tons of copper,
4,000 to 5,000 tons each of lead and zinc, perhaps
30,000 kilos of silver and an unknown quantity of
gold to jewelers, local banks and the mint. The
prices for domestic sales are essentially world
prices or a little cheaper.

A refined product that has not yet been mentioned, as it is not produced at any of the three
refineries, is mercury. From the famous Santa
Barbara mine at Huancavelica, this is sold for export by Minerco to the United States, its annual
value reaching some $1.2 million.

Examined critically, the metal-refining business
in Peru shows various faults that could be eliminated.
First, the glaring shortage of zinc-refining capacity

should be remedied. For many years, plans have existed for building a refinery (with associated plants)
near Ancon, but only in the late 1960's were there
signs that the project was really under way--probably
using Japanese finance. The refinery will have to
count on supplies of concentrate from Cerro de Pasco
and Santander--both major producers, the latter having
its own U.S. refinery--and it is clear that the project has political implications. Nevertheless, it
should certainly go ahead, as at the moment Peru is
receiving effectively 50 per cent of the value of
over 70 per cent of its zinc production--i.e., losing
some $125 million yearly. Second, it is shocking
that La Oroya is not working to capacity in copper
production. Its uncompetitiveness may be owing to
excess profits on its operations, but many people
would say that inefficiency and generally out-dated
practice were more to blame. The refinery is, at
the moment, a virtual monopoly and it should not be
allowed to abuse its position. Third, there is
clearly scope for an electrolytic copper refinery in
southern Peru, coupled with an extension to the Ilo
smelter. Such an extension will have to be made for
Cuajone, and extra capacity should be built into it
to handle the production of other mines of the area,
if not also of those Bolivian mines that export via
Peru. The present proposals for the electrolytic
refinery are for a 125,000-ton-per-year plant at Ilo,
with Belgian technical aid and finance. Apart from
the increased earnings the country would get by these
measures, and the extra employment afforded, the nation's exports would have a more secure sale in world
markets. Concentrates can only be sold to smelters,
but refined products can be sold to any metal fabrica-
tor.

    Such projects require careful study and a large
investment. This investment should ideally be made
by Peruvians, but it is unlikely that any Peruvian
capitalist will do so. This leaves the State. Chile,
which operates on a much narrower economic base than
Peru, has State-owned (ENAMI) smelters producing
51,000 tons of blister copper yearly (more than La
Oroya) and refineries producing 84,000 tons (of which
45,000 tons from blister copper is from the Kennecott-

owned* El Teniente mine). There is no reason to
think that Peru could not do the same and come to
some agreement with the foreign companies with regard
to supplies. The financing of these projects deserves special mention as it raises some very obvious
but, nevertheless, not generally appreciated points.
Consider, for example, the proposed zinc refinery.
Suppose it can be built at a cost of $200 for every
ton of refined zinc capacity. (The figures used here
are purely for argument--no actual cost being avail-
able--and they will, of course, vary with the size
of the plant, subsidiary plants, etc.) Refining zinc
locally will earn the country's foreign exchange reserves an extra $100 per ton, so if the plant is im-
ported and paid for in U.S. dollars two to three years
after it enters into operation, it could be completely
paid for. However, the plant has costs in soles
(electricity, labor). As it earns no soles, dis-
counting side products like sulphuric acid or local
sales of zinc, it can only meet its local costs by
changing dollars into soles, at the current rate of
exchange. Suppose these local costs are the soles
equivalent to $60 per ton. If the plant is to pay
off its building costs only out of its profits, it
will take five to six years, instead of two to three.
In view of foreign interest rates alone, it is obviously desirable that the whole of the plant's dollar
earnings be used to repay the costs of construction
as fast as possible, but this implies that the government would have to meet the soles operating costs by
issuing money (as loans, gifts, printing it if necessary) without a foreign exchange backing in the central bank reserves. It will be objected that such
an issue of money would be most unorthodox, not to
say irresponsible--likely to lead to domestic infla-
tion--but is this so? What difference would the
dollars in the reserve make to domestic inflation if
they did exist as a backing to the issue? The answer
is none, unless they were bought back and used for
importing. This chain of reasoning can be followed
a long way, and will be taken up in Chapter 13, but
for the moment it is worth emphasizing two points.

---

*In process of nationalization in 1971.

The construction of a plant as a zinc refinery illustrates that "paying for the plant" in dollars and
"making a profit" domestically are two distinct concepts, only linked by the parity of the two curren-
cies. Second, if the plant operator is the State,
as opposed to a private business, it is in its power
to choose between or combine these concepts by alter-
ing exchange parities or issuing money without foreign
currency backing. Thus, two political problems are
really at the basis of the whole project: the "profitability" of nationalized enterprises, and the principle of the international monetary system known as
the "gold exchange standard."

Peru's current metal exports are worth some $450
million yearly (depending on world prices), of which
nearly $70 million are from iron. Without any in-
crease in the extraction from the mines, or, in other
words, depletion of national reserves, it should be
possible to raise earnings by nearly $35 million
simply by refining zinc and turning all the copper
to blister copper. A further $15 million could be
produced by refining lead,* refining the blister copper and recuperating the silver as bullion from these
processes. If 40 per cent of these products were
shipped in nationally registered boats, an extra $3
million could easily be raised; and when Marcona has
50 per cent of its fleet registered in Peru, the State
may gain a surprisingly large additional bonus from
taxing its profits. None of these moves could be
considered unreasonable let alone revolutionary, but
between them they could produce up to $55 million a
year—a 12-per-cent increase.

_____

*A Rumanian firm has offered to build a 40,000-
ton-per-year lead smelter.

11

MINING
INSTITUTIONS
AND
LAWS

Mining institutions fall into three main categories. The first is that of education--professional
training and professional associations. The second
is formed of all those bodies that officially regulate and supervise the industry--government departments and the legislation itself. The third category
is concerned with financing the mines--the banks.
Each of these three categories will be discussed
separately.

EDUCATION AND PROFESSIONAL
ASSOCIATIONS

It is natural to consider first the training of
the miner himself (meaning the worker, the obrero--
the term minero has often been used in Peru to sig-
nify mine owner), although, in general, he has no
formal training whatever. The Peruvian miner has
been referred to often simply as the indio, and, indeed, in the sierra miner is virtually synonymous
with Indian. This implies that the miner, through
no fault of his own, is normally not only without
formal technical education but often without any
formal education of any sort. He may well be illit-
erate in remoter parts. Younger miners, however,
will be sons or nephews of miners, born on mine

sites, educated at the primary schools of the company
and who in their later teens will go down the mine
(19 is the minimum age for under-ground work). Although he will have little formal, or no technical,
education, he will already know a lot about mining.
As a baby, he will have swung on his mother's back
as she toiled up to the pithead or tunnel entrance
bearing his father's lunch in an enamel dish (with
a lid to keep it hot) to be sent to him under-ground.
He will have climbed all over the external workings
as a boy. As a youth, he will have handled explosives making fireworks for fiestas. His whole up-
bringing will be full of legends and stories of the
mines--their superstitions, their dangers, their accidents, wonderful discoveries of lost veins, strikes,
riots, earthquakes. When he has his first job, he
only will be experiencing what he has heard of all
his life. He will learn by watching, copying and
experience. It should be pointed out here that, although his life is centered on the mines from boy-
hood, even in the grimmest accounts of colonial or
later mining in Peru there are no records of the
miner's child ever being sent under-ground (or women
either)--a situation very different from most other
countries in the world.

In the larger mines, some technical training
will be given by the company, but often this concentrates on the workers who are responsible for maintaining mechanical equipment rather than on the miner.
The miner may also receive training from the mine
engineers, although there are few who are really prepared to give a demonstration of laying a charge to
blast a difficult face as opposed merely to giving
instructions for doing it. In some parts of the
sierra where mining is not common, it may be that a
man comes to work in a mine without any previous ac-
quaintance with it. Such a man will receive his
training by working beside experienced miners from
other regions, Puno being the main exporter of itin-
erant miners. In the large mines of the coast, for
example Marcona, the situation is very different.
Here, much of the work consists of driving heavy
vehicles rather than clambering about under-ground,
and much non-Indian labor is employed. Such workers

will probably have no technical education or previous
mine experience but will have worked with civil engineering contractors.

Between the miner and the mining engineer (ingeniero de minas) are a large number of other jobs
that are not specifically concerned with mining,
such as accountants, electricians, camp police,
cooks, transporters, etc. Most of these people will
be mestizos (of mixed blood) and have basic primary
education, with secondary education for the most responsible posts. There are, of course, school teach-
ers, doctors, social workers, chief accountants, etc,
who must all have professional qualifications to
practice, and most of them will have a university
degree. Racially, these posts will be filled by
non-Indians--Negros are rare in any post in the industry. In foreign companies, these positions may be
filled partially by foreigners.

The main technical training aimed directly at
the industry is that of mining engineer. In Peru,
they graduate effectively from only one university,
the Universidad Nacional de Ingenieria (UNI), although a small university in Cerro de Pasco also
gives the title, and San Agustin, in Arequipa, plans
to follow suit. The UNI (formerly the Escuela de
Minas--see Part I) has been operating since 1876,
and until very recently its prime function was that
of a school of mines. Now, however, many other dis-
ciplines are taught. Mining students take a five-
year course of which the first two, under the new
university legislation, are common to all under-
graduates. In the third year, a sort of introduction
to specialization takes place, and during the remaining two years the student specializes in mining,
metallurgy or geology--in 1969, the fifth year
counted 15, 11 and 3 students in each discipline,
respectively. (These figures are a bit low. Normally, up to 40 students graduate yearly.) A very
wide variety of courses is offered but, unfortunately,
not always available. The UNI has great difficulty
in retaining staff as a good mining engineer can earn
two to three times the salary in the industry, without counting perquisites (housing, schools, health).

Additionally, the problems and strain of working in
a university--full of disorders and troubles, as are
most universities--does not add to its attraction as
a place to work. The student of mining, apart from
matriculation fees (nil for those in need), has to
pay for his books and his food and lodging. Limited
student accommodation is available. Scholarships
are also available for students, some provided by
the UNI, some by mining companies and some by a U.S.
charitable organization, which is to make up to 28
grants of 8,000 soles each annually ($200) on condi-
tion that 50 per cent will be repaid from earnings
on graduation. The mining companies' scholarships
are approximately 15,000 soles each, perhaps eight
from U.S. companies (Cerro de Pasco, Southern Peru)
and one from Atacocha (other Peruvian companies contribute to the charitable scheme mentioned earlier).
The students run their own system of loans and an in-
expensive book shop. Thus, the student of mining
engineering is relatively well provided for, it being
possible for almost everyone in his last two years
to have a grant if he deserves it. Only relatively
well because even a scholarship of 15,000 soles would
maintain only someone who was living at home or with
relatives in Lima. A student from the sierra who had
no relatives in Lima would need 25,000 soles yearly
to keep himself even very modestly.

The Peruvian universities mark the courses with
a complicated system of credits. Credits are given
for attendance, for practicals, for mid-term exams,
for final exams, each course having a different
quota. If the total number of marks is not sufficient, the course must be taken again. Course A may
have as an obligatory prerequisite a pass in course
B, and if course B has been failed a student's progress is severely jeopardized. By European standards,
the system is perhaps over-rigid, but in Peru it is
probably not inappropriate. All students of mining
engineering complete 12 months of practical work in
mines, three months in each of their first four
years. Sometimes, they will work during the brief
August holiday as well, often to earn money in the
mine. Apart from formal studies, the UNI contains a
good geological museum, a concentrator plant, and
the students edit a bi-annual magazine called _Minas_.

Once graduated with the proud title of _ingeniero_, the student may do further studies abroad. Perhaps five foreign scholarships are awarded yearly to the United States, United Kingdom, Belgium, etc. More likely, the graduate will look for work, which he will easily find in the national mining industry. It would be invidious to comment on the level of the graduate's ability, but even those foreigners most given to criticizing things Peruvian admit that the modern graduate in mining engineering of the UNI is much more able than in the past. Apart from natural lack of experience in any recent graduates anywhere in the world, the Peruvian mining engineer is in no way inferior to his foreign counterpart. On the other hand, the mining departments of the UNI may be criticized fairly for lack of research. In nearly 100 years' existence, no significant technical innovations have been developed, the university confining itself to teaching knowledge and methods that have largely originated in other countries. For such a mining country as Peru, this is strange, but whatever the reasons in the past a major cause now is lack of funds. Very few of the teaching staff are on full-time pay, let alone being paid for research. There is not enough money for the universities, one reason being that there are too many of them with consequent enormous overheads. In Lima alone, there are four major universities (San Marcos, UNI, La Catolica, La Agraria), without counting many minor ones, and government funds are not sufficient for them all. Under these circumstances, one wonders why the mining industry itself does not support research in some form or other in the UNI, but here a familiar problem arises--who could support it? The large U.S. companies could, of course, but U.S.-financed research would be viewed with considerable suspicion, to put it mildly, in a Peruvian university. The bigger national companies could support it, too. Half a million soles yearly would finance a small project, and this would only be .5 per cent of the value of the annual production of a 400-ton-per-day mine. Tax concessions could be got for such grants. In other countries, former students who have become prosperous in industry hasten to establish research grants, endow laboratories, etc. (their names figuring

prominently somewhere in the titles), but not in
Peru. The Peruvian capitalists, with few exceptions,
do not think in this way.

To practice his profession, the newly graduated
mining engineer must become a member of the Colegio
de Ingenieros del Peru. This is a professional body,
established by the government to look after legal
aspects, and is divided into chapters, one of which
is for mining engineers. The Colegio takes disci-
plinary action in cases of non-professional conduct,
supplies technical experts to assess the government
and expert witnesses in law cases and technical documents (contracts, etc.) must be signed by its members
to have legal validity. The engineer may also join
the Sociedad de Ingenieros del Peru, a social society
with club rooms, which occasionally publishes a review called Informaciones y Memorias. He will more
probably join the Instituto de Ingenieros de Minas.
The Instituto is a dynamic technical society, pub-
lishing a review (Mineria) every two months or so
and holding an important Convencion every two years,
to which come many foreign delegates. The Instituto
has as members over 150 of the 300 to 400 mining
engineers in Peru.

In addition to the mining engineers, the university trains another group of professionals almost exclusively for the mines--i.e., geologists. The
oldest geological school is that of San Marcos, from
which some 25 geologists graduate yearly. The university suffers from all the staff and financial
problems of the UNI and, consequently, its work is
seriously handicapped. The students take a five-
year course, and almost 90 per cent of them go
straight to the mines on finishing. There is now an
active demand for geologists from the industry, the
old idea that a mining engineer was sufficient being
abandoned. Cerro de Pasco, in particular, employs a
large number in prospecting. Some students go to
the petroleum industry, some get scholarships abroad
(Mexico and Chile now offer them) and some go to
government departments (geological survey, road building). Besides San Marcos, even more geologists
graduate from San Agustin in Arequipa--perhaps 40

yearly, and a few, as mentioned earlier, come from
the UNI. Some confusion exists over the geologists'
professional qualifications, and San Marcos gives
academic degrees (bachelor and doctor) as well as
professional ones (<u>ingeniero geologo</u>). This confusion is reflected in the professional societies.
Most geologists, including foreigners, belong to the
Asociacion de Geologos, which they would regard as
their professional body, but the State officially
recognizes the more recent Capitulo de Ingenieros
Geologos of the Colegio. Thus, many doctors of geology are now trying to get the (inferior) title of
ingeniero geologo. The geologists have a scientific
society called the Sociedad de Geologia, which, unfortunately, is not now as active as it has been.
It publishes a <u>Boletín</u> occasionally, containing
scientific articles, and the Asociacion de Geologos
runs geological weeks with lectures and visits (Arequipa, 1969).

Besides mining engineers and geologists, there
are one or two other careers closely linked with the
mines. San Marcos and other universities train law-
yers in mining law, and there is an associated Instituto Nacional de Derecho de Mineria y Petroleo
with some 120 individual members, which publishes a
bi-annual journal. Chemical engineers from the UNI
are, on the other hand, frequently employed in the
concentrator plants of the mines.

The foregoing associations are essentially professional or scientific and are linked to careers
and degrees provided by the universities of Peru.
Apart from them are two other societies that represent the industry--the mining companies. The first
is the Sociedad Nacional de Mineria y Petroleo,
which is comprised of all the major companies together with suppliers and some individual members.
It is some 65 years old and produces a <u>Boletín</u> every
two months, besides fortnightly and monthly statis-
tical leaflets for its members. A yearly publication
<u>Perú Minero</u> is also edited. The society exists, of
course, to defend its members' interests and may be
called a pressure group. It can be counted on to
pronounce on new legislation and government measures

and maintains a few full-time paid research staff to
back its arguments with the necessary statistics. A
similar body concerned with the small mines is the
Sociedad Progreso de la Pequena Mineria, which has
nearly 400 members and also produces a <u>Boletín Minero</u>
every two months. Many of these members are, in
fact, national owners of medium-sized mines, and it
may fairly be said that the society represents the
Peruvian mine owner, whereas the Sociedad Nacional
includes foreign mines and suppliers whose aims and
political tenets are not always identical. The small
miners listed as society members mostly live in Lima,
although there are some in Puno, Trujillo, Cajamarca,
etc., and it is probably not as representative as it
would like to be--for obvious reasons, some small
miners living in such remote spots and being relatively too unsophisticated for the society.

As will be appreciated, there is no shortage of
societies and bodies for defending the interests of
the industry or its members. Nor is there a shortage
of journals, and there are often very interesting
articles published. Nevertheless, one could criti-
cize the societies on one or two points. For example,
reverting to a former theme, it is odd that between
them no schemes are run to finance research, give
scholarships for special studies, endow a university
chair, etc. It is also a pity that, considering its
mining history, there is no public mining museum in
Peru. Despite the existence of some affiliated
groups (e.g., of the Instituto de Ingenieros de Minas
in Cerro de Pasco, La Oroya, Toquepala), the organi-
zations are all very centralized in Lima and they can
only be used by mining engineers on leave. One would
think that a gathering place with a small restaurant,
library and lecture room in, say, Huancayo would be
very welcome, but none exists. Finally, the most
striking omission is that of a national miners'
union (for the mine laborers). Unions are only organized at the mine level, and their importance will
be discussed in Chapter 12.

GOVERNMENT AND LEGISLATION

Since 1969, mining matters are handled by the newly created Ministerio de Energia y Minas, having previously belonged to the Ministerio de Fomento y Obras Publicas. The Minister (under the revolutionary government a member of the armed forces, the present one being General Jorge Fernandez Maldonado S.) is advised by a Director Superior, under whom are three main departments, one of which is the Direccion General de Mineria with its own departmental director. The Minister is also advised by various consultative bodies, the mining one being the Consejo Superior de Mineria. The Consejo is comprised of seven ex officio members (the Minister himself, Director Superior, etc.) and six others elected by the major mining institutions (Sociedad Nacional de Mineria, etc.) or professional groups (Departmento de Minas of the UNI, etc.).

The main organization handling day-to-day affairs is the Direccion General de Mineria. Under it come the 15 Jefaturas Regionales de Mineria in Arequipa, Ayacucho, Cerro de Pasco, Cajamarca, Cuzco, Huaraz, Huancavelica, Huancayo, Huanuco, Ica, Lima, Piura, Puna, Tacna and Trujillo. These register all claims, supply technicians to verify their validity and exact situation and handle, in the first instance, all problems of their areas--disputes, accidents, projects. The definitive register of all concessions is kept in the Direccion General. (This sensible system has grown directly out of the Diputados and Tribunal de Mineria of the colonial Nuevas Ordenanzas de México). The total number of people employed in mining administration in the ministry is less than 200. Under the Direccion General also comes the Servicio de Geologia y Mineria, which provides two important services. The first of these is the geological map of Peru. Various previous maps of a general nature have been produced since Steinmann and Lisson's of 1924, the most important of which is Bellido and Simons' of 1955, and, of course, mining or academic studies of limited areas have existed for a long time (Rivero made a geological

map of Cerro de Pasco in 1827). However, the present
project whereby the country is divided into half-a-
degree squares, which are systematically being mapped
on a 1:100,000 or 1:200,000 scale, is the first attempt at a detailed map of Peru. The work is going
ahead fast with the help of British and French geologists, and in 1969 over half of the non-jungle area
of Peru was either under study or already published.
The second service is that of geological consultancy
to the mines, and also of mineralogical advice, etc.
The Servicio also has a good library that is open to
the public.

The Direccion General de Mineria exists to exe-
cute and supervise the observance of the rulings of
the mining legislation, the 1950 Código de Minería.
It is clearly not possible to analyze in detail such
an important piece of legislation here, and all that
will be attempted is a rough sketch of its contents
together with a discussion of some controversial
items. Moreover, the Código de Minería is due to be
replaced in 1971 by a new Ley General de Minería,
the basic outline of which was given in 1970.

The Código de Minería is firmly rooted in Peruvian traditional mining law, whose landmarks have
already been stated to be Toledo's 1574 legislation,
the Nuevas Ordenanzas de México (applied to Peru in
1786), the 1877 temporary legislation and the 1900
Código de Minería. The 1950 Código de Minería opens
with the statement that the mineral substances belong
to the State, but that anyone is free to prospect for
them. The State may give concessions to exploit
mines, certain people (particularly public officials)
being ineligible as concessionaires. The Código de
Minería then follows with articles concerning the
dimensions of concessions and the concessionaire's
rights. An important section detailing the concessionaire's obligations comes next, which contains the
canon (tax) he must pay (50 soles per hectare per
year for all metaliferous concessions except gold--
for which he must pay 4.50 soles) and the much dis-
puted, altered and sometimes abrogated clauses on
the sobre-canon (supplementary tax or fine) for non-
exploitation after five years' possession (Article

51), tax concessions for depletion (Article 54) and
the signing of special contracts with the government
for marginal mines (Article 56). Then come various
sections about the lapsing of concessions (owing to
non-payment of canon or sobre-canon), the freedom of
the State to exploit its own mines as it sees fit,
the register of concessions, the official organization (Direccion General de Mineria, etc.) and all
the procedures for staking a claim and getting a concession, including cases of opposition. The last
major section (Chapter 4) considers mining contracts,
laying down norms for forming mining companies, for
transferring the ownership of concessions, for regulating loans, mortgages and pledges in the industry,
etc. The Código de Minería closes with some rulings
about its initial enforcement and the destination of
funds arising from the various charges and fines mentioned beforehand. The essence of the legislation,
one may say, is that anyone (Peruvian or foreign) may
stake a claim and own a concession, provided he pays
certain (small) dues and charges. He is obliged to
observe safety rules and labor legislation, he is
encouraged by various financial incentives and he is
fined for not working the concession.

Controversy has arisen from the clauses that affect the State's revenue in the exploitation of concessions, and it is fair to say that if there were
no foreign companies working Peruvian mines such controversy might never have arisen. It is generally
believed by the public that the foreign companies
are not paying Peru (i.e., the State), or at any rate
used not to pay, fairly for what they have gained
themselves from mining. This controversy has not
focused on the territorial canon (even a 1,000-hec-
tare concession only pays some $1,250 yearly) but on
the tax paid by the big companies, so it is necessary
to sketch the Peruvian tax system.

Taxation on mining companies is levied on their
profits, and in 1969 the main rate (for profits above
500,000 soles yearly) was 35 per cent. In addition,
all Peruvian companies had to pay a 25-per-cent tax
on the net profit (i.e., on 65 per cent) for all
dividends they paid out, by way of an advance on the

shareholder's personal taxation. Foreign companies
similarly had to pay 30 per cent (making a total tax
of 54.5 per cent), as it was presumed that all their
profits went in dividends to shareholders or holding
companies abroad. All exporters paid a 4-per-cent
export tax on the f.o.b. value of their minerals,
which was only an advance toward their profit tax,
the balance of which fell due on March 30 of the
next year. Thus, the crux of the matter is, what
were the profits? Profits are earnings (normally
f.o.b., but the company may export on its own account) less costs, depreciation, amortization, interest payments and, in the past, depletion. The books
must be kept in soles. Depreciation is allowed at a
maximum rate of 3 per cent on buildings and constructions, and on machinery according to its useful life--
although the mines would like this according to the
mine's life, as they claim it is often impracticable
to move old equipment out from remote and exhausted
mines. Amortization is on development (exploratory,
mine preparation) expenses and is charged per ton of
ore extracted. Depletion was to cover the exhaustion
of the mine reserves and used to be similarly charged.
Interest payments on borrowed capital pay 40 per cent
if paid abroad--e.g., to the parent company of a foreign mining company--but are otherwise tax free.
These have been the main profit tax rulings--there
were, of course, minor variations on them. However,
the actual rates of taxation on profits were altered
in 1970.

    The first cause for discussion was depletion.
The theory behind depletion presumably ran as follows: When a mining company is formed, various people
join together, some of whom contribute capital in the
form of cash, others in the form of the mine reserves.
Shares are issued in accordance with the capital paid
up, and the cash capital is invested in, say, machinery and preparatory work, which are later written
off in depreciation and amortization. In the same
sense, the mine capital (the reserves) is written off
in depletion, tax being charged on the net profit after these deductions and the shareholders rewarded
with the remains. However, in a country where it is
the basis of the Mining Code that the State owns the

mines, it is the State that contributes the mine
capital and one might logically expect that the State
be issued with shares, or at least be paid rather
than penalized for the exhaustion of the mine. In
fact, after innumerable public discussions, depletion
was effectively abolished. It existed in name still
until 1970, but it functioned as an investment allowance. Depletion, up to the lesser of 15 per cent of
the value of the concentrates at the mine and one
third of the tax-payable profit (before deducing depletion), was allowed only if re-invested produc-
tively within three years. In practice, some 10 per
cent of the gross value of the sales of a company
would be re-invested tax free in this way. In 1970,
mine depletion allowances were eliminated and Article
54 abrogated.

The second controversy centered on Article 56,
the granting of special contracts (with tax concessions) to marginal operations with heavy capital investment. It could be argued with reason that this
article should never have existed and in 1970 it,
too, was abrogated. It applied only to foreign companies in practice, and none of them mined marginal
deposits by international standards; the "risk" that
they wished to ensure against was not the unprofit-
ability of the mine but rather the political "risk"
of investing in Peru. The original Article 56 was
not precise, but essentially it fixed lower profits
taxes until the investment should be recovered. This
gave rise to the row with the Southern Peru Copper
Corporation, which continued paying the lower taxation two years after many people claimed it had recovered its investment. Article 56 was then amended
to specify more clearly how the recuperation of the
investment was to be determined and to fix a minimum
total tax of 40 per cent for foreign companies bene-
fiting from such contracts. On the other hand, accelerated depreciations were permitted, the compulsory
re-investment of depletion was suspended, tax stability was guaranteed for six years after the end of
the contract and investment allowances made for five
years after. The law was, in short, drawn up to attract the investor by various concessions, and there
was grave danger that a weak government might hand

away more and more to get the prospective miner to
start exploiting his mine. However, the ability to
sign special contracts does have certain advantages--
as evidenced in the case of the Homestake Mining Company, which as a counterpart to the tax concessions
agreed to spend 60 per cent of its $10-million in-
vestment in Peru. Without a special contract, there
are no legal means whereby the percentage of the investment spent on Peruvian goods and services may be
controlled--other than by indirect taxation on imports. Article 56, as it stood, also guaranteed the
availability of foreign exchange for re-exporting the
recuperated investment and subsequent profits, and
disputes arose as to whether this should be within
the exchange certificate system or not. The article
referred to enlargement of existing plants as well
as to opening new mines.

The third debated article was number 51. Originally, it read that if, after five years, the concessionaire could not show that he spent more than
50 soles per hectare per year, a sobre-canon equal
to the canon would be charged (and allowed against
future taxes on profits). As the Código de Minería
explicitly concedes concessions only for exploration
(up to five years) or exploitation (indefinite), but
not for sitting on, Article 51 as it originally
stood was a very ineffective means of penalizing
those who did not work the mines. It was later
changed (1965 and 1966) to give a five years' grace
period from June, 1965, after which the sobre-canon
would be introduced starting at four times the canon
and doubling every year, and the criterion as to
whether a mine was being worked was that its annual
production should exceed one sixtieth of its reserves.
However, new legislation in 1969 gave the large mining companies until the start of 1970 to put forward
a schedule for exploiting their unworked mines, and
this had to start in March or April, 1970, and be
duly followed under penalty of losing the concession
altogether. This move, for various reasons, is
highly salutory: Many large mines have been unworked
for decades, although fully explored and the reserves
known (Cerro Verde since 1917); the holding of
unworked mines is against the wording of the law and

the whole tradition of Peruvian mining; and, most
important, the companies were using their position
as potential investors to blackmail the government
into granting concessions under Article 56. The
1965-1966 legislation would not have started to bite
until 1972 or 1973. Under the new law, almost all
the unworked copper deposits, Cuajone excepted, had
reverted to the State by the start of 1971.

It is worth pointing out that these controversial points illustrate well the colonial legal heri-
tage in the mining industry. Depletion was objected
to on logical grounds--the mine does not belong to
the concessionaire but to the State (the Crown). The
facility to grant special contracts has existed since
the very first days of the conquest, Charles V charging tenths instead of fifths on certain mines while
they were still developing. The non-exploitation of
mines was penalized by the concession being confiscated from Toledo's first legislation onward.

Before leaving the subject of taxation, it
should be added that the mining industry is allowed
reduced import taxes on articles necessary for working the mine that are not available in Peru. These
taxes average perhaps 35 per cent of their f.o.b.
value in the port of embarkation. On other items,
taxation could average 100 per cent. After the 1967
devaluation, a temporary export tax of 10 per cent
was introduced, which--such was the outcry--was immediately turned into a profits tax advance, and
later further softened in various ways (e.g., it was
not payable if certain government bonds were bought
with it). Finally, the industry pays certain special
dues, apart from the canon, for official services--
inscription of concessions in registers, official
recognition of concession boundaries on site, etc.

The 1970 legislation also created the State-
owned company Minero Peru. It is intended that this
company shall handle the large mining operations that
in the past would have been in foreign hands. In
particular, Minero Peru is responsible for the concessions that have reverted to the State for failing
to comply with Article 51 or the more recent legisla-

tion. The two most likely to be immediately tackled
are Cerro Verde (exploitation) and Quellaveco (exploration). A further provision in the new legislation is for the State commercialization of mineral
products and State ownership (Minero Peru) of all
future refining plants. It also appears that the
ambitious new industrial legislation is to be extended to the mining industry, creating worker participation in the capital and the running of mining
companies--forming thereby the Communidad Minera.

It remains to discuss very briefly the special
passages in the mining legislation that refer to the
small miners (pequenos mineros). Various clauses in,
and modifications to, the Mining Code have allowed
small miners lower canones (20 soles), freedom from
import duties and reduced official charges (e.g.,
for advertising claims in El Peruano, the official
newspaper). A small miner was defined as having less
than 1,000 hectares of concessions and producing less
than 1,000 tons per month, the value of that production being less than 500,000 soles. In 1969, radical
new legislation was introduced defining them, broadly
speaking, as producing less than 10 million soles
yearly and more than 100,000 or 500,000 for concessions less than 300 and 1,000 hectares, respectively--
i.e., a minimum production is required, corresponding
to less than half a ton a day. Apart from incentives
on the lines of the former ones, but better, the new
law also permits rapid depreciation of equipment (up
to 100 per cent yearly), permits investment allowances (depletion may be invested in housing workers),
sets up a financing fund and authorizes the Banco
Minero to increase its lending to small miners and,
finally, grants special additional tax concessions
to those working in new and remote areas. The law
should prove a powerful stimulus, perhaps more to
the enterprising mining engineer who sets up on his
own than to the sierra Indian, and it should also
discourage bogus small miners who do not achieve the
minimum production levels (e.g., at Hualgayoc), as,
apparently, their canon and sobre-canon are to be
the same as for the big mines.

CAPITAL FOR THE MINES

A commercial mining company may seek finances from five main sources: the export houses, the commercial banks, the Banco Minero, the stock market or from abroad.

It has been stated in Chapter 10 that the annual purchases of concentrates and minerals by the export houses amount to some $60 million, or 2,500 million soles. A small proportion of this sum may be regarded as finance in the form of advances to the producers. Essentially, such advances are short term but loans against future production (avios) can be for up to two years. Longer-term loans may well lead to the lender establishing an interest in the mining company, and there are various such cases, facilitated by the fact that some of the exporters are mine owners in their own right. Unfortunately, it is not possible to say what percentage of the above total purchase figure could be considered as loans for investment, but it is almost certainly very small. New legislation obliging the export houses to make annual reports detailing their operations should lead to some clarification of their role as financiers, which is at present kept very secret owing to competition between them. Their potential is clearly relatively big.

The commerical banks are relatively unimportant sources of capital. In 1969, loans to the mining industry stood at some 180 million soles, which represented 1 per cent of their total loans and less than 5 per cent of the annual production of the nationally owned mines alone. A policy of selective credit designed to favor the mines, among other industries, has been introduced by the military government, so this situation may change. At the moment, the commercial banks are probably not technically equipped to assess mining investments. A single case will serve as illustration. The San Juan de Lucanas mine had as shareholders members of the Wiese

family and also had borrowed money from the Banco
Wiese. Because of mismanagement, the mine ran into
financial trouble and got a 10-million-soles loan
from the Banco Minero to pay off surplus labor and
invest in mine preparation. At the same time, the
member of the Wiese family most interested and capable in mining matters died. The mine foundered
further, 4 million of the 10 million soles are alleged
to have been used to pay off the debt to the Banco
Wiese (instead of to prepare the mine), and the Banco
Minero took control of the mine, auctioned it off to
recover their own debt, but not finding a buyer
started to operate it successfully on their own account. The former owners took an action against the
Banco Minero. Such a story does not reflect credit
on the mining experience of the commercial banks and
does not encourage them much in further activities
in that field.

The Banco Minero has, since the mid-1960's,
grown into the most important source of domestic finance for the mining industry. The Banco was founded
in 1942 and until 1964 led a very tranquil existence,
but since then has blossomed into activity, its loans
to the industry growing at up to 50 per cent per
annum. In 1969, they were 888 million soles: 315
soles on medium and long term; 143 soles, short term;
390 soles, indirect loans (discounts, etc.); 40 soles
being under recovery by legal action. Besides supplying finance, the Banco buys and sells minerals
(5 million soles worth yearly); operates two concentrator plants, one in Hualgayoc the other in Huachocolpa, and administers a third in Catac (three others
have been sold to former clients who have grown);
maintains a research laboratory in Callao; gives
technical assistance and loans from subsidiaries in
Huaraz, Huancayo, Juliaca, Nazca and Trujillo; and
supplies mining equipment to small miners. The Banco
is also in charge of the financial studies for the
proposed zinc refinery. On its total loans, the
Banco Minero charges an average of 6 to 7 per cent,
but it is empowered to give 5-per-cent loans to small
miners (loosely defined as those without, or with a
very small, concentrator) up to a total not exceeding
1.5 million soles. There is no doubt at all that the

Banco has served to set many small miners on their
feet, an example being the famous Millotingo silver
mine, which initially used the Tonsuyoc concentrator
that it has since bought from the Banco. Financially, the Banco Minero draws its resources from an
approximate 1-per-cent export tax on all minerals
and concentrates. In 1968, for example, this represented about 140 million soles, 80 per cent going to
increase the Banco's capital and 20 per cent to the
profit-and-loss account. Since this latter account
also receives 25 per cent of last year's profits
(75 per cent being capitalized or put to reserves),
the year's operations frequently show an agreeable
profit--which is satisfactory for silencing those
critics who maintain that State institutions are always inefficient. Without these subsidies to the
industry (after all, they are the purpose of the
Banco), losses would be made. It also benefits from
cheap (4 per cent) rediscount facilities at the Banco
Central de Reserva. In short, the Banco, besides
serving the mining community well, gives the appearance of a profitable business, when in reality it is
subsidizing the less-favored members of the industry--
as it should be. There is still much scope for its
growth. A medium-sized mine such as Madrigal, which
is to treat 500 tons per day, required an investment
of 400 million soles in 1969. By its statutes, the
Banco is forbidden to lend more than 10 per cent of
its effective capital, which in 1969 was about 600
million soles, to a single client--so even at an annual growth rate of 50 per cent, it will be 1973 before it can finance any other than smallish projects.
It is a much smaller enterprise than its Chilean
counterpart, ENAMI. Organizationally, the Banco depends indirectly on the Ministerio de Energia y Minas.
It employs under 400 people.

Of the 40-odd national mining companies, only
nine are quoted on the Lima stock exchange, the Bolsa.
Their total share capital is 427 million soles, much
less than the Banco Minero's loans, and much of this
has not been subscribed directly but arisen through
the capitalization of profits or revaluation of fixed
assets after devaluations of the sol. Despite the
pre-tax profits of 50 per cent (without counting

depletion) on total operating costs, which some of
the quoted companies can show, there is very little
activity in their shares. In general, the shares,
although quoted, are only sold in large blocks and
are held by very few people. The small saver, in
fact, cannot buy mining shares--or, indeed, hardly
any shares at all--and no encouragement is given to
him to do so. An interesting article in the Bolsa's
monthly publication maintains that one of the many
reasons for the lack of activity on the exchange (it
meets for only 15 minutes daily) is the lack of public confidence in the Sociedad Anonima (S.A.), the
limited company, which is not obliged to report its
activities in sufficient detail and is often controlled by a few powerful shareholders. Since there
exists no legal machinery for forming Sociedades de
Responsibilidad Limitada (private companies) in Peru,
it is not possible to legislate adequately for public
companies without affecting every business in the
country that calls itself "S.A.," which would be
ridiculous. Despite all the difficulties of the
stock market, it is surprising that the foreign companies have not raised, or been forced to raise,
some of their capital there. None of them are
quoted, the absence of that Peruvianized institution,
Cerro de Pasco, being particularly noticeable. In
1970, however, Northern Peru considered floating a
$25-million debenture in Peru for Michiquillay--a
sum two-and-a-half times greater than the total capital in mining shares already mentioned--but nothing
came of this project.

The fifth source of finance is foreign and is
for importing equipment. For replacing relatively
low-value equipment (e.g., rock drills), only very
short-term loans are available, and these, as has
been said, are often advanced by the export houses.
The Banco Minero, for example, finances some $4-
million worth of imports of this sort yearly. However, larger capital equipment--over $100,000--is
often financed by the seller who may give 80 per cent
credit over five years. Such credit is given against
a bank guarantee and is only offered to an established mine whose dollar earnings are a good security.
It is very hard to say how much capital expenditure

is made by a mine on imported goods, as the figure
fluctuates greatly and the classification of what
are capital goods is uncertain, but a figure of $15
million yearly should give an order of magnitude.
(A further $5 million to $15 million may be spent
locally, either paying cash or with credits from the
Banco Minero and commercial banks.) If credit for
importing capital goods is taken as up to five years,
at any given time the mining industry may be expected
to be indebted abroad for such items for $20 million
to $30 million—a figure agreeing with those given
by the Banco Central de Reserva. Total spending on
capital equipment would appear to be well within the
former depletion allowance for the industry as a
whole. In other words, for normal plant or mine expansion—for the purposes of internal bookkeeping—
if pre-depletion profits were large enough the depletion allowance was large enough. In some cases,
e.g., Southern Peru, the depletion allowance proved
excessive, and failing to find a productive enterprise to invest its money the company applied to pay
tax on it and export it as profits instead.

When it comes to opening a new mine, the situation is very different. For the foreign company,
foreign finance has usually been sought—finance to
the order of hundreds of millions of dollars. Even
they have had difficulties in getting such finance
at high interest rates, and as the Eximbank of the
United States frequently plays a role, political considerations also intervene. Cerro de Pasco has
sought capital by mergers, a proposed one with Beth-
lehem Steel being prohibited on anti-trust grounds.
At the moment, a tendency to use Japanese or European
finance is discernible. The Peruvian mining company,
except for the disastrous case of Panamerican Commodities, does not apply for and would not get foreign finance to start a new mine. Between the Banco
Minero and the commercial banks, $1 million or even
$2 million might be raised by a single company, but
the other sources of capital—the export houses and
the stock market—would almost certainly not be
forthcoming unless the mine owner were prepared to
surrender his control. Where is the owner to a concession to be worked at 100 tons daily or more to
get his capital? Where indeed?

CONCLUSION

Briefly commenting on the three themes treated, it can be said that in the Peruvian mining industry training and professional matters are fairly well organized, those of the miner/worker excepted; that the State bodies and legislation are impressive and very much on the move; and that the capital market is inadequate and obscure.

12

THE

MINING INDUSTRY

IN

THE ECONOMY

It is the purpose of this chapter to analyze the influence of the mining industry on the Peruvian economy. Chapter 13 is devoted to a discussion of national policy concerning the mining industry based on the present analysis.*

---

*The figures used are only approximate, but, it is hoped, not too much so. They are largely based on statistics in the <u>Boletín</u> of the Banco Central de Reserva, the <u>Reseña Económica y Financiera</u> of the same institution, the <u>Anuario de la Industria Minera del Perú</u>, <u>La Minería en el Perú</u>, the Peru/Bolivia review of the Economist Intelligence Unit and such information as it has been possible to acquire from the mining companies themselves, from their suppliers and from the buyers of their products. Really precise data is not available, and if it were so it is doubtful how meaningful it would be, given the instability of even this relatively stable industry. An example: in 1968, the imports of capital goods for mining fell 38 per cent (<u>Reseña Económica y Financiera</u>) as a result of the 1967 devaluation. If the big copper projects go ahead, they will rise several hundred per cent. The purpose of the figures is to indicate the relative importance of the item discussed.

THE INDUSTRY AS A BUYER

The industry spends annually about 4,000 million
soles ($100 million) on goods and services. This is
2 per cent of total demand, which even at fixed
(1963) prices has $\pm$ 5 per cent annual fluctuations.
Perhaps 20 to 30 per cent of this expenditure is on
capital equipment, the remaining 70 to 80 per cent
being on explosives, tires, plastic raincoats, nails,
cement, etc.--all the thousand and one (or better,
several tens of thousands) items that the industry
consumes. There is a marked tendency recently for
the proportion of imported goods and services to
fall, a tendency owed largely to a buy-Peruvian campaign run by Cerro de Pasco. (It should be pointed
out that the larger foreign mines, in 1967, still
used 70 per cent of their spending for importing,
while the medium and smaller mines used less than
30 per cent.) Total imports for the mining industry
may tentatively be put at $50 million--some 12 per
cent of the foreign exchange value of the industry's
own exports, and some 7 per cent of Peru's total imports. Thus, as a buyer the industry is not very
significant, and even as an importer, where its share
is larger, its importance is decreasing.

Nevertheless, certain aspects of the mines' expenditure on goods and services are sufficiently important to deserve underlining. The first group is
roughly that of metal products (iron and steel) and
comprises flotation cells, ball mills (and balls for
them), conveyor systems, storage bins, grinders and
crushers. Most of this machinery is fairly easily
manufactured, and there are some half dozen works in
Lima and Callao equipped with machines for bending,
cutting and making angles in steel plates out of
which they can construct almost anything required.
Pieces that have to be founded are often sub-con-
tracted to two or three big foundries (Fundicion
Callao, MEPSA) or a greater number of small work-
shops. The design of the equipment is frequently a
copy. A mine asks for replacements for the broken
roller system of a conveyor belt, the designer measures it up and draws it, the replacement is made and

soon the factory can offer a whole conveyor belt system based on the design. The orders given by the
mines are an important influence in the development
and diversification of such a basic industry as metal
founding and fabricating.

The value of orders given in this field vary
wildly. A smallish concentrator plant costs 20 million soles, so three orders one year and none another
causes a $1.5-million change. The effect of an eco-
nomic squeeze on other buyers of metal products is
tragically apparent. In 1969, one of the largest
foundries (two electric-arc furnaces, two induction,
one petroleum and a small blast furnace) was almost
idle for want of orders--an incomprehensible state
of affairs in a country so much in need of capital
equipment and where so many people are under-employed.
This distressing waste of material and human resources is one of the characteristics of an under-
developed country, and it is one advantage of the
mining industry that its prosperity does not depend
on domestic conditions but on world prices, so it
can continue placing orders when others cannot.
(The concomitant of this is, of course, the effect
of external depressions on domestic demand.) In this
respect, it is sad to see that Cerro de Pasco and
Southern Peru (with others) set up their own foundry,
MEPSA, to which their orders preferentially go. In
particular, MEPSA supplies a large part of the 250-
million soles annual market for balls and linings
for ball mills--its two mining owners must guarantee
it nearly 90 per cent.

The steel plates are imported, national supplies
not yet being available for the market, while the
iron and steel for founding are from scrap or Chimbote. Imported steel costs in 1969 were $171 per
ton c.i.f. Callao.

An important aspect of the mines' purchases is
that part done locally in the sierra, on timber, for
example, or indirectly, on food. In 1967, 76 million
soles were spent on timber, 80 per cent of which was
national. What is spent locally out of wages must
be at least ten times that figure, and its effect on

remote rural areas can be imagined. In Caylloma,
for example, ten hours on a shocking road from Arequipa, the mine spends locally, directly or indirectly, 30 million soles per year. The effect on stock-
raising alone is considerable. In central Peru, the
Cerro de Pasco Corporation decided to enter this
field on its own account, partly owing to complaints
about land poisoning by La Oroya's fumes, and un-
wisely bought about 300,000 hectares of rough grazing.
This has since been confiscated under the agrarian
reform.

Perhaps the most spectacular demonstration of
the extended influence of the mines is to be seen in
transport. A considerable number of the roads in
Peru owe, if not their construction, at any rate
their maintenance and survival almost entirely to
the mines. An excellent new road to Cobriza from
Pampas (five hours) is a recent example, but others
have been built in the past (e.g., Quiruvilca to
Pasto Bueno), and whenever a mud slide occurs it is
always the mine at the end of the road that is the
first to send bulldozers to clear the passage for
themselves and everyone else. The mines, or the
transport contractors they employ, are also responsible for importing a large number of trucks and
pick-ups, which sooner or later serve a wider public.*
The very large mines excepted, the industry or its
contractors perhaps spend $3 million to $5 million
annually on these vehicles. Cerro de Pasco has a
large fleet of its own and uses contractors, but re-
lies principally on the railway, (which would probably close without it); Southern Peru uses its own
private railway and, like Marcona, special heavy
trucks for the mine. In Marcona's case, it got permission to re-export to Australia a fleet of unwanted
dump trucks (exporting vehicles, regarded as capital
goods, is generally prohibited) as, apparently, they
were of no use to anyone else--an instance of the
isolation of the really big mines, whose old equipment is frequently fit only for scrap.

———————————

*New legislation has granted Volvo a monopoly in
truck manufacturing in Peru.

The mines also consume a certain number of products made almost exclusively for them. Reagents for
concentrator plants, valuing $3.4 million yearly,
are largely imported; only lime, copper sulphate and
zinc sulphate being made locally. The two U.S.
firms, Cyanamid and Dow Chemical, who dominate the
market, have no plans for manufacturing in Peru.
The necessary raw materials, although simply made,
are not available, and the market is said to be too
small. The tax concession given to the mines for importing these necessary products thus works nega-
tively in the sense that it reduces the incentive to
manufacture locally. Explosives, on the other hand,
are largely local. Perhaps half of the $5-million
market represents AMFO, made at the mines, the remainder being dynamite--95 per cent manufactured in
one factory near Lima. Cerro de Pasco and other
mines, plus German and Belgian companies, have a
stake in this factory. Another Peruvian factory in
Arequipa blew up with horrible loss of life in 1969.

Finally, the mines represent a $2- to $3-million
market yearly for power generating equipment. The
437-megawatt installed capacity is more than 50 per
cent hydroelectric, Cerro de Pasco's enormous 190-
megawatt plant dominating. The company sells energy
to neighboring mines, but, in general, mines build
to supply their own needs and have none to spare for
other mines or villages. This somewhat anti-social
attitude is undoubtedly owed to the scarcity of
water. There are very many mines in the sierra that
have to cut production between August and October,
and often they will maintain a stand-by diesel set
for these occasions. Diesel capacity is 58 megawatts, but running costs are high. Two soles per
kilowatt hour is typical, the cost of transporting
the fuel being an important contribution, and the
engines must be uprated 20 to 40 per cent for the
altitude. Diesel capacity is replaced or increased
15 per cent per annum, entirely with imported equipment. Fuel and oil for all purposes costs the industry some $3 million a year. In Ilo and Marcona,
electricity is generated from steam turbines.

In the national economy, the spending by the
mines is not very significant but locally, in the

sierra, it can be decisive in keeping an area economically alive. The industry's relative impervious-
ness to domestic recessions makes it a factor of
stability for those industries who sell to it, but
it is a pity that the large companies, Cerro de Pasco
in particular, have only partially resisted the temptation to secure their own supplies, thereby vitiating
this useful function. However, that company has recently started a healthy buy-Peruvian campaign,
holding exhibitions of the company's needs to stimulate national industrialists. It is probable that,
not considering spending on the major new mines, the
mining industry's import bill can be reduced $10 mil-
lion to $20 million without overtaxing Peruvian in-
dustry.

THE INDUSTRY AS AN EMPLOYER

Of the 3.7 million people economically active
in Peru, the metal-mining industry employs 45,000 to
50,000--less than 1.5 per cent. For what the figure
is worth, the average pay is about 60,000 soles
yearly or over 160 soles per day--a very good figure
by Peruvian standards. However, this average con-
ceals a vast range of variations from the huge salaries of foreign executives to the 40 or 50 soles that
the miners may get in remoter parts of the sierra.

Considering first the miners/workers: They number some 40,000, slightly over half of whom are actually in the mines, the remainder working in the
concentrator plants, administration, generating
plants and a not insignificant proportion (3,000) in
the smelters and refineries. Pay in the large mines
is better than in the small ones, but the main dis-
tinction is really between pay in the big coastal
mines (Toquepala, Marcona), which was in 1967 nearly
70,000 soles per year per man, and pay in the sierra.
In the sierra, wages for the same year were from
17,000 soles in Huancavelica and Puno to nearly
40,000 soles in Pasco. These differentials reflect
the productivity of the workers (much higher in the
mechanized big mines), the wealth of the mines and,
to some degree, the competition for labor between

them--it is not possible to pay really low wages in
Pasco and Junin owing to the large number of mines
in that area.

How are wages agreed upon? In each mine, the
workers form a union (sindicato), and every year
wage claims are made, resulting typically in 10-per-
cent increases--whose real value is difficult to
assess as the cost of living rises very unsteadily
and is, in any case, only calculated for Lima-Callao.
However, most people would agree that real wages and
living conditions do improve from year to year in
the industry, albeit not as fast as might be desired.
The unions, in general, work independently of each
other. They are organized by the workers themselves
and meet in out-of-work hours. There are no paid
officials. Their bargaining power is tied tightly
to local conditions of employment, and their wage increases depend to a considerable degree on the social
conscience of the management. In many parts, the
miners also own small-holdings (chacras) and the
whole labor force disappears at seed-time and harvest,
so in the better-run small mines a fair amount of
mutual tolerance is required between manager and
workers. In the big mines of the center or the
coast, the situation is different. The workers'
small-holdings, if they have any, are left to the
care of sons or brothers, and the unions are more
organized. For instance, there are 14 unions in the
Cerro de Pasco company and they work more or less in
harmony. More or less, since 12 belong to the Confederacion de Trabajadores del Peru (CTP), a group
controlled by Alianza Popular Revolucionana Ameri-
cana (APRA), officially recognized and given to mod-
eration in its demands. Its leaders are trained in
Lima at a school financed by the big mines and in
contact with North American unions--and, some say,
the CIA. The two remaining unions belong to the un-
official Confederacion General de Trabajadores del
Peru (CGTP), a much more radical (some would say
Communist) body that is growing in importance and
seems more effective in its actions in defense of
the workers. But despite these political overtones,
the mine workers are essentially very poorly organized and cannot really be said to achieve for their

members a fair share of the industry's earnings;
profits--pre-depletion but post-depreciation and post-
taxation--in 1967 (according to official statistics)
were 40 per cent more than the total wages and salaries bill and over double the workers' wage bill on
its own. It should be remembered that, Marcona and
Toquepala excepted, the miners are Indians and work
in situations that few other races could survive in,
i.e., they are indispensable unless replaced by
machines.

If the question of labor is discussed with the
mine managers, they will quickly point out that the
mines pay a great deal better than agriculture, or
indeed than many industries. In agriculture, wages
of 20 to 30 soles a day are typical and no mine's
minimum wage is nearly as low as that, without counting bonuses and perquisites. As a whole, the industry reckons to spend 70 per cent more than its wage
bill on such things--schools, hospitals, subsidies
to the store. All mines have a hospital (sometimes
two) unless they are near one operated by the State,
in which case they have a first-aid post with a
nurse. In principle, the worker pays 6 per cent and
the employer 14.3 per cent of the wage toward social
security, unemployment fund, pensions and, in the
case of the employer, two other funds; but if the
mine has a hospital, i.e., normally, these figures
are reduced to 3 and 8.3 per cent, respectively.
The worker goes to the mine hospital or the State
hospital if that contribution is paid. His wife and
family are not, apparently, the legal responsibility
of the mine but, in fact, represent the main clien-
tele of the mine hospital.

However, no legislation, hospital equipment or
social security are sufficient to counteract the
rigors of living at 4,700 meters and, to put it
bluntly, the ignorance and carelessness of many of
the Indians in looking after themselves and their
children, plus the inadequate housing provided by
the mines. An illustration will serve. Raura, a
mine surrounded with glaciers, but with a well-
equipped hospital, two doctors, a social worker,
three or four nurses and a medicine bill of 50,000

soles per month, takes care of 600 workers and employees in all. The workers have perhaps four to
five live children each--60 to 70 per cent die in
their first two years of life largely because of
pneumonia and other respiratory complaints; houses
hold up to eight persons to a room--and sometimes
two families, with results that can be imagined;
there is free coal but no hot water on tap at all--
and cold water only at the end of the row. The in-
tensity of the cold between 6 p.m. and 6 a.m. has to
be felt to be believed. Raura's climate is exceptional, but the picture is not untypical. Apart
from educating the miners a bit in looking after
themselves, there is no doubt that the companies
should build much better houses for them. Cerro de
Pasco is a particular defaulter, but few sierra mines
have even tolerable housing. The need for better
housing is most felt in central Peru with its vicious
climate, and since nearly all the mines there have
long histories and huge reserves there is no excuse
for not meeting it.

It is the ambition of most miners, if they have
ambitions for their families, that their children
should get a better education and get away from the
mines, but few would want to see them promoted into
the class of mine employees for they, too, lead a
hard life. The 7,000 to 8,000 employees in 1967
earned from 40,000 soles in Ayacucho to over 200,000
soles in Tacna (Toquepala), averaging some 110,000
soles--good salaries, when housing and medical care
are also considered. But the mine engineer has his
own particular problems. First, very few mines have
adequate secondary schools, if they have any secondary school at all, so sooner or later the engineer
is alone in the sierra and his wife and family in
Lima, Arequipa or other large coastal towns. Often,
it is almost impossible for husband and wife to meet
except during the annual vacation, as weekends are
quite inadequate for traveling the vast distances
involved. In the· smaller mines, life can be very
lonely for someone without personal resources. The
weekly film and the occasional local fiesta do not
compensate for the long evenings with few diversions.
Peru being in the tropics, it is always dark by

7 p.m., so there is little opportunity even for fish-
ing or walking in the hills. The dedicated father
resigns himself to it and devotes his energies to
his work and to earning a good salary to pay for his
children's education--which can be shockingly expensive if they are sent to what are regarded as good
schools. Such, too, is the attitude of most of the
550-odd foreign employees who are in Peru primarily
for the money. Their average salary is some $10,000
to $11,000 yearly. (The big mines do indeed pay
senior staff in dollars--it is taken as a sign of
promotion to be transferred to the dollar pay roll.)

     The two big coastal mines are exceptions to the
remarks about conditions. Although they are in isolated spots, they are linked by fast roads to towns
(Tacna, Nazca), and the camps have good housing, excellent pay and are agreeably laid out--Toquepala
much better than Marcona. These mines, of course,
are very wealthy, but a feature of their activity is
the productivity. Toquepala, for example, produces
about 1.3 million tons of ore and some 50,000 tons
of concentrates per month, employing a total of
3,200 people--400 and 15 tons, respectively, per person. A sierra mine, say Cercapuquio, produces perhaps 20 tons of mineral per person per month (and
half of that is from old tailings) and 1.5 tons of
concentrates. Newer mines, even in the sierra, ac-
centuate the productivity trend. Cobriza handles 60
tons of ore per month per person and 6 tons of concentrate. Cobriza plans to install television in
the concentrator plant to cut down on labor even further. This tendency must be deplored. It is true
that progress cannot be stopped completely, but
there is no evidence that the larger mines are about
to go bankrupt owing to excessive wage bills. Moreover, in a developed country, one can argue that if
workers are displaced in the mines then others are
employed manufacturing trucks or television equipment,
but this is not so in Peru since all such equipment
is imported. One can also argue, and such an argument will be taken up later, that the mines are essentially non-productive as they use labor to produce
goods that are not consumed domestically but exported.
But this is a theoretical argument that applies to

the industry in the economy rather than to local conditions in a mining area. The local reality is that,
far from there being a labor shortage, there is endemic unemployment. The mines, as a whole, are not
significant employers of labor in the economy as a
whole, but, as in the case of their buying, the employment they do offer is often vital in a limited
area. The case of Chilete, mentioned earlier, illustrates this, and it is hard to imagine what the departments of Pasco and Junin would be like without
the employment given by the mines.

For all its hardships, work in the mines offers
better conditions than the Peruvian Indian generally
enjoys in the sierra and offers him better pay than
he can get in many parts of the country, sierra or
coast. A trend to replace labor by imported machines
is to be seriously regretted, particularly as those
mines doing it are among the most able to support
increased labor costs.

THE INDUSTRY AS A PRODUCER

The gross national product (GNP) of Peru for
1968 may, at current prices, be put at some 180,000
million soles. The total value of the production of
the mines for that year was approximately $470 mil-
lion to $480 million, or 18,500 million soles--10
per cent of the GNP. However, this latter figure,
which includes smelting and refining and SOGESA, also
includes intermediate consumption by the mines that
may be put at 25 to 30 per cent, reducing the gross
product of the mining industry to some 7 per cent of
the GNP. Again, 4, or at most 7, per cent of these
figures for mine production represents domestic consumption as opposed to exports, so the "value added"
by the entire mining, smelting and refining industry
to Peru to those products that are actually of use
in Peru is less than 0.5 per cent of the GNP. In
other words, the mines as domestic producers are almost insignificant.

However, the little production that there is
for the domestic market is, nevertheless, important,

metals occupying a fundamental position in all econ-
omies. First and most important is steel. SOGESA,
as has been said, has been producing about 100,000
tons yearly in the form of billets, wire rods, corrugated rods for the construction industry and angled
sections, although this latter capacity is not used
since two other companies (in Lima and Arequipa) make
the same product from SOGESA's billets and national
capacity is in excess of demand. These companies
are likely to install electric furnaces for smelting
scrap, and perhaps pellets from Marcona, thus further
trespassing on SOGESA's ground. Another company,
PROLANSA, and its associated Alambresa, with factories
near Callao and Chimbote, makes galvanized sheets
for roofing, galvanized wire, ordinary wire, springs
and meshes--as do three or four various other smaller
concerns. SOGESA is to have a galvanized sheet capacity of 30,000 tons per year, too. A U.S. subsidiary, Armco, makes small steel tubes; a German
company, Ferrum Peru, galvanized tubes up to 4 inches;
and a Peruvian company makes up to 20-inch, spiral-
welded high pressure pipes. There are also some
smaller Peruvian companies in the tube business.
Where the raw materials for these products are produced by SOGESA they are used, but, otherwise, much
steel is imported (tens of millions of dollars). In
the 1970's, SOGESA's annual capacity should be
270,000 tons, which will include the 150,000-ton extension for hot- and cold-rolled sheets and save
Peru a further $25 million in imports. Even then,
however, a substantial part of the domestic market
for steel will not be covered, including tinplate,
most special and stainless steels and heavy sections
for construction.* The Peruvian steel industry is
only in its infancy, but it is probable that it would
never have been born at all were it not for the iron
fields of Marcona. Thus, a single mine, although

----

*In 1967, imports totaled nearly $60 million, of
which the most important items (and sources) were:
hot- and cold-rolled sheets (Japan, Belgium); tinplate (Canada, United States, France); steel alloys
(Australia, United States, Chile); and large steel
tubes (Mexico). See also the end of Chapter 9.

reserving only a small part of its production for
domestic consumption, is the cause of a domestic industry that should have in the 1970's, if Chimbote's
ancillary steel companies are included, a gross product worth about $60 million at the cost of less than
$5 million in lost exports.

The iron processed in Peru is not sufficient for
the domestic demand, since it is not transformed into
enough distinct products, but all other metals that
are mined do satisfy the country's needs, although
their imports are virtually nil. Copper is consumed
predominantly in two large (Indeco, Pirelli) and one
small (Coprelsa) cable works. Between them, they
manufacture power cables, telephone cables, simple
insulated wire and wire with insulating varnish for
armature windings. Their raw material is copper wire
bars from La Oroya. The two large firms are foreign-
owned, Indeco being a 60-per-cent Cerro de Pasco subsidiary, and between the three of them they could
probably consume 10,000 to 15,000 tons annually. Unfortunately, in 1969, they were not working near
capacity, but plans for extending the chronic telephone system plus the power cables needed for the
Mantaro scheme should improve the outlook for the
1970's. Meanwhile, Coprelsa has been exporting a
part of its production to Germany. There are, of
course, other small domestic users of copper--brass
foundries, radiator manufacturers, etc.

Lead, and particularly antimonial lead on which
La Oroya is now concentrating, is used in the motor
industry for battery plates. Much of this is recuperated from scrap, together with copper, by a
Danish firm that has set up a 50-50 subsidiary with
Cerro de Pasco. Zinc is used for galvanizing and
alloys, but neither it nor lead are really as important in value or as a basis for a wider industry as
iron and copper. Silver, however, fulfills a rather
special role, as it employs a large number of small
craftsmen and jewelers and is, undoubtedly, one of
the attractions for foreign tourists.

Certain metals that the mines do not produce
are used in Peru--aluminum being an important one,

particularly since it has come into favor for high-
tension cables. A more ridiculous case is nickel.
The mint has seen fit to start issuing coins with a
25-per-cent nickel content. No nickel is mined in
Peru (although there are deposits near Ayacucho),
and for technical reasons the coins must be minted
in France. The price of nickel has, at times, quad-
rupled.

There is little prospect of a radical increase
in domestic metal consumption except in the case of
iron and copper, and even copper would probably be
exported finally as electrical conductors of one
form or another if a substantial decrease in the
proportion exported as cathodes or blister occurs.
Since the two major producers of these conductors
have other factories of their own in other parts of
the world, one may wonder how hard they are likely
to push the expansion of their Peruvian ones. In
both steel and copper products, it is probable that
capacity will continue to be in excess of demand for
some time. It is both extraordinary and tragic to
see such expensive equipment as is installed for
handling these metals lying idle (1969) when there
is so much need in Peru for what they could produce.

THE INDUSTRY AS AN EARNER
OF FOREIGN CURRENCY

It has been said that the total value of the
production of the mines, smelters and refineries is
some 10 per cent of the GNP. That figure includes
all their spending, wages, profits, taxation and provisions for depreciation, etc.--a fair measure of the
industry's total domestic importance. However, its
national importance is far greater than what that
figure would indicate. The mines represent just over
50 per cent of Peru's export earnings. In 1968, the
individual metals' percentage incidences in the
value of total metal exports were roughly as follows:
copper, 47.5 per cent; iron, 16.5 per cent; silver,
16.5 per cent; zinc, 8.5 per cent; lead, 7 per cent;
bismuth, 1.5 per cent; molybdenum and tungsten, each
0.5 per cent; others, including mercury, cadmium,

gold, antimony, tellurium, tin, selenium, indium and manganese, the remaining 1.5 per cent. (These figures should be halved to get percentages of total exports.)

However, it must not be imagined that all the $420 million that were 1968's approximate f.o.b. export earnings come to rest in Peru. Besides the $50-odd million that the industry spends yearly on imported goods and services, it needs a further $100 million of foreign exchange. Table 1 is reproduced from the Reseña Económica y Financiera of the Banco Central de Reserva.

Bearing in mind that the foreign companies, which represent 85 per cent of the gross production, are the only ones to re-export profits, depreciation and interests and also have a higher percentage of foreign purchases (69 per cent for 1967), Table 1 might be roughly summarized as follows:

Foreign mining companies

Percentage of total sales spent in Peru   60
Percentage of total sales spent abroad or
    exported   40

National mining companies

Percentage of total sales spent in Peru   90
Percentage of total sales spent abroad   10

These figures are not exaggerated. A more likely estimate for 1967 is that the foreign companies spent 45 per cent of their earnings abroad in one way or another, but this has been reduced to allow for Southern Peru's entry into the normal taxation scheme (in 1968) and for a smaller proportion of foreign purchases by foreign companies as a whole.

Thus, if the industry's gross production (SOGESA excluded) is put at $460 million (1968 approximation) and it is imagined that all the mining companies were Peruvian, the net gain in foreign currency would be about $410 million as opposed to $290 million. If it

TABLE 1

Percentage Distribution of the Gross Value of Production of the
Metal-mining Industry, 1967

Used in the Country		Used Abroad	
Remunerations	17	Profits remitted	14
Purchases (goods, services)	11	Purchases	13
Taxes	15	Depreciation	9
Re-investment of profits and depletion	20	Interests	1
Total	63	Total	37

is objected that the Peruvian companies would have
had to import more equipment and borrow foreign capital for the big mines, so that only the profits out
of the repatriations of the actual foreign companies
would have come to rest in Peru, the figures still
would be $355 million (hypothetical case) and $290
million (actual case). This difference is similar
to the estimated increased annual earnings produced
by building zinc, lead and copper refineries and re-
organizing the marketing of the products as discussed
in Chapter 10. Thus, it is not xenophobia that
causes the Peruvian to question the activities of the
foreign mining companies--a simple fact that they are
foreign is responsible for a loss in foreign exchange
earnings that may yearly be estimated, at least, at
$50 million or, at most, at $110 million. During
each of the years 1967 and 1968, net long-term capital inflow to Peru was approximately $100 million.
It is tempting to conclude that if the mines had been
developed by Peruvian owners (with or without foreign
loans) in the first place, their additional earnings
would now cover the country's importing of foreign
capital.

Leaving aside the question of foreign ownership,
Table 1 may be adjusted to refer only to exports and
be rewritten for 1968 approximately as follows:

TABLE 2

Distribution of Expenditure by Metal-mining
Companies, 1968

Expenditures	Per Cent	Million Dollars	Billion Soles
Wages, purchases and invest- ment in Peru	50	225	8.9
Taxation in Peru	15	68	2.6
Profits, depreciation, pur- chases abroad	35	157	6.1
Total	100	450	17.6

What is the mechanism whereby this distribution
is made? Since 1967, when the certificate system
was re-introduced after the devaluation, all exporters
are issued with exchange certificates for their foreign earnings. Exports are only permitted against
specified documents of credit. These documents are
handled exclusively by the national banks, and when
those banks deliver (as they are obliged to do) the
corresponding foreign money to the Banco Central de
Reserva they are issued in return with the exchange
certificates, which are, of course, passed on to the
original exporter. Thus, the exporter receives in
return for his minerals and concentrates certificates
that have a nominal value in foreign currency.
These certificates have a limited life, as little as
three days, in which time the exporter can use them
himself or sell them to someone else by endorsing
them. During their life, they are used for buying
back foreign currency, but only when authorized to
do so by the relevant government departments (Ministerio de Hacienda, etc.). Specifically, the mining
industry uses them for exporting profits and recouping capital in the form of depreciation. They can
also be used for importing. Should the life of the
certificates expire, because the holder cannot sell
them or does not want to, they can be cashed in for
soles at the Banco Central de Reserva. The certificate rate is (in 1969) 38.70 soles to the dollar and
is virtually completely stable.

The system exists to control the buying and
selling of dollars that are the product of exports
and, also, to supervize the repatriation of profits,
etc., by foreign companies operating in Peru. It is
a fair system that operates apparently well. It is,
therefore, somewhat surprising to find that, until
1970, only exporters were effectively submitted to
it, that is to say only those people who actually
earned foreign currency and who, therefore, might be
supposed to have a greater freedom in disposing of
it. But this was not so. There was nothing to stop
private individuals from buying foreign currency on
the free (giro) market (at 43 to 44 soles the dollar)
and sending it away where they willed. They could
also hold accounts in foreign currency in Peru. In

1969, these stood at some $90 million, compared with
the central bank's $100 million net foreign currency
reserves. In the 1968 balance of payments,* there
is an item labeled "Errors, Omissions and Short-term
Capital" representing $107 million outgoing. This
is to be compared with a commercial surplus of $193
million, a transfer and services deficit of $160 mil-
lion and a long-term capital surplus of $101 million,
all of which combined produces a net surplus of $27
million. The point is that it would be ridiculous
to direct efforts toward producing commercial surpluses (controlling imports, aiding exports), toward
reducing services deficits (making freighting in national boats obligatory, controlling repatriation of
profits) and toward angling for foreign capital
(seeking loans, attracting foreign investors) if virtually nothing was to be done to control essentially
speculative movements in short-term capital whose
operations are on the same scale and whose fund of
foreign currency in Peru alone was almost as large
as that of the Banco Central de Reserva. This, presumably, was the reasoning behind the May, 1970, exchange control regulations that converted the foreign
currency holdings to soles and ordered the repatriation of external accounts. The central bank's reserves rose to $316 million in June, 1970.

Following the use of the exchange certificates
a stage further, the mining industry may be supposed
to cash in (in accordance with Table 2) $225 million
yearly to meet their Peruvian expenses. They receive
soles in exchange at the 38.70 rate, producing 8.9
billion soles. If this figure is adjusted to include
the expenses corresponding to the industry's production for national consumption as well, it becomes
some 9.9 billion soles, but the total value of the
goods released on the domestic economy (this includes SOGESA) is only 1.2 billion soles at the very
most. Thus, the industry is causing a monetization
of 8.7 billion soles per year--a figure to be compared

---

*The breakdown to individual items is by no means
as thorough as might be desired, but the major characteristics are clear.

with the largest government budgetary deficit of 5.7
billion soles in 1967. It is true that the issue of
these soles is backed by dollars in the Banco Central
de Reserva, but that does not reduce their domestic
inflationary effect. They are hardly even used to
produce non-salable items of public utility such as
roads (the most the government ever spent on roads
was 2.0 billion soles in 1966). This 8.7-billion-
sole expenditure produces very little for the Peruvian public--except more paper dollars.

Likewise, $68 million are converted into 2.6
billion soles and paid to the government as tax.
The government can count on this money as income and
so include it in the budget, the Banco Central de
Reserva being able to discount a correspondingly
greater quantity of government paper and issue notes,
if need be, to the government against the dollars.
In short, these $68 million entitle the government,
other things being equal, to spend more. The logic
of these proceedings is not clear. How does the
existence of dollars in the Banco Central de Reserva
justify the government in spending more money? Or
better, why should the government not spend more
money if the domestic economy requires it without
the dollars backing it? Leaving this question aside,
the 2.4 billion soles paid in tax, when raised to
2.7 billion soles to account for the domestic as
well as export sales, is about 10 per cent of the
central government's 26-billion-sole 1968 income.

The sum of the two former figures (225 + 68 =
$293 million) is the profit made by Peru on the cur-
rent international payments account. However, the
remaining $157 million represents, many Peruvians
would argue, the loss made by the country on the
whole operation as it is the difference between the
f.o.b. value of the metals exported from Peru and
the amount of dollars received for them. This $157-
million deficit may be reduced by considering the
value of the metals produced in Peru for national
consumption (some $30 million), the value of capital
goods imported (although some are of doubtful productive value--some $15 million) and, possibly, even the
value of consumer goods that are imported or gained

by the country. Even so, they would say that there
is a deficit of some $70 million per year. It will
be objected that this argument is not fair, that the
metals do not have that value as a capital asset,
that their sale price is the result of the mining
and processing industry and that, in the ground,
they are almost worthless, but this argument is be-
lied by those persons who most use it--the foreign
mining companies who do not seem to have regarded
their unexploited concessions as worthless.

Another objection is that the argument does not
consider large-scale capital movements. Current
capital spending is included and re-investment net
of depreciation represents $50 million of the $293
million entering Peru yearly, but really big initial
investments, such as Toquepala, have not been duly
taken into account. No such investments have taken
place since the late 1950's but they probably will
in the 1970's, so an attempt will be made here to
analyze their effect, particularly on the balance of
payments. In the short term, the effect is obviously
very positive.* If a $300-million investment is
imagined, 60 per cent of which is spent in Peru,
there is a $180-million increase in the balance of
payments. Suppose 40 per cent of local and 80 per
cent of foreign spending is on goods and services on
which depreciation and amortization can be charged
(e.g., plant machinery and mine preparation work).
The country receives $168 million worth of what one
may call assets in addition to the payments bonus.
(This reckoning assumes that the assets created

---

*So, at any rate, reason would lead one to be-
lieve. If, however, one looks at the historical
record, it is most surprising to find that when Marcona (1952-1954) and Toquepala (1956-1960) were initiated, instead of showing substantial increases,
the central bank's dollar reserves fluctuated badly
and devaluations occurred. In the first period, the
sol dropped some 15 to 19 soles to the dollar and in
the second, from 19 to 27 soles. This must have considerably reduced the two mining companies' costs in
Peru.

locally have actually been called into being by the
investment, not simply bought. Moreover, it assumes
that they are assets––it is not questioned whether
a ball mill is really of use to the national economy.) Moreover, $108 million of consumer spending
power is liberated, a sum equal to 15 per cent of
the central government's total annual spending. All
this money spent in soles––where does it come from?
The central bank has largely printed it in return
for dollars.

One can next try to draw up a balance for the
entire life of the mine (see Table 3). It is supposed that it runs for 30 years, earning $150 million
yearly, 95 per cent from exports. (Other figures,
which it is hoped are not unrealistic, are put in to
complete the illustration.) A surplus of foreign
currency of $2,717 million is generated, $90 million
per year. If one attempts a capital account, valuing the metals lost to Peru at the profit made on
their extraction and the metals sold in Peru at their
cost price (the figure below is sale price, but this
is compensated by the fact that the value put for
the metals exported is actually the profit on total
extraction), the result is:

Losses		Gains	
Metals gone	675	Surplus on for- eign payments	2,717
Surplus on capi- tal a/c	2,307	Metals supplied in Peru	225
		Residual equip- ment	40
Total	2,982	Total	2,982

These figures are very gratifying to those pre-
disposed in favor of large foreign investments of
the sort discussed. The big gains for the country
are to be compared with the $675-million profit for
the company. However, the figures are somewhat

TABLE 3

Effect on Balance of Payments of Spending by a Sample Mine

Outgoing	Million Dollars	Incoming	Million Dollars
Total spending abroad out of costs (12)*	540	Initial spending in Peru	180
Post-tax exported profits (including spending abroad out of profits) (15)	675	Sales of metals abroad (95)	4,275
Depreciation and amortization on total capital spending, initial 168 subsequent (7) 315	483		
Sale of residual equipment in Peru	40		
Subtotal	1,738		
Surplus on foreign payments	2,717		
Total	4,455	Total	4,455

*The figures in parentheses are percentages of the total sales.

deceptive. The balance-of-payments surplus has been
produced at the expense of massive spending in the
country, spending that is uncontrolled by the government, certainly inflationary, and severly reduces
the government's own freedom of movement in the same
field. Moreover, this spending is the most important
way in which the foreign currency can effectively be
gotten for the country, taxation representing a mere
quarter of the payments surplus. Should the government try to increase the share it gets directly by
raising taxation, it could force the industry to cut
costs further, but it can also have a negative effect. Once taxation on profits is above 50 per cent
(in Peru it is 54.5 per cent), it can become profitable for the companies to spend their money on unnecessarily expensive equipment that they can recoup
tax-free later, and even if this stage is not reached,
the incentive for avoiding extravagance is certainly
small. If, on the other hand, taxation is reduced,
the company has a bigger incentive to cut costs and
the government's income might or might not rise, but
the country's total foreign currency revenue will
certainly fall. Thus, from the country's point of
view, inflationary expenditure on a domestically un-
profitable activity is an essential prerequisite for
earning foreign currency.

Moreover, considering this capital account, it
is still the paper surplus that dominates. Without
it, the huge capital surplus would be a loss. Should
the level of domestic sales of the company increase,
a capital surplus on the actual goods could be produced, but, of course, at the expense of the balance
of payments. In the extreme case of all the mine's
production being consumed domestically, there is a
large payments deficit equal, at least, to all the
profits and depreciation removed from the country,
while the capital surplus only exists if the value
(cost price) of the goods produced exceeds this--
i.e., if profits are near or over 50 per cent of
sales, there is a capital loss as well as a foreign
exchange one.

From this one may conclude that if there must
be foreign mining (or manufacturing) companies

supplying the domestic market, it is in the country's interests that they make no profit. A foreign mining company exporting is preferable and, in fact, this is what they, and the industry as a whole, do. In this case, in return for metals the country receives dollars, which, in their majority (say 75 per cent of the net surplus), are released in inflationary form on the economy as a necessary counterpart to their arrival in the central bank reserves. The remaining 25 per cent of the net surplus goes to the government directly and will probably also be released--one hopes on something domestically more productive than mining.

CONCLUSION

Reviewing the domestic effect of the industry as a whole one can say:

1. As a buyer and employer, the mining, smelting and refining industry, while locally important, is not very significant nationally. Insofar as it is significant, its operations consist of largely inflationary spending, the counterweight being the dollars gained for the reserves. As a producer for the domestic economy, it is of very marginal importance, although it is hoped that this importance--especially the iron and steel industry--will grow. It is highly desirable that such productive activities are in national hands, as they earn no foreign currency with which to service the charges of a foreign capitalist.

2. As an exporter, the industry is the dominating source of foreign currency for Peru. This currency is earned normally via domestic spending, taxation and capital movements. National companies are much more efficient earners than foreign ones because foreign companies export profits, depreciation and amortizations and tend to spend a higher proportion abroad on goods and services. Exceptional capital movements, namely very large initial foreign investments, have much the same effect as that achieved by printing money, except that there are large dollar gains for the reserves.

Thus, the essential importance of the mining industry in Peru consists of the fact that it earns
dollars. Apart from its small domestic production,
the justification for its other domestic activities
depends on this. It is only fair to ask, what is
the real use for these dollars?

13

THE FUTURE
OF
THE INDUSTRY

In any under-taking, it is desirable to decide
where one is trying to go before actually setting
out. Thus, a discussion of the future of the mining
industry and the decisions that are being, or should
be, taken about it presupposes some objective for
the industry. The objective assumed here is that
the industry should contribute as much as possible
to the welfare and development, in the widest sense,*
of the Peruvian people. The objective is not that
the mining industry should grow for growth's sake,
still less is it that the industry should serve as a
cheap source of raw materials for the richer countries of the world, and it goes without saying that
it is not the enrichment of a few persons, foreign
or national. If these latter aims coincide with the
primary aim, well and good; if not, they must be
waived. Since, however, the industry's primary importance is that of an exporter, a dollar earner, a
discussion of mining policy involves a discussion of
the economic policy of the country as a whole, even
if very briefly. The more local economic effects of
the industry (employment, etc.) have already been
detailed; and although much remains to be done in

---

*Article 14 of Pope Paul VI's Populorum Progres-
sio.

those fields, the industry as a whole must be discussed in the context of the economy as a whole.

NATIONAL ECONOMIC POLICY

So much needs to be done in Peru that one can
only wonder how any government manages to decide on
its priorities.* Whether it be roads or irrigation,
housing or health services, agriculture, local industry or education, the field for building, manufacturing and employing seems unlimited. Whatever particular choice a government may make, one thing is
certain: There is no need to invent work. In a
country where the majority of people live in what
one may justly call hovels, are under-nourished, often uneducated and frequently die at an early age
from lack of proper attention, the problem is clearly
not that of persuading them to buy a second car to
keep the factories active. Nevertheless, as has been
pointed out earlier, the incredible truth is that
there are large numbers of people out of work, or
under-employed. There can be no doubt, therefore,
that the first priority is to employ people in satis-
fying, as far as possible, the basic needs of the
community as a whole.

Easily said. Before the Spaniards came, the
Incas ordered people out to work. Thus, on one
famous occasion, the Inca Pachacutec put 40,000 men
to dig, in ten days, an irrigation canal that has
watered the Ica Valley ever since. Nowadays, however, people have to be paid, and from where is the
money to come? There are two possible sources within Peru--private and government. For various reasons, private investment is of secondary importance,
although it is 80 or even 90 per cent of total investment, which is 20 to 25 per cent of the GNP.
The main reason, of course, is that private investors

---

*A good, short, description of Peru, its people
and its recent history is given in Marcel Niedergang,
Les 20 Amériques Latines, Volume 2 (Paris: Editions
de Seuil, 1969).

are not interested in social spending, which is what
the country most needs. As manufacturers, they are
involved in building or equipping the schools, hospitals and power stations, but their activity is conditional on the State's and their investment conditional on their activity. This is so in most countries of the world, but perhaps more so in Peru,
which, for better or for worse, is traditionally
wedded to the idea that major projects are initiated
by the Inca, the Crown or the government. Second,
the supply of money to private investors is controlled
by the State, which fixes, via the Banco Central de
Reserva, the banks' legal reserves, their maximum interests rates, etc. Third, in a country where so
much of the capital is concentrated in so few hands
and where the company owned by a large number of
small shareholders is unknown, political considerations have an inordinate effect on private investment plans. If a few key people take fright or decide to hold their hands, they affect the whole
economy. The government controls these people via
the "atmosphere of confidence" it creates or does
not create. (It may be surmised that these people
have tended, at times, to control the government.)
Finally, there is no effective pressure on private
capital to invest in useful local activities. In
particular, capital could be exported at will until 1970. Much capital that is not exported is invested in speculative building, which is then for
rent or sale at prices that can only be paid by foreign executives or diplomats--anyone but the people
really in need of houses. In short, private capital
is often socially irresponsible.* The honorable exceptions are critically dependent on economic policy
and government spending for their success. The government is the major influence in the real development of the country.

If the government is the major influence, there
must be many governments who have felt that this influence only really shows its negative aspects. The

---

*Cf. Populorum Progressio, second part of Article
24.

government has not the money for the tasks that face
it.   Central government income for 1968 was some 24
billion soles (local government takes approximately
another 16 billion), essentially from taxation.*
This is the money the government has to spend, the
Banco Central de Reserva being able only to discount
government paper to cover seasonal differences between government income and expenditure, and being
severely limited in its lending powers to the government.** Government expenditure is certainly a bit
misdirected--the armed forces, for example, take 20
per cent of it--but even if it were not so, it is
probable that a balanced budget would lead to unemployment and a very slow rate of development--as,
indeed, happened in 1969 and 1970. Governments that
want to be financially respectable and orderly, e.g.,
the military one that took power in 1968, find at
once that this undermines all their plans for trans-
forming the country. On the other hand, if the government runs deficits as it so often has done (nearly
50 per cent of the central bank's 22-billion-sole assets are its credit with the government or State
banks), the economy may move, but sooner or later a
devaluation occurs, e.g., 1967. This phenomenon is,
of course, common throughout the world, but it is
very much accentuated in Latin America, in general,
and Peru, in particular. (In a very interesting
series of articles, M. Paul Fabra*** has analyzed the
causes of the choice between inflation or unemployment, which seem to be the only two possibilities
facing the economics of the major free-market countries of the world. His conclusion is that much of

---

*These figures were also approximately those for
1969 and 1970, but a radical increase is envisaged
for 1971 and 1972 with a two-year total budget of
116 billion soles.

**Articles 46 to 48 of the Ley Orgánica of the
Banco Central de Reserva.

***"L'Inflation et la Société de Consommation," Le
Monde, Sélection Hebdomadaire, June 26 to July 2,
July 3-9, 1969.

the blame is attributable to the excessive profits
made by producers, particularly those of consumer
goods. If this is so, it can be imagined how much
worse will be the effect in Peru, where profits owing
to the uncertainty of the market are that much higher
and, moreover, are often exported, thus hitting directly, rather than indirectly, at the parity of the
national currency.)

This shortage of capital has led both Peruvians
and interested foreigners to think that a third
source might be sought--namely, foreign. It is a
pity that the word "capital" is used, as it is somewhat abstract. "Money" is a better term, it makes
one think of actual notes and coins, and then, at
once, the essential truth is brought home. These
notes and coins are not soles but, in their majority,
dollars.

THE USE OF DOLLARS

It is perhaps somewhat naive to ask what is the
use of dollars in a country whose currency is soles,
but if it is a naive question then there must be a
simple answer to it.

The first and most obvious answer is that the
dollars are needed for importing. How many dollars
are needed yearly for this purpose? Since the beginning of 1968, when restrictions were imposed, imports have fallen sharply by 23 per cent ($820 million
in 1967, $630 million in 1968 and even less since
then). The restrictions were against all imports
that had a locally manufactured equivalent. It is
clear that there used to be much unnecessary importing. What foreign visitor to the "under-developed"
country of Peru is not astonished by the number of
sumptuous limousines on the shockingly surfaced
streets of Lima, by the ultra-modern office equipment
used by companies whose turnover is insignificant or
even, to consider a quasi-import, by the number of
persons who seem to be able to take holidays in
Miami, Paris or Japan? If dollars are used for importing, it is not the same as saying that they are

needed for importing. Of course, a certain amount
of foreign currency is required for imports even if
all frivolous use of it was stopped, and it is the
business of economic planners to decide what that
amount is and ensure that it is procured. Both government and private industry need the foreign currency, and it should be pointed out, perhaps unnecessarily, that both are on the same footing for getting
it. The government has to buy it from the Banco
Central de Reserva like anyone else. Its capacity
for buying is limited to the amount of money it has
allocated to other tasks in the budget. In short,
the entity that most needs foreign currency for importing big turbines for hydroelectric projects,
rolling mills for steelworks, etc., namely, the State
and its corporations, is limited in what it can get
by domestic financial considerations--even though
the foreign exchange may be available in the Banco
Central de Reserva. Thus, certainly foreign currency
is needed for importing, but how much? And how can
matters be better arranged domestically to ensure
that it is preferentially available to those who
really need it for useful capital equipment? And
why dollars? It certainly is strange that whereas
in 1968 Peru's imports were 38 per cent from the
United States and 62 per cent from other countries
(of which West Germany was 13 per cent; Argentina,
11 per cent; Japan, 7 per cent) the foreign exchange
reserves of the central bank, excluding some 40 per
cent held in gold, were virtually 100 per cent in
U.S. dollars. (The same proportion may be surmised
for the commercial banks, who do not publish details.)
Presumably, then, the central bank reserves have
some other purpose than paying for imports. What
is it?

A second use for dollars is as a backing to
domestic currency. Central bankers have been compared to gnomes in the past and there does seem to
be a certain fairy-tale quality about them. To
many people, besides M. Jacques Rueff,* the idea

---

*"Ce Qui Doit Arriver Arrive," Le Monde, Sélec-
tion Hebdomadaire, June 5-11 and 12-19, 1969.

that one piece of paper is of value because it can
(in principle, and only, then, to a certain fraction
of its nominal value) be exchanged for another piece
of paper is purely and simply ridiculous. In 1968,
the Banco Central de Reserva's gold and dollar reserves covered 35 per cent of the notes in circulation. The dollars are labeled piously "payable in
gold." Apparently, in the United States, the gold
reserves cover less than 25 per cent of domestic
circulation alone, and are quite incapable of meeting the demands of overseas creditors holding dollars. One tends to discern schizophrenia in international monetary circles. On the one hand, it is
said that gold is outmoded, not to say prehistoric,
and that the world's economy should be liberated
from its stranglehold; while on the other hand, pro-
hibitions are put on the buying and selling of gold
by individuals and governments, the official price
(unique among metals) is rigidly controlled, governments are persuaded to hold paper "payable in gold"
(it is not) and, worst of all, they are lectured
that their domestic note issue should be backed by
this paper--advice that the printers of dollars do
not follow themselves. Some people even argue that
the dollars are better than gold--although one would
surely think that, in the last analysis, gold plate
for the President's table would look better than
dollar wallpaper should the international monetary
system collapse--but however one argues the gold
versus dollars case, one is missing the main point.
The stranglehold that exists is that of central bank
reserves as a whole--gold, dollars and all other
foreign currency. Why should the issuing of money
be restricted by any other considerations than the
needs of the people of Peru? Why is a 35-per-cent
coverage acceptable? Why not 75 per cent or 1.5 per
cent or any arbitrary figure once the 100 per cent
has been abandoned? Is the pitiful unemployment,
misery and stagnation of a whole country a price
worth paying to balance the books to an arbitrary
percentage? Perhaps this is what Pope Pius XI was
thinking about when he denounced the "international
imperialism of money" way back in 1931.*

---

*Quadragesimo Anno.

But, accepting the situation as it is, what is
done with these foreign currency reserves? Since
virtually no currency maintains its value, the reserves must be put out to loan. In 1969, some $40
million to $60 million were on short-term, and a
slightly smaller quantity on long-term, loan abroad.
Why abroad? Because, once again, dollars are of no
use in Peru. Thus, the very Banco Central de Reserva of Peru, in a country supposedly starved of
capital, lends its money abroad. It may safely be
assumed that it is placed on the Euro-dollar market
and finds its way back to the big United States
banks. There, it will probably be used to finance
projects in the United States, but it may even be
lent again to Peru. Surely, these reserves could be
put to a better use. One possibility is to buy the
mines' products with them and take advantage of
movements in world prices. Since a portion of the
reserves is never touched--if they drop that low, a
devaluation occurs--a portion that may be valued at
least at $40 million (a fraction of the long-term
loans), the central bank could easily afford to ride
out any temporary fall in copper prices and to choose
one metal, which (unless both the foreign mining companies' and Peru's policies are quite crazy) has an
assured future. If such a policy tided a mine over
a bad period, it would, at any rate, have helped a
few miners and their families.

A third answer to the question "what is the use
of dollars?" is easy. Speculation. If dollars
really are vital to the country's progress, then it
is extraordinary that a free market in them has so
long been tolerated. As has been said before, some
$90 million worth of foreign currency were held in
accounts in Peru, and, until 1970, the public could
buy dollars in relatively unlimited quantities without any need to apply for permission. Compare this
to the exchange controls in the "developed" countries
of most of Western Europe. How many dollars or
Swiss francs were, and still are, held by Peruvians
outside Peru? Nobody knows, but even such orthodox
journals as The Economist state that the flight of
capital from Latin America is much larger than is

generally supposed.* A free market is a luxury that
few countries can afford--not even the United States
nowadays, where "voluntary" controls and travel taxes
have been applied. Peru was acting rightly, if be-
latedly, in applying exchange controls in May, 1970.

Finally, dollars serve to pay debts. In 1969,
Peru owed about $850 million abroad of which $770
million were payable within five years, i.e., at the
rate of $170 million a year (including interests,
etc.), which is nearly 20 per cent of the country's
annual export earnings. How did such huge debts
arise? Certain debts are because of genuine importing of useful goods and services, but, even here,
all is not quite as it should be. When foreign companies tender for a project, it generally goes to
the cheapest offer (although the effect of bribes,
which reflect as much discredit on the giver as they
do on the receiver, should not be discounted). Once
the project is well under way, the contractor asks
for more money. If the State does not pay, he walks
out. The State is powerless to refuse his demand
without sacrificing the project for several years.
It is virtually powerless to take legal action or
retaliatory measures against the contractor. Such
blackmail is not unknown. However, much of the debt
has not been accumulated from any useful import of
goods and services. It is from foreign loans to finance government projects, in accordance with the
idea that dollars are suitable for meeting soles expenses. From 1966 to 1968, some 60 per cent of the
Peruvian government's deficit was financed externally
in this way. This idea has been taken on, albeit
with some reluctance,** and is based on the former
idea that the central bank can issue notes against
dollars. Thus, the government gets a loan of the
dollars, cashes them in at the central bank, and the
bank pays the government soles--the only apparent
inconvenience being that the amount of dollars to

---

*Economist para América Latina, October, 1969.

**Felipe Herrera, President, International Devel-
opment Bank, at Vina del Mar, Chile, May 16, 1969.

pay back is greater than the amount received, because
of interests. Leaving aside the question already
put (why does the central bank not lend the soles to
the government without the dollars, if the expenditure is justified?), it should be said at once that
the interests payable are not the only inconvenience.
The lender soon makes his presence felt further.
Would it not be better for Peru to employ foreign
consultants (from the lender's country) to examine
the feasibility of this exciting jungle highway project? Surely, a foreign contractor (from the lender's
country) could handle the work better than a national
one. (Of course, he must be adequately compensated
for having to work in such a remote spot as eastern
Peru.) Soon, there will be not much need to turn
the dollars into soles as they are all being spent
in dollars directly. Alas, the day comes when the
debt is to be repaid. The exciting jungle highway
may or may not have benefited the Peruvians. One
thing is certain, it has not earned any dollars to
repay the debt. If, on the other hand, the loan had
been invested in some industry that did earn dollars,
what use would it have been to Peru? An exporter is,
after all, not making his products available on the
local market. Most of Peru's huge foreign debt has
been formed quite unnecessarily. One can only ask
further, should Peru really feel obliged to repay it,
at any rate in the scheduled lapse of time?*

If these reasons for seeking dollars are examined, it seems clear that only the first is justifi-
able--importing. The fourth reason, debt paying, is
only a consequence of the three former ones. Dollars
are wanted for importing, a quantity that must be
decided in accordance with overall economic plans,
but it may well be a quantity less than is supposed.
In any case, it might be a better idea to get
deutschmarks or yen. If the government or private
investors really need money for domestic spending on
really useful projects, the central bank should issue
it. (From the Ley Orgánica of the Banco Central de

---

*Overseas Development Institute, Review, No. 3
(1969), pp. 38 and 39.

Reserva, one might well ask who is supposed to rule Peru, the bank or the government?) Private speculation should be killed by exchange controls and private foreign deposits should be turned into soles and the foreign currency put to the benefit of the nation as a whole, as has now been done. The foreign debt should be run down as far as possible, not paid if inconvenient, and certainly no new debts, unless absolutely necessary, should be contracted.

These measures might provoke a panic among the monied classes of Lima, but such people represent a very small minority of the people of Peru. The majority of the country would be completely unaffected by them in any negative sense; on the contrary, if they lead, as they should, to work being provided, together with schools, roads and hospitals, that majority would receive very considerable benefits. It will be objected that inflation would rapidly appear. Considering the slack in the economy, this may be doubted, particularly when imports and speculation are controlled. But the threat is certainly there-- a threat in no small measure owing to the excess (not shortage) of exporting industries that already pump inflationary liquidity into the economy without the corresponding goods on which to spend it and to the preponderance of foreign manufacturing companies, who in boom times make such large profits that their exports of currency (some $50 million in 1966) seriously and adversely affect the balance of payments. But, should the choice arise between devaluing the sol or stifling the country's development, the former course should always be chosen. This course is not popular with Peruvian governments for obvious reasons, and they point to cases (Uruguay) that have followed it without success. Devaluations, however, are not to be used to prop up the liberal, free-exchange economy that is here in question,* but to further the country's welfare, and must be accompanied by other necessary measures. Thus, it could be argued that the sol should officially be maintained below its market value to discourage black

*Populorum Progressio, Article 58.

market speculation and reduce dollar exports of profits and depreciation by foreign manufacturers who
earn in soles and favor a tourist surplus (the danger
that foreign companies buy up Peruvian ones being
controlled by legislation). The industrialization
of Brazil under President Kubitchek is an example of
the relative success of such an unorthodox policy of
government spending. As for the dollars that _are_
needed for importing, they are earned independently
of the exchange rate, except that if the sol is too
under-valued the foreign-owned exporters will make
bigger profits to export, although, in this case,
the government itself will also get directly a higher
proportion of the money they leave in Peru.

Thus, the real answer to the question "what are
dollars needed for?" is that foreign exchange, not
necessarily dollars, is needed for importing essential capital equipment that cannot be manufactured
in Peru. The rest of the country's real development
can be looked after by an expansion of selective
credit or, put more bluntly, printing money to good
purpose.

THE MINING INDUSTRY

The mining industry's most important role is as
an earner of foreign money, money which, according
to what has just been said, serves only for importing. In the long term, it should be the objective
of a country endowed with such natural resources and
such human problems as Peru's to import as little as
possible, and what it must import should preferentially come from its similarly situated neighbors.
Even in the short term, importing should be mini-
mized--for example, by making tools as well as goods
in Peru. (Such a course would train people in making
machine tools at the expense of defective products
at the beginning, but defective products can still
have a use. An imported machine for making wire net-
ting may be cheaper to run and give a more reliable
product, but it is unlikely that a nationally manufactured machine will fail to work at all.) However,
in the short term, Peru (in 1969) is burdened with

the foreign debts already mentioned, and it is apparently the policy of the government to earn for the country much more foreign exchange than has in the past been earned. (In this policy, they have been remarkably successful to date [1971].) It is not possible to pronounce on the wisdom of such a policy without a profound knowledge of the Peruvian economy and its future projections, but it is possible to discuss the implications of this policy for the mining industry.

Easily, the most satisfactory method of developing the mining industry is by promoting the medium-sized nationally owned mines. They are more efficient earners of foreign currency; they train and give confidence to more Peruvians in decision-making posts; several medium-sized mines scattered over Peru are much more socially beneficial than one giant mine in one location only; and, finally, they are technically and financially within the nation's capabilities. It has been said that capital for the mines is hard to come by and this is so in fact, but not so in principle. If 400 million soles are taken as a typical investment for a medium-sized mine, then such a sum could certainly be "made available" from government sources once every two years without badly disturbing the budget. It would, after all, be only 1 per cent of the central government's annual expenditure and would also be an investment. However, such a rate of development, even doubled to allow for a miraculous procurement of capital from private national sources, would only yield a further $5 million each year in foreign currency. Thus, even over ten years, with a new national medium-sized mine opening every year, only $275 million would be produced--a figure to be compared with a foreign debt that has reached $850 million. In short, while much is being done and much more still could be done to foster national mines, no practical policy for them is going to enable them to produce the amount of foreign currency that is apparently required.

The next means whereby the mining industry can increase foreign earnings is by further foreign

investment. In this context, only the really big
mines are considered: first, because they predominate; second, because it is only they that really may
need foreign expertise and capital. Investments in
Cuajone, Michiquillay and Cerro Verde would represent
a sum of $600 million to $800 million over five years
if all were to go ahead jointly under foreign control.
This does not include the phosphates deposit of Bayo-
var in Piura, which, added to them, would make a
total of about $1 billion. The copper concessions
alone would, when operating, then earn over $300 mil-
lion yearly. Everything would depend on the contracts signed between the companies and the government, but if it were assumed that the contracts were
so written that the companies spend 60 per cent of
their investment and later leave the same percentage
of their earnings in Peru, the net gain for the foreign reserves would be some 80 million per year until
1975, and then nearly $200 million yearly for the
life of the copper mines. Recently, it has become
fashionable to attack large foreign companies exporting primary products from under-developed countries
as the archetypes of imperialism, and they are compared very unfavorably with the new "enlightened"
foreign company manufacturing in the country for the
domestic market. However, if a villain must be
sought among the foreign companies, it is surely the
latter type of company and not the former. The foreign manufacturing company, unlike the mining company, earns no foreign currency with which to pay
for his exports of profits, etc. Instead, he siphons
capital out of the country, often in return for a
product of very doubtful value--one thinks of soft
drinks. He is in direct competition with other producers, in particular national ones, and his avowed
aim is to take their share of the market. To this
end, he uses his superior capital resources to import
more elaborate machinery (and cut his prices in extreme cases), and, in certain fields, it is clear
that national companies cannot hope to compete (e.g.,
car manufacturing), not because they cannot make the
product but because foreign competition will deliberately kill them. In his battle for the market, the
foreign manufacturer invades the whole cultural life
of the nation. He defiles the streets with his

advertisements, the radio and television are interrupted with his propaganda and a whole alien way of
life is forced upon the host country. Compare this
to the mining company that sits tight in the mountains, is not in competition (except very indirectly)
with national companies and has no need to advertise
its products locally, or persuade, cajole and bully
the public into adopting habits they do not necessarily want and probably cannot afford.

Nevertheless, the foreign mining company does
have its own, although lesser, drawbacks. The major
one, of course, is its enormous economic power. If
the copper projects had gone ahead under their former ownership, and other factors had not changed,
the American Smelting and Refining Company would have
controlled (through its 51.5-per-cent ownership of
the Southern Peru Copper Corporation and 100-per-cent
ownership of the Northern Peru Mining Company) over
25 per cent of Peru's exports, and would have contributed in taxation some 7 or 8 per cent of the
government's income. The Cerro de Pasco Corporation
(22.25-per-cent stake in Southern Peru) will still
represent (with Cuajone) 15 per cent of exports and
4 or 5 per cent of government income. With the best
intentions in the world, it is impossible that these
two companies should not have made their weight felt
in the political field--they already do--and in extreme cases, have felt tempted to exert pressure
through the U.S. government. Moreover, as has been
pointed out, the foreign investment in these new
projects would be essentially inflationary. The
operation of the mines is also essentially inflationary since the foreign exchange to be earned by the
country (excluding the 25 per cent of net earnings
collected in taxation) must be spent in its soles
equivalent. And then the copper is gone. On the
reasoning that a bird in the hand is worth two in
the bush, it has been argued that dollars today are
better than copper tomorrow, that copper will be replaced by substitutes and so forth, but who knows?
There is no doubt that in granting the operating contracts to the foreign companies the government would
have been laying up political troubles for the future
and probably economic ones as well.

An alternative to more foreign investment for
new mines is to nationalize the existing foreign
mines in operation--in particular, the really big
ones. This would immediately produce $70 million,
perhaps $80 million, extra per year for Peru in for-
eign currency earnings--almost the same amount likely
to be produced yearly by the new copper investments
before they actually start production. Since it
represents the profits and depreciation at present
exported, it would presumably go straight to the government who could then pay the foreign debt with it,
import capital equipment or use it as they see fit.
The government, perhaps, would feel free to release
the same amount of soles internally that the foreign
investors would have done, except this time, it could
be spent on useful public works. In the future, nationalization would produce less dollars than what
the new mines would when working, but perhaps the
State would feel able to put one of those mines into
production on its own account. It is quite likely
that the nationalization would enable the foreign
debt to be paid off without any increase in production.

Such a nationalization would be regarded as a
very radical step, but certainly not wicked. Na-
tionalizations are common in Western Europe (e.g.,
the United Kingdom), although not of foreign companies, and have already been practiced on mines in
Chile and Zambia. Besides, they are morally justified.* However, they do bring certain problems.
The first problem for Peru would be that of compensation. Since the foreign mining companies, unlike
the International Petroleum Company (IPC), have not
broken the law (even their fiercest detractors can
only point to occasions when they have taken advantage of the feebleness, not to say venality, of past
governments), they would presumably have to be compensated. What for? Some would say that they have
already recouped and more all the money they have
spent in Peru, which is certainly true, and that they
should have no compensation. The companies would

---

*Populorum Progressio, Articles 23 and 24.

probably claim compensation for the value of their
assets in Peru. This would produce a dispute. In
1965, Southern Peru had already claimed $106 million
in tax exemption for depreciation and amortization
out of what they state to have been a $216-million
investment. Since then, they have charged more and
probably re-invested only a very small amount, so
it is unlikely that the company could claim that its
assets were worth more than $50 million. Cerro de
Pasco is more difficult. According to the company's
annual report, fixed assets in Peru are, very approximately indeed, $100 million--not including the mining
properties, which the company claims as assets for
the benefit of its shareholders, but which by Peruvian law belong to the State (they are valued at $30
million). The situation is complicated by factors
like depletion, which is charged at different rates
in the United States and in Peru. Marcona's assets
are still more uncertain, and those of the smaller
foreign mines are even more vague, but a total figure
of $200 million for the book value of all foreign
companies' assets should give an order of magnitude.
This sum could be paid off in three years with the
proceeds of nationalization, but the government would
probably settle for a longer period, paying interests.

The second problem produced by nationalization
would be the running of the mines. Toquepala should
not present many difficulties, but the Cerro de Pasco
empire would be a formidable task for any newly arrived executive, expert or not. Marcona would give
rise to other problems, as the company would probably
refuse to allow its fleet to be used for shipping unless given very favorable conpensatory terms. Peru
could certainly attempt the mines' administration
with not unreasonable chances of success, since there
are many national mining executives, albeit of
smaller concerns. If tackled seriously and responsi-
bly, and assuming labor troubles did not intervene
(cf. Bolivia), the problems could be overcome.

Third, there would be a political storm. If
the country had to seek technical aid from the Soviet
countries, the storm would be greater, but it is
unthinkable that the United States would actually

revert to force against Peru. At the most, "amend-
ments" would be applied, and Peru could retaliate by
not paying her debts to U.S. commercial and government banks.

Looked at dispassionately, the course of nationalization of the existing foreign mines would be
difficult, but certainly not impossible. Pursued
with determination and justice, the increased earnings would almost meet the needs of the existing
foreign debt, and credit could probably be got (even
if from unorthodox sources) to pay such compensation
as might be agreed upon. As has been said, apart
from political considerations and national pride,
one big advantage of the measure would be to give
the government increased scope for spending domestically on public works.

Perhaps the wisest, but most difficult, course
to steer to increase foreign currency earnings from
the really big mines would be that chosen by President Frei in Chile when he came to power. This
course consists of developing the new mines as mixed
companies, the State in partnership with private (not
necessarily U.S.) capital. Such a system might work
as follows: The new mine requires an investment of
$350 million, $150 million of which (including interests) is borrowed abroad; the remaining capital is
paid by the State ($100 million) and by the foreign
partner ($100 million). Of this, $210 million are
spent in Peru preparing the mine and building plant,
etc. When the mine starts producing, it earns $150
million yearly, $15 million of which are spent outside
Peru on imported goods and services. Wages, goods,
etc., in Peru take $45 million; the remaining $90 million goes to depreciation ($30 million) and taxation
($24 million), and the profits ($36 million) are
divided equally between the company and the State.
Depreciation of $25 million is allocated yearly to
pay off the loan capital, which takes six years (11
years from when the mine started), and the depreciation pays off the residue of the owners' capital for
another six years. When all the capital is paid off,
the State raises taxation from the former level of
nearly 45 per cent to nearly 55 per cent. After 20

years, including the five preparatory ones, the balance of the operation is as shown in Table 4.

TABLE 4

Operations of a Mixed Company
(in millions of dollars)

Year	Foreign Exchange Earned	Govern- ment's Earnings	Foreign Partner's Earnings
1-5	110	-100	-100
6-11	537	267	123
12-17	612	342	198
18-20	345	210	60
Total	1,604	719	281

The figures are, it is hoped, realistic and
speak for themselves. The State's initial expenditure, which, in any case, would be in soles and would
be less than 1 billion per year, is recouped in eight
years, and from then on the operation earns up to 2.8
billion soles yearly (albeit in dollars). The foreign company's tax-paid discounted cash flow corresponds to an 11.5-per-cent rate of interest. The
foreign exchange earned for the country averages $80
million yearly. The advantages of such a scheme are
obvious. The investment, particularly the cost in
foreign money, is borne by foreigners--the lender
being reassured by the participation of another for-
eigner in the project. The State gets technical assistance on the project, and Peruvians are trained
in the management of such a huge investment. The
foreign partner earns at a good rate and is tolerably
guaranteed against arbitrary measures that he might
suffer were he not in partnership with the State.
Indeed, he will share in any tax concessions and

high depreciation rates that the government may grant
to the State corporation running the mine with him.
The country, in 20 years, gains $1.6 billion in for-
eign exchange, only 55 per cent of which is spent in
inflationary form on this otherwise useless activity,
compared with the 75 per cent that is typical at the
present time.

But a policy of partnership is not easy, as the
State will be attacked on the left wing, and the foreign investor will know that it is only a matter of
time before the government will feel capable of running the mine on its own. He will thus plan for a
shorter period for recouping his investment or perhaps shy off altogether. It is clear that, even on
the favorable picture given so far, the balance-of-
payments' surplus over ten years is not of the size
of Peru's foreign debts. It will be necessary to
run two mines in this way, and it would probably
prove insuperably difficult both to negotiate and
then to exploit them together.

The best way to develop the mining industry is
by promoting the medium-sized national producer--
but in the foreseeable future, it is most improbable
that they will generate the amount of foreign currency that is apparently required, largely to meet
the international debts of Peru. By direct foreign
investment, those debts could be met--at the cost of
future earnings. By nationalization, they could almost be met--and perhaps they and the additional compensation could be avoided together in the political
turmoil. By a partnership, the country would be committed to conventional respectability and would have
to borrow further, or permit new foreign investors,
in parallel with the mixed-ownership mine, to pay
its existing debts. In view of what has happened in
Chile, the prospect of success in this moderate
course would not appear to be very great.

If the foreign debt could be ignored, Peru would
do much better to continue developing the medium-
sized mines, leaving the large unworked concessions
as natural reserves for the time when the country may
need the metals itself.

CONCLUSION

Historically, economically and emotionally, the mines are a major force in Peru. At the start of the 1970's, the projects for them are of crucial importance, as they will define not merely the future course Peru wishes to take but also control, to a large extent, the economic development of the country. The big concessions are the decisive projects. Article 59 of <u>Populorum Progressio</u> states, with reference to international contracts, that the rule of freely given consent is subordinate to the demands of natural justice. In other words, should the foreign companies concerned with these concessions impose, or try to impose, unequal terms on Peru in the proposed mining contracts, they are guilty of "economic dictatorship" against the people of Peru, and must be prepared to reap the consequences. Should Peru refuse to be imposed upon and in desperation be driven, and not unreasonably, to refuse any new concessions and to nationalize existing ones, the companies and their governments should not react hastily. If the rest of the world has more to offer Peru than it has to take from it, it is high time it was clearly demonstrated after so many centuries of plunder. There is a real possibility that Peru, in pure self-defense, may be forced to turn its back on the world and seek its own salvation alone.

It may sound from the former paragraph that, in fact, the future of the mines depends on the outcome of a battle between Peru and the foreign companies. In a sense this is so; and the first round of this battle has already taken place with the reversion of unworked concessions to the State. The foreign companies, however, are not heartless, grasping capitalists determined to exploit the poor to their utmost--on the contrary, many of their top executives are very well aware of the social implications of their activities and are very concerned to fulfill their obligations as best they can. After many decades in Latin America, they frequently are much attached to the country in which they work. But the sad truth is that the companies' and Peru's interests

are different, and hardly even complementary. The
foreign companies are not scoundrels. The real
scoundrel is the system that has permitted them to
act as they have done, the system that has allowed
them to buy up all in their path, to spend initially
soles they did not have and to pay their wages and
taxes later with soles they have never earned. This
system, which is institutionalized as the international monetary system, in general, and the gold exchange standard, in particular (but which has a long
history dating at least from 1897 in Peru, before
these names were invented), consists essentially of
a powerful country persuading a smaller one that "my
money is better than yours: You should, therefore,
hold it in your reserves and only issue domestic
money against it; you must pay your debts to me in
my money, and I will pay my debts to you in my money
also; if you accumulate a surplus of my money, you
must buy more from me or invest it in my industries;
above all, it must clearly be understood that my
money, although international, is only printed by me."

     The two major results of the success of this
propaganda are (1) to force the poorer country to export excessively (earn foreign, rather than national,
currency), the exports being raw materials--since
that is what the richer country wants; and (2) to
force it to import excessively (propaganda alone can
not create a use for foreign currency once earned),
the imports being manufactured goods--which the
poorer country would be much better employed producing itself. A variation to this is for the capitalist of the richer country to set up a manufacturing
industry in the poorer country, paying for the investment and exporting his profits in his own money.

     This system, in the name of the law of the free
market, free trade, etc., is best summed up by the old
joke "'It's every man for himself,' said the elephant
as he danced among the chickens." In Article 26 of
Populorum Progressio, Pope Paul VI states "This lib-
eralism without control, which leads to dictature,
was justly denounced by Pius XI as the generator of
the 'international imperialism of money.' There is
no better way of condemning such an abuse than by
solemnly remembering that the economy is at the service of man."

NOTE ON VARIOUS TYPES
OF PESOS
AND OTHER MONETARY UNITS
IN CIRCULATION
IN VICEREGAL PERU

Students of the first 150 years of viceregal
Peru are constantly confused by the diversity of
monetary units. The confusion existed at the time,
too; the Viceroy don Melchor Navarra y Rochaful
(1684-1689) complained bitterly in his memoirs about
the various types of peso in use and stated that he
had attempted to standardize on the peso corriente.
In general, it may be said that there were essentially
two types of silver pesos--the peso ensayado of just
over 13 reales and the peso or peso corriente of 8
reales. These had sub-types of approximately equal
values, the differences owing to the costs incurred
in turning silver bars into coin.

If we try to understand the origin of these
terms, we must go back to the gold peso--the peso de
oro or castellano. This peso (or weight--peso means
weight) was one fiftieth of a marco, there being two
marcos to the pound. (The Spanish pound weighed
460.1 grams, 1.5 per cent more than the pound avoir-
dupois.) When the conquerors first came to Peru,
there was no local mint, coins being unknown to the
Incas, and, in consequence, a severe shortage of
currency. The practice thus rapidly developed of
trading in quantities of refined silver. This quantity, once the quintos reales (royal fifths) had
been paid and its purity guaranteed by official

assay, was known as the peso ensayado and valued the
same as the peso de oro. Since, very roughly, gold
was worth ten times silver at the time, the peso ensayado was approximately one fifth of a marco of
silver. When the Lima mint opened in the 1560's--
and was later transferred to Chuquisaca and Potosi--
silver coins known as reales were put into circulation (67 struck from each marco). Thus, the peso
ensayado was equivalent to 67/5 or approximately
13.25 reales. So thought the royal officials whose
pay had been arranged in pesos ensayados, and when
they began to be paid in coin they demanded this number of reales for every peso ensayado of their sti-
pend. The viceroys, however, insisted that if the
officials were paid in coin they should receive only
12.5 reales--the difference representing the cost of
minting. This figure was continually in dispute because the authorities themselves admitted that the
cost of minting was not as high as this approximate
6 per cent. The peso ensayado thus fluctuated between 12.5 and 13.25 reales when paid in coin.

What was the value of a marco of silver before
paying the quintos reales, etc.--silver known as
plata corriente? Alonso Barba, in his El Arte de
los Metales, states that it was worth 50 reales, corresponding to 67 less 1.5 per cent tax (derecho de
Cobos), less one fifth, less 3 reales (1 for senoraje,
2 for braceaje). Thus, one fiftieth of a marco, or
one peso if we use peso with its original meaning of
weight (as applied to the peso de oro), was worth
one real. The coin struck with value of 8 reales
was known as the real de a ocho, or real "multiplied
by eight." It would then buy a peso de a ocho of
plata corriente, i.e., eight fiftieths of a marco.
From this, it is a very short step to calling the
coin of 8 reales a peso de a ocho reales, peso corriente de a ocho reales or peso corriente for short,
particularly if it is remembered that illegal trading
was done in plata corriente. All these terms are
found in the early documents and they imply a shift
in meaning of the words "de a." Whereas the real de
a ocho, peso de a ocho, peso corriente de a ocho
clearly imply a real or a peso (one fiftieth of a
marco) of plata corriente "multiplied by eight," the

later use of a peso de a ocho reales or peso corriente de a ocho reales should be taken to mean a peso "composed of" 8 reales. It may be presumed that it was thus that the 8-real coin became known as the peso corriente, and later simply as peso when the other forms of peso fell into disuse. (The pesos de a ocho were crudely translated into English as "pieces of eight.")

As with the peso ensayado, the peso corriente de a ocho reales had another associated peso but this time of greater value--the peso de a nueve reales. This had its origin in those officials whose stipends were fixed in terms of pesos corrientes of 8 reales, but who were paid in silver bars because the production of coins by the mint was insufficient to meet the demand. The 9 instead of 8 reales were supposed to compensate the recipients for the inconvenience of being paid in bars.

In fact, the source of confusion should have disappeared as soon as the mints were established in Peru, but the fact that many official salaries had originally been drawn up in pesos ensayados and the insufficient production of the mint at Potosi--the only one for silver for 100 years from the 1580's-- so far away from the centers of expenditure (Lima) caused the old names and the old practice of paying in silver bars and tejas (square pieces of silver used [illegally] as coin) to be perpetuated.

As for gold, which had been the original standard when the conquerors arrived, it soon disappeared from the monetary scene. Not only was production limited, silver easily dominating the mining industry, but also its minting was not allowed. Indeed, Viceroy don Melchor Navarra y Rochaful implies that no gold coinage at all circulated in Peru--i.e., not even Spanish. A brief issue of gold coins in Cuzco in the late 17th century came to a stop after two years. It is interesting to note that already by Barba's time (the 1630's), the value of gold with respect to silver had risen from 10 to some 12.5 times, owing to the relative scarcity of the former metal. Thus, the peso de oro, if it had then been

in circulation, would have been worth 25 per cent
more than the peso ensayado, although they were originally of equal value--i.e., some 18 instead of
13.25 reales.

A further monetary unit current in the early
years was the ducado. This name was a survival from
a Spanish coin abolished in the 1530's, and the ducado in America was never more than a unit for ac-
counting--there existed no corresponding coin. Its
use survived, for some reason, in the naval accounts
for a considerable time. The ducado was worth five
sixths of a peso ensayado, or five sixths of a peso
de oro, originally. As the gold value increased,
the ducado remained pegged to the silver peso ensayado
rather than to the gold peso de oro.

The silver coins actually struck and in circulation in Peru were the pieces of 8 reales (the
peso), 4, 2, 1, .50 and .25 reales--a strictly binary
system.

For the purpose of translating into modern cur-
rencies via the metal content of the coins, the foregoing may be briefly summarized as follows:

Silver

The peso, peso corriente, peso de a ocho = 8
reales
The peso ensayado = 13.25 reales

(There were 67 reales to the marco, or 134 to the
pound of 460.1 grams. In 1728, this number was
changed to 68, the extra real was reserved by the
Crown to meet the costs of minting the improved
coins.)

Gold

The peso de oro = one fiftieth of a marco (one
hundredth of a pound) of gold

Imaginary

The ducado = 11 reales, approximately

Thus, if we assume pure silver was worth $2.00 per troy ounce, pure gold worth $40 per troy ounce and make allowance for the purity of the Peruvian metals, then the

       peso corriente = 6.72 Swiss francs = $1.64*
       peso ensayado = 11.15   "   "   = 2.72

and the

       peso de oro   = 22.80   "   "   = 5.56
       the ducado   = 9.31   "   "   = 2.27

     The subject is further complicated by the purities of the metals, but this effect was only marginal since the purities were high and relatively constant—gold, 22.5 carat; silver, 11 dineros 4 granos (12 dineros = 100 per cent purity and there were 24 granos per dinero), normally. Also, the practice of evaluating all the units in maravedis (copper coins that did not circulate in Peru and were badly debased in Spain) often confused as much as it helped. For the record, one peso ensayado was worth 450 maravedis; the real, 34 maravedis; and the purity of a marco of silver also was measured in maravedis—the pure marco valuing 2.400 maravedis.

_____

     *With one U.S. dollar equal to 4.10 Swiss francs.

B

**NOTE
ON UNITS
OF
LENGTH**

```
1 pie (foot) = 0.2746 meters
1 vara = 3 pies = 4 palmos = 0.8359 meters
1 palmo = 0.209 meters
1 paso geometrico = 5 pies = 1.393 meters
```

Longer units:

```
1 estadio = 125 pasos geometricos
1 milla (mile) = 1,000 pasos geometricos
1 legua (league) = 20,000 pies = 5.572 kms.
```

Unit of height:

For measuring heights and depths, a rough unit called the estado was used. It corresponded to a man's height and used to be reckoned in some 7 pies. Thus: 1 estado = 1.95 meters, approximately.

APPENDIX

C

NOTE
ON WEIGHTS USED
IN PERU
IN THE MINING
INDUSTRY

The weights used in Peru were as follows:

		1 marco	= 230.0465 grams
1 libra	=	2 marcos	= 460.093 grams
1 arroba	= 25	libras	= 11.5 kilos
1 quintal	= 4	arrobas	= 46 kilos
1 cajon	= 50	quintales =	2.3 metric tons

Although various means of measuring the _ley_ or grade were employed, the most common was in marcos per cajon. From the above table it is clear that:

$$x \text{ marcos per cajon} = 0.1 \ x \text{ kilos per metric ton}$$
$$= 3.27 \ x \text{ troy ounces per long ton}$$

Unfortunately, in Huancavelica it seemed to be the custom to measure grade in libras per carga. (Often, the larger unit is not mentioned and the words "per carga" must be inferred.) The carga does not appear to have been a standard weight. The _Diccionario de la Real Academia de Madrid_ suggests that a carga was 3 quintales, but these quintales seem to be composed of 105 or 144 libras. One reference of Montesinos (1682), referring to the distillation furnaces called javecas, says "Cada horno se carga con 15 arrobas de metal. . . ." If carga is taken

to refer to the charge of the furnace, then this passage may give its weight--i.e., 15 arrobas. It would
be natural to measure the grade in this way, the
amount of mercury produced by the furnace from a
standard charge. If a carga = 15 arrobas = 375
libras, it also nicely averages the two values of
the _Diccionario_. With this assumption, x libras per
carga = 2.67 x kilos per metric ton.

D

ESTIMATION
OF THE GRADE
AT WHICH
SILVER MINING PAID
IN THE VICEROYALTY

If silver is valued at 50 reales per marco (Barba), a grade of x marcos per cajon was worth 50x/8 pesos at 100 per cent recovery.

Assuming the mine is operated with P additional workers for every man at the face (in the account of Huancavelica by the Viceroy Marques del Castel Fuerte, this number lies between 2 and 3) and that one man at the face extracts some 5 quintales per day (implied in same account and justified by modern experiments), some 10(P+1) man-days or _jornales_ are required to extract a cajon. At 4 reales per jornal, a cajon costs 5(P+1) pesos.

Refining costs are in two parts. Labor, additives, etc., are estimated by Barba to cost 17 pesos. If mercury is assumed to have been "consumed" at the rate of one libra for every marco of silver produced (this was the standard assumption at the date) and it costs N pesos per quintal, then the total cost of refining is 17 + Nx/100 pesos.

Thus to "pay" $50x/8 > 22+5P + Nx/100$

or $x > (17,600+4,000P)/(5,000-8N)$ marcos per cajon.

Example: If mercury sells at 90 pesos per quintal and P=2, the ore was profitable with

$$x > 25,600/(5,000-720) = 6 \text{ marcos per cajon}$$
$$= 0.6 \text{ kilos per metric ton}$$
$$= 19 \text{ troy ounces per long ton}$$

Note 1

In practice, costs would probably be somewhat higher to allow for other factors such as transport, overhead, storage, etc. Moreover, the costs would vary considerably from one mine to another depending on the depth, the hardness of the rock, the use of explosives, etc. The calculation does not pretend to give more than a very rough indication of the profitable grade at which viceregal miners worked.

Note 2

It was the practice for miners to reckon the grade in terms of what it actually yielded; for this reason, recovery has been placed at 100 per cent. If, however, it is desired to talk of the actual grade or quantity of metal in the ore, all the figures for grade should be multiplied by $100/E$, where E is the percentage efficiency of the process used. For mercury amalgamation, Barba implies E was approximately 85 per cent.

I. METALS
AND EXPORTS
II. PRODUCTION
OF MAJOR METALS
(RECOVERABLE)

I.   Metals and Exports
(in millions of dollars)

Year	Metals Exported	Total Exports	Trade Surplus	Soles per $
1945	20	104	19	6.5
1950	45	194	7	15
1951	69	253	−27	15
1952	70	239	−49	16
1953	68	222	−71	17
1954	80	248	−2	20
1955	96	271	−30	19
1956	115	311	−72	19
1957	116	330	−120	19
1958	105	292	−88	23
1959	110	315	−2	28
1960	200	433	58	27
1961	220	496	27	27
1962	201	540	3	27
1963	202	541	−15	27
1964	274	667	87	27
1965	298	667	−62	27
1966	362	764	−52	27
1967	385	757	−61	40
1968	454	866	236	43
1969	480 E	864	260	43
1970	540 E	1,095 E	468 E	43

E = Estimate

Sources: Annual reports, "Memoria [date]," of the Banco Minero; Anuario de la Industria Minera, formerly published by the Instituto Nacional de Investiga-cion y Fomento Mineros, now published by the Servicio de Geologia y Minerias; Daniel Rodriguez Hoya, ed., La Minería Metálica en la Economía Peruana (Lima, 1969); Banco Central de Reserva statistics published quarterly in Reseña Eco-nómica y Financiera.

II. Production of Major Metals (Recoverable)
(in tons)

Year	Copper (000's)	Silver	Zinc (000's)	Lead (000's)	Iron (millions)
1945	29	350	47	53	--
1950	33	418	77	62	--
1951	35	521	89	78	--
1952	30	453	102	83	--
1953	34	556	127	99	1.4[a]
1954	40	594	130	108	2.1
1955	41	660	150	121	1.8
1956	45	602	153	123	2.9
1957	55	741	136	136	3.3
1958	52	751	123	125	3.3
1959	51	865	133	121	4.5
1960	184[b]	1,016	157	131	5.2
1961	198	1,055	171	137	5.5
1962	165	1,031	184	133	5.9
1963	180	1,094	195	149	6.6
1964	176	1,070	237	151	6.5
1965	180	1,134	254	154	7.1
1966	200	1,059	284	162	7.8
1967	191	1,036	305	160	8.9
1968	201	1,064	322	152	9.0
1969	199 E	N.A.	315 E	155 E	N.A.
1970	187 E	N.A.	329 E	164 E	N.A.

[a]Marcona began production.
[b]Toquepala began production.
E = Estimate
N.A. = Not Available

Note: Much more detailed statistics separating refined from semi-refined products and concentrates are available in the sources cited, together with production of bismuth, mercury, cadmium, selenium, tellurium, gold, indium, antimony, tin, tungsten and molybdenum.

Sources: Anuario de la Industria Minera, formerly published by the Instituto Nacional de Investigacion y Fomento Mineros, now published by the Servicio de Geologia y Minerias; La Mineria en el Perú (Annual, Lima: Editores Tecnicos Asociados S.A.); annual reports, "Memoria [date]," of the Banco Minero.

F

SOURCES
OF INFORMATION

It is not possible to give a detailed biblio-
graphy (except for the historical sources that follow
these comments) since so much of the information has
been acquired from journals, from the press and from
personal visits. What follows, therefore, is an indication of what were the sources of information for
this book rather than an exhaustive list of publications.

For general information about Peru, Marcel
Niedergang's <u>Les 20 Amériques Latines</u> (Paris: Editions de Seuil, 1969) and the Lima press (<u>El Comercio,
Oiga</u>) are the political sources, while <u>South America--
A Natural History</u> (London: Hamish Hamilton, 1971),
by Jean Dorst and the series entitled "Documental del
Peru" (Lima: Informacion, Opinion Publica, Publici-
dad y Encuestas--Editores [IOPPE-S.A.], 1967), in
which a book about each department is being issued,
provide geographical backgrounds. The author has
also visited 21 of the 24 departments--Tumbes, San
Martin and Madre de Dios being the exceptions.

On geological matters, the <u>Boletín de la Sociedad Geológica del Perú</u> (BSGP), the publications of
the erstwhile Instituto Nacional de Investigacion y
Fomento Mineros (INIFM) and the explanatory booklets
that go with the maps published by the Servicio de

Geologia y Mineria have been largely used. In particular, Volumes 31 (geological map of all Peru) and 33
(Estructura y Levantamiento de los Andes by Ulrich
Petersen) of BSGP, together with several articles by
Professor J. V. Harrison on Central Peru and Norman
D. Newell on Ica and Puno have been consulted. Much
has been learned from Ingeniero E. Ponzoni's course
on the geology of Peru in the Universidad Nacional
de Ingenieria and, especially, from conversations and
trips with Dr. J. J. Wilson, O.B.E., whose survey of
the Ancash area has also been consulted.

On mines, there are so many articles in the different mining journals (listed in Chapter 11) that
it is impossible to detail them. Mention should be
made of the publications of the 1969 Convencion de
Ingenieros de Minas (including La Minería Metálica
en la Economía Peruana), the annual publication La
Minería en el Perú, and the Anuario de la Industria
Minera published by INIFM. In addition to published
information, the author has also collected his own,
with innumerable visits to companies and institutions.
The following mines or plants were visited personally
in 1968 and 1969: Millotingo, Pacococha, Condestable,
Raul, Casapalca (Department of Lima); Morococha, Puquiococha, Cercapuquio, La Oroya (Department of Junin); Cerro de Pasco, Huaron, Atacocha (Department
of Pasco); Santa Barbara, Cobriza, Caudalosa/Castro-
virreyna (Department of Huancavelica); Cerro Verde,
Caylloma (Department of Arequipa); Toquepala (Department of Tacna); Ilo (Department of Moquegua); Marcona (Department of Ica); San Juan de Lucanas (Department of Ayacucho); San Antonio de Poto/Natomas
(Department of Puno); Catac, Santo Torribio, Ticapampa, Conduzo/SOGESA (Department of Ancash); Quiruvilca (Department of La Libertad); Michiquillay,
Hualgayoc, Paredones (Department of Cajamarca); Turmalina (Department of Piura).

For economic and allied information, Carlos
Malpica's Los Duenos del Perú (Lima: Ediciones
Eusayos Sociales, 1968) and the publications of the
Lima stockmarket have been used for investigating
company structure, while the Economist Intelligence
Unit and the Boletín and Reseña Económica y Finan-

<u>ciera</u> of the Banco Central de Reserva have supplied
macro-economic information. Much has also come from
the pages of <u>El Peruano</u>, the government's official
newspaper, in particular the text on legislation.

Finally, views on development in the wider sense
have certainly been influenced by the annual review
of the ODI (London) and by Pope Paul VI's <u>Populorum
Progressio</u>, while innumerable articles in <u>Le Monde</u>
have undoubtedly also contributed. The author is,
however, entirely responsible for what he has written.

Acosta, Padre Jose. De Procuranda Indorum Salute.
    Madrid: Edition of the Coleccion Rivadeneira,
    1954.

_____. Historía Natural y Moral de las Indias.
    Madrid: Edition of the Coleccion Rivadeneira,
    1954.

Antze, Gustar. Metallarbeiten aus dem nordlichen
    Peru. Hamburg, 1930. Spanish edition, Lima:
    San Marcos University, 1965.

Arana, Pedro P. Minas de Azogue del Perú. Lima,
    1901.

Barba, Alonso. El Arte de los Metales. Reprinted,
    Lima: Real Tribunal de Mineria, 1817.

Bardella, Gianfranco. Setenta y Cinco Años de Vida
    Económica del Perú. Lima: Banco de Credito
    del Peru, 1964.

Burzio, Humberto F. Diccionario de la Moneda Hispano-
    Americana. Santiago, Chile: Fondo Historico y
    Bibliografico, 1958.

Cieza de Leon. La Crónica del Perú. Madrid: Austral
    Edition, 1945.

Fuentes, M. A., ed. Memorias de los Virreyes. Ma-
    drid, 1859.

de Gamboa, Francisco Javier. Comentarios a las Or-
    denanzas de Minas. Madrid, 1761.

Helms, Anthony Zachariah. Travels from Buenos Aires
    by Potosi to Lima. London: Richard Phillips,
    1807.

Jimenez, Ingeniero Carlos, et al. Síntesis de la
    Minería Peruana en el Centenario de Ayacucho.
    Lima: Ministerio de Fomento, 1924.

Juan, Jorge y Ulloa, Antonio de. David Barry, ed.
    Noticias Secretas de América. Madrid: Biblio-
    teca Ayacucho, 1918.

Llano Zapata. Memorias Histórico-Físicas-Apologeticas
    de la América Meridional. Cadiz, 1761. (Re-
    printed, Lima, 1904.)

Lothrop, S. K. Inca Treasure as Depicted by Spanish
    Historians. Los Angeles, 1938. Spanish edi-
    tion, Lima: San Marcos, 1964.

Maffei, E. y Rua F., R. Apuntes para una Biblioteca
    Española de Libros sobre Minería. . . . Madrid,
    1871.

Pastor, Rey. La Ciencia y la Técnica en el Descub-
    rimiento de América. Buenos Aires: Esposa
    Calpe Argentina, 1942.

Raimondi, A. El Peru. Various editions, Lima, 1858-
    1913.

_____. Notas de Viajes. Alberto Jochamowitz, ed.
    Various editions, Lima, 1945-1948.

de Rivero, M. Colección de Memorias Científicas Ag-
    rícolas é Industriales en Distintas Epocas.
    Brussels: Imprenta de H. Goemaere, 1857.

_____ and Pierola, Nicholas de. Memorial de Ciencias Naturales y de Industria Nacional y Extranjera. Lima: Imprenta de la Instruccion Primaria por J. F. Solorzano, 1828.

von Tschudi, J. J. Peru, Reisekizzen aus den Jahren 1834-1842. Graz: Akademische Druck u. Verlaganstalt, 1963.

Vargas Ugarte, Ruben. Historia General del Perú. Lima, 1966.

Velarde, C. E. La Minería en el Perú. Lima, 1908.

Posco, 160
Power generation, 263
PROLANSA, 216, 270
Proustite, 130
Pucara formation, 11, 116, 119, 126
Pumps, steam, 83
Puna surface, 12, 81
Puno, 58, 84, 196, 197
Pyrargite, 130

Quintos, 36, 51
Quito, 65

Railways, 17, 89, 94, 103, 222-23
Real, 51
Rescate, 40
Reverberatory furnace, 52, 85, 204, 211
Rio Blanco, 230
Roads, 17
Rolling mills, 214
Rosicler, 29, 52, 130, 138

San Agustin, Universidad de, 242
San Jose (Huaron), 109, 230
San Juan, 156
San Marcos, Universidad de, 242
San Mateo, 59
San Nicolas, 157, 158
Scholarships, 240
Seaports, 19
Sechura desert, 5
Selenium, 209
Senoraje, 51
Servicio de Geologia y Mineria, 245
Sherman Silver Act, 97
Shipping, 225, 226
Shrinkage, 129
Sierra, 6
Silver, 15, 24, 60, 75, 96, 116, 128, 129, 137, 141, 167, 180, 209, 233

Socavon, 30, 126
Sociedad Nacional de Mineria y Petroleo, 100, 243
Sociedad Progreso de la Pequena Mineria, 244
SOGESA, 111, 213
Soroche, 29, 52
Square set, 121
Steel, 53, 212
Stock exchange, 255
Stratigraphy, 10

Tacana, 28
Tacna, 150
Taxation, 91, 97, 154, 247-48
Tectonics, 13
Tellurium, 209
Tetrahedrite, 169
Tin, 179, 198
Tinyahuarco, 105, 230
Tocochimbos, 24, 51
Training, 237-38
Transport, 16, 221-22, 262
Tribunal de Mineria, 67, 83, 91, 93, 245
Trujillo, 84
Tungsten, 105, 126, 128, 175, 176, 210, 212

Unions, 265
United States, 97, 227
Universidad Nacional de Ingenieria, 239

Vanadium, 105

Wages, 265
Water-jacket furnace, 89, 91
Wolframite, 176
World War I, 108

Yauyos, 90

Zinc, 14, 110, 116, 123, 142, 179, 206, 233-34, 271
Zinc refinery, proposed, 233-34, 235

PEOPLE

Abadia, Pedro, 83
Acosta, Padre Jose de, 29 et seq., 39, 47 et seq.
Agia, Padre, 34, 44

Amat, Viceroy Manuel de, 64, 65, 65, 77
Arias, Dr., 33 et seq.
Arias Davila, Jesus, 128, 132, 139

334

Atahualpa, Inca, 23, 26
Avila, Garcia de, 193

Babinski, 90, 96, 161
Baertl family, 122, 138
Ballesteros, Tomas, 66
Balta, President Jose, 93
Barba, Padre Alonso, 25, 29,
  46, 53-54, 72
Becerra, Jose Antonio, 47, 73
Benavides, Alberto, 137
Born, Baron, 69
Brazini, Alberto, 144, 147

Cabrera, Amador, 27, 32, 37
Capellin, 47
Castel Fuerte, Viceroy Marques
  de, 60, 61, 63
Castellar, Viceroy Conde de,
  62
Castilla, President Ramon, 86
Charles III, King, 65, 67
Charles V, Emperor, 51, 54,
  251
Chatenet, Mauricio du, 96
Cieza de Leon, 24, 27, 28, 36,
  53, 192
Cochrane, Carlos, 147
Coquette, 72
Corro, 60
Corzo, 50
Croix, Viceroy Teodoro de, 69,
  77
Crosnier, 89

Dammert family, 197
Dunstan, Simon, 106, 188
Durand family, 91, 106, 184

Elhuyar, Fausto de, 69
Escobedo, Jorge, 67, 68
Esquilache, Viceroy Principe
  de, 35, 56

Fernandez Maldonado S., General Jorge, 245
Fernandini, E. P., and family,
  96, 124, 136
Francisco Fray (Bishop-Elect
  of Potosi), 61
Fuchs, Federico, 155

Galjuf family, 119
Gallo Diez, Francisco, 120
Gamboa, Francisco Javier de,
  47, 55, 60, 65

Garces, Enrique, 27, 133
Gil y Lemos, Viceroy Francis-
  co, 71
Gildemeister family, 104, 105,
  127
Giles family, 122
Grace, Michael, 94, 95, 101,
  103
Grundy, William, 106
Gutierrez brothers, 93

Habich, Eduardo de, 91
Helms, Zachariah, 48, 69, 193
Heverling, 96
Hochschild, Mauricio, 111,
  144, 146
Hugon, Pedro, 88
Humboldt, Baron Alejandro von
  4, 54, 68, 74, 87

Iglesias, President, 94

Juilland, 196

Kuhn, Francisco, 69

Larrieu, 89
Lemos, Viceroy Conde de, 58,
  61, 63
Linan y Cisneros, Viceroy Mel-
  chor de, 39-40
Llano Zapata, 43n., 59
Loret de Mola, 131

Mahr, Ricardo, 96
Malaga Santolalla, Fermin,
  105, 175
Malinowski, 89, 94
Mancera, Viceroy Marques de,
  61-62, 64
Marroquin, 66
Medina, Bartolome de, 28
Meiggs, Henry, 90, 94, 103
Miculisich, 104
Monterrey, Viceroy Conde de,
  33, 34
Montesclaros, Viceroy Marques
  de, 33, 34, 42
Montesinos, 34
Mothe, Francisco, 71

Nordenflicht, Baron von, 69-
  70, 82

Ocana, Rodrigo de, 66
O'Higgins, Demetrio, 32, 68,
  77, 192

335

MINES, MINING AREAS AND MINING COMPANIES

W. F. C. Purser first visited South America in 1965 to give a course on computer control at the Universidad Nacional, Buenos Aires. He traveled extensively in the southern part of the continent, lecturing at various other universities and to the staff of process industries. In 1968, he was awarded an ODI Fellowship to go to Peru for two years to study the mining industry of that country, a study that resulted in the present book. He taught at the Universidad Nacional de Ingenieria, Lima. Subsequently, he was visiting professor at the Universidad de Chile, Santiago, before returning to Europe.

Mr. Purser has a degree in mathematics from the University of Cambridge, England, but has spent most of his working life in the field of computers and automation, particularly in the process industries-- steel, oil, chemical and paper. He has published various technical papers on computing and process control, and he now works for Systems Programming Ltd. International, London, as a consultant.

Mr. Purser was born in Dublin in 1937. He is married and has three children.

RENEWALS 458-4574

DATE DUE

APR - 6	◄		
GAYLORD			PRINTED IN U.S.A.